Introduction to Dynamic Programming

SERIES IN DECISION AND CONTROL

Ronald A. Howard

INTRODUCTION TO DYNAMIC PROGRAMMING

by George L. Nemhauser

DYNAMIC PROBABILISTIC SYSTEMS (In Preparation)

by Ronald A. Howard

Introduction to

DYNAMIC PROGRAMMING

George L. Nemhauser

Department of Operations Research and Industrial Engineering
The Johns Hopkins University

JOHN WILEY AND SONS, INC.
New York • London • Sydney

Library of Congress Catalog Card Number: 66-21046
Printed in the United States of America

TO

Loring G. Mitten

Preface

Dynamic programming is used to solve complex optimization problems. This book presents the theory and computational aspects of dynamic programming. It is an applied book, designed for operations researchers, management scientists, statisticians, engineers, and social scientists.

Scientific decision-making involves model building and then solving the model to determine an optimal solution. Many models, encompassing different disciplines and areas of application, are amenable to solution by dynamic programming. These models contain many decision variables and have a mathematical structure which is such that calculations of the optimal decisions can be done sequentially. When and how the calculations can be done sequentially is the essence of dynamic programming. Sequential optimization loosely means determining the optimal decisions one at a time. Often the ability to determine decisions one at a time makes a problem computationally feasible.

Extensive applications have been made in inventory theory, allocation problems, control theory, search theory, and chemical engineering design. By identifying the mathematical structures amenable to dynamic programming analysis, it is hoped that new applications will be developed. This problem is the subject of Chapter II. It is preceded by a brief discussion of model building, the dynamic programming approach, and optimization in Chapter I. Chapter II presents the basic approach of multistage problem solving and when it can be used in optimization. By knowing when it is theoretically possible to use dynamic programming, an analyst can decide whether it is possible to solve his problem by dynamic programming. But, knowing that something is possible is different from knowing exactly how to do it.

Chapters III and IV are the "how-to-do-it" chapters. Basic computations are the subject of Chapter III—how the dynamic programming formulation is obtained, how the computations are organized, the preparation of flow charts for computers, the data requirements, and sensitivity analysis. The exercises are especially essential in Chapter III. They demonstrate the basic ideas of dynamic programming formulation and solution. It is absolutely necessary to solve problems to understand dynamic programming. Methods for doing computations as efficiently as possible are given in Chapter IV. This is most crucial when expensive computer time is used.

Chapter V extends the results obtained for deterministic multistage decision models to stochastic and competitive models. In Chapter VI the usual assumption about the serial structure of adjoining stages is removed to extend the analysis to processes with branches and feedback loops. Models with an infinite number of decisions are discussed in Chapter VII. The relationship between dynamic programming and the calculus of variations is revealed. Some general conclusions and a discussion of applications are given in Chapter VIII.

Almost every new idea introduced is illustrated with a detailed analysis of one or more examples. The form of the examples assumes that a model has already been constructed, so that attention can be given to its dynamic programming formulation and solution. In this framework, one can relate his own problems to the problems in the text by adding the necessary context to the examples. Furthermore, organizing the problems according to their mathematical structure will be of great advantage to those interested in developing new applications.

The development of dynamic programming is almost exclusively due to Richard Bellman and his colleagues at the Rand Corporation. His books and papers furnished a large fraction of the source material for this text. Professor L. G. Mitten of Northwestern University introduced me to dynamic programming. His interest stimulated mine. I am thankful to him for encouragement and for valuable suggestions on the organization and technical content of the book. I hope the book makes him proud. Dr. William W. Hardgrave read a draft of the manuscript in detail. His comments were invaluable in transforming the manuscript from draft to final copy. My wife, Ellen, has helped immensely with style and grammar—a difficult task considering her lack of interest in the subject matter. All of the several reviews obtained by John Wiley have helped to improve the book. A draft of the book was used in a one-semester two-hour-per-week course at Johns Hopkins which I taught jointly with Dr. Mandell Bellmore. I am grateful to him and the students who found numerous errors while suffering through the rough draft. I would like to express my appreciation to Mrs. Helen Macaulay of Johns Hopkins for her excellent typing of part of the first draft and the entire second draft of the manuscript, and to Miss Jane Shaw of Leeds University, U. K., for typing a considerable portion of the first draft. I am also grateful to Michael Magazine for reading the galley proofs and assisting with the preparation of the index.

George L. Nemhauser

Baltimore, Maryland
April 1966

Contents

I

Introduction

1. Background

Dynamic Programming is an approach to optimization. Optimization means finding a best solution among several feasible alternatives. The term "a best solution" is used because there may be more than one optimal solution.

The representation of a problem in abstract or symbolic form is known as a *mathematical model*. Characterizing optimization problems by mathematical models goes back to the Greeks, if not further. Attributed to Greek mathematics is the solution of problems such as finding the geometric figure of minimum perimeter that encloses a given area.

Theories of optimization existed long before the development of the calculus. Nevertheless, the formal development of optimization theory came from the calculus. After the invention of the calculus, mathematicians worked actively on optimization problems. The theory was developed for mathematical models containing continuous variables and differentiable functions. Many of the problems studied were of geometrical background. Although the theory provided solution procedures for problems with several variables, the theory was not adequate to deal computationally with models containing a very large number of variables. However, a few variables were generally sufficient to characterize most of the geometrical problems of interest then. The classical development of optimization theory through the calculus was essentially complete by the end of the nineteenth century. A good exposition is contained in *Theory of Maxima and Minima* by Hancock [35].

In the 1940's there was a reawakening and change of direction in the study of optimization theory. This renaissance was stimulated by the war effort. Two parallel but interrelated occurrences are especially significant;

the work of scientists and mathematicians on military operational problems, and the invention and development of the digital computer.

The scientific approach to military problems, and then, after the war, to industrial and other institutional problems, became the field of study known as *operations research*.† The formulation and solution of mathematical models of optimization is an integral part of operations research. These models of complex logistic, production, and distribution systems are generally characterized by a large number of variables, and are often of a form not amenable to solution by the calculus.

Pioneer operations analysts simultaneously developed models and solution techniques. Their notable successes were partly due to the rapid evolution of high-speed digital computers. Given a machine that could do thousands of calculations per second, it became practical to think about solving problems containing hundreds or even thousands of variables. This realization stimulated the study of iterative optimization schemes and eventually led to the development of linear and nonlinear programming, dynamic programming, and various search methods.

The evolution of these methods and their refinement may be thought of as the renaissance of optimization theory. The motivation for this regenerated interest stems from operations research. Thus modern optimization theory is usually studied in conjunction with operations research. However, it can and has been applied to problems completely within the domain of traditional disciplines. It is possible to study the methodology without making reference to digital computers. However, as the success of the methods depends largely on digital computers, we shall consider the role of the computer.

2. Mathematical Models of Decision Making ‡

A mathematical model is a symbolic representation of relations among the factors in a problem of decision making. The basic components of the model are:

1. *The variables* $D = (d_1, d_2, \ldots, d_n)$—those factors that can be manipulated to achieve the desired objective. These variables are commonly referred to as independent or decision variables.

2. *The parameters* $Y = (y_1, y_2, \ldots, y_p)$—those factors that affect the objective but are not controllable.

3. *The measure of effectiveness* (R)—the value, utility, or return as-

---

† Some general references on operations research are Churchman et al. [23], Flagle et al. [30], and Saaty [60].

‡ Ackoff [1] contains an excellent discussion of mathematical decision models.

sociated with particular values of the decision variables and parameters. The measure of effectiveness, alternatively called the utility measure, criterion function, objective function, or return function, is a real-valued function of the decision variables and parameters, which can be represented as

$$R = R(D, Y)$$

There is a wide variety of commonly used measures of utility, such as cost, profit, rate of return. It will be assumed that a specific measure of effectiveness can always be chosen that will adequately reflect the important differences among different values of the decision variables.

4. *The region of feasibility* (*S*)—in most circumstances the decision variables are limited in the values they can assume. These limitations are generally given by specifying a region of feasibility or constraint set (*S*). The feasible values for the decision variables must be contained in the set *S*, that is, ($D \in S$). Sometimes it is possible to represent all or a part of the constraint set by equations and/or inequalities of the form

$$g_i(D) \begin{array}{c} \leq \\ = \\ \geq \end{array} \Bigg\} \; 0, \qquad i = 1, \dots, m.$$

Equations and inequalities that determine the region of feasibility are usually called constraints or restrictions.

Any *D* satisfying the constraints is known as a feasible solution to the model. The decision-making problem is to find a feasible solution that yields high value or return. An optimal solution (*D**) is defined as a feasible solution producing the greatest possible return, that is,

$$R(Y) = R(D^*, Y) \geq R(D, Y), \qquad D \in S$$
$$= \max_D R(D, Y), \qquad D \in S$$

For every problem, the optimal *R*(*Y*) is unique (when it exists) but there may be more than one optimal solution.†

In most real situations it is satisfactory to find a solution yielding a

---

† The question of existence rarely arises in a real problem but must be explained mathematically. First, if *R* has no upper bound, no maximum is said to exist. A simple example will suffice to explain the second possibility. Suppose $R(D, Y) = D$, where *D* is a real scalar variable restricted to the open interval $0 < D < 1$. The function $R(D, Y)$ has many upper bounds: the smallest is unity. This smallest upper bound is called the *supremum*. Since there is no value of *D* in the open interval, $0 < D < 1$, which yields the supremum, no maximum is said to exist. For almost all problems of practical interest the supremum and maximum are equivalent. We shall only speak of maxima and minima although we could use the more general terms suprema and infima.

near-optimal return. However, the optimal return is established since it is not usually possible to evaluate the goodness of a nonoptimal solution.

The great advantage of a mathematical model is its generality and ease of manipulation. Any sort of sensitivity analysis, such as changing values of the variables, parameters, constraints, or even changing the functional relationships, is most easily accomplished when there is a mathematical model of the system. But these enhanced investigative powers are not attained without cost. The amount of mental effort and analysis required to construct a mathematical model of real-world phenomena is great. First, the system must be described unambiguously. The variables must be identified and a single measure of utility chosen. The relations among the variables must be expressed mathematically. One of these relations is the utility measure and the remainder are constraints.

A solution to a model can be no better than the model itself. Consequently the model must be an accurate representation of the system. But how accurate? Unfortunately, there are no hard and fast rules. The appropriate accuracy of the model depends upon how accurate a solution is needed and how decisions change as the model is modified. Often this can be determined only by trial and error. But it is generally good advice to try the simplest model first. Additional accuracy is likely to mean additional cost and time in constructing the model, and a more accurate model may be difficult to solve and yield no better results.

Various simplifying procedures can be attempted. Decision variables and parameters apparently having negligible effect on the return can be eliminated. The nature of the variables can be changed from continuous to discrete or vice versa. Often in a first model stochastic variations in the parameters are ignored. An obvious simplification is to approximate the return function and constraints by, say, linear functions. We must compromise by balancing solvability and reality. The compromises that must be made will, in part, depend upon the power of the solution techniques. Obviously, sharper optimization tools permit the use of more complicated models.

It is difficult to present a mutually exclusive and collectively exhaustive classification for mathematical models of decision making. But it is useful to make some distinctions. In *deterministic* models the return is given unambiguously by specifying values for the decision variables. There are no uncontrollable or random variables. In contrast, *stochastic* or *probabilistic* models contain random variables that cannot be controlled and whose values are given by probability distributions. A deterministic model can be considered as a special case of a stochastic model, in which each random variable assumes a particular value with probability 1 and all other values with probability 0. In this sense it is possible to treat the two cases together. For the sake of clarity, we shall defer discussion of stochastic models until we have developed the theory and computational aspects concerning deterministic models. A further classification in this direction is *competitive* or *game-theoretic* models, in which different variables are subject to different decision makers' control. We shall elaborate on these classifications in Chapter V.

The continuous or discrete nature of the variables is another mode of classification. This breakdown will be useful in the discussion of computational aspects of dynamic programming in Chapters III and IV. Basically, a continuous variable can assume any real value in an interval, whereas a discrete variable is restricted to a finite number of values in an interval.

Different forms of the objective function and constraints yield still another division of mathematical models. A meaningful grouping is between linear and nonlinear models. In a linear model the objective function is

$$R(D) = c_1 d_1 + c_2 d_2 + \ldots + c_n d_n$$

and the constraints are linear inequalities. Later, we make a very crucial distinction between objective functions of several variables that are separable and those that are not. This technical difference will not be explained now, but will be expanded upon in great detail in Chapter II. An example of a separable function is

$$R(D) = r_1(d_1) + r_2(d_2) + \ldots + r_n(d_n)$$

However, an arbitrary function of n variables is not separable. Closely related to the notion of separability is single-stage versus multistage model. In a single-stage decision process all decisions are made simultaneously, while in a multistage decision process the decisions are made sequentially. This division is not based entirely on the physical characteristics of the process, since it is often possible to create artificially a multistage process from a single-stage one. We would imagine that there are considerable computational advantages to making decisions one at a time rather than all at once. This is the *raison d'être* of dynamic programming.

3. General Approach of Dynamic Programming

Having constructed an appropriate mathematical model, we must choose an optimization technique to solve the model. The way we determine an optimal solution depends, of course, on the form of the objective function and constraints, the nature and number of variables, the kind of computational facilities available, taste, and experience.

Often, before performing the optimization, it is desirable to make some changes of variables and transformations. In contrast to simplifying the model, these preparatory operations preserve the properties of the model completely. The transformed model has the same optimal solution as the original, but is of a form that can be optimized more easily.

Basically, dynamic programming is such a transformation. It takes a sequential or multistage decision process containing many interdependent variables and converts it into a series of single-stage problems, each containing only a few variables. The transformation is invariant in that the number of feasible solutions and the value of the objective function associated with each feasible solution is preserved. The transformation is based on the intuitively obvious principle that [10]

an optimal set of decisions has the property that whatever the first decision is, the remaining decisions must be optimal with respect to the outcome which results from the first decision.

Later, we shall restate the *dynamic programming principle of optimality* using new terminology. Although the principle of optimality seems both obvious and simple, it can more appropriately be described as powerful, subtle, and elusive.

We may say that a problem with N decision variables can be transformed into N subproblems, each containing only one decision variable. As a rule of thumb, the computations increase exponentially with the number of variables, but only linearly with the number of subproblems. Thus there can be great computational savings. Often this saving makes the difference between an insolvable problem and one requiring only a small amount of computer time.

Certain problem areas, such as inventory theory, allocation, control theory, and chemical engineering design, have been particularly fertile for dynamic programming applications. The property basic to these problems is that decisions can be calculated sequentially. The method of sequential calculation is the essence of dynamic programming.

For example, consider a chemical process consisting of a heater, reactor, and distillation tower connected in series. It is desired to determine the optimal temperature in the heater, the optimal reaction rate, and the optimal number of trays in the distillation tower. All of these decisions are interdependent. However, whatever temperature and reactor rate are chosen, the number of trays must be optimal with respect to the output from the reactor. Using this principle, we may say that the optimal number of trays is determined as a *function* of the reactor output. Since we do not know the optimal temperature or reaction rate yet, *the optimal number of trays and return from the tower must be found for all feasible reactor outputs.*

Continuing sequentially, we may say that, whatever temperature is chosen, the reactor rate and number of trays must be optimal with respect to the heater output. To choose the best reaction rate as a function of the heater output, we must account for the dependence of the distillation tower on the reactor output. But we already know the optimal return from the tower as a function of the reactor output. Hence, the optimal reaction rate can be determined as a function of the reactor input, by optimizing the reactor together with the optimal return from the tower as a function of the reactor output.

In making decisions sequentially as a function of the preceding decisions, the first step is to determine the number of trays as a function of the reactor output. Then the optimal reaction rate is established as a function of the input to the reactor. Finally, the optimal temperature is determined as a function of the input to the heater. Finding *decision functions,* we can optimize the chemical process one stage at a time.

An allocation process can be similarly analyzed. Suppose we want to allocate funds to three research projects, A, B, and C, to maximize expected revenue. Since total funds are limited, the amount allocated to each project depends on the allocations to the other projects. However, whatever funds are given to projects A and B, the allocation to C must be optimal with respect to the capital remaining. Since we do not yet know the optimal allocation to projects A and B, *the optimal allocation and revenue from C must be determined for all feasible amounts remaining,* after allocations have been made to A and B. Furthermore, whatever allocation is made to project A, the allocations to B and C must be optimal with respect to the funds remaining after the allocation to A. To find the optimal allocation to project B, we find the allocation maximizing the revenue from B together with the optimal revenue from C, as a function of the funds remaining from the allocation to B. Finally the optimal allocation to A is determined, to maximize the revenue from A plus the optimal revenue from B and C, as a function of the funds remaining after the allocation to A. In reality, funds are allocated to the three projects simultaneously. The sequential allocation is a mathematical artifact allowing us to make the decisions one at a time.

The same idea can be applied to optimize the trajectory a missile takes to its target. A trajectory consists of a set of directions from the launching pad to the target. There is a surface consisting of the set of all points one mile from the target. Not knowing which of those points the missile should pass through on an optimal trajectory, we determine the optimal paths to, say, minimize travel time, from each of these points to the target. From the surface of all points two miles from the target, the optimal path to the target is established by minimizing the time to reach the surface one mile away together with the optimal times from the one-mile surface. This sequential decision process is continued along surfaces a constant distance from the target until the launching point is reached.

Our intention in this section is only to stimulate an interest in dynamic programming. The basic questions are: What are the underlying principles? When can they be used? How can they be used? Where can they be applied? We shall deal with these questions, almost in turn, in the succeeding chapters.

Dynamic programming was certainly practiced long before it was named. Wald's work on sequential decision theory [65] contains the seed of a dynamic programming approach. The two papers by Dvoretzky, Kiefer, and Wolfowitz [26, 27], on inventory theory are certainly in the spirit of dynamic programming.

Undoubtedly, however, Richard Bellman is the father of dynamic programming. His research at the Rand Corporation in the 1950's led to the publication of a large number of significant papers on dynamic programming, culminating in his first book on the theory of dynamic programming first published in 1957 [10]. He invented the rather undescriptive but alluring name for the approach—*dynamic programming*. A more representative but less glamorous name would be *recursive optimization*. We shall use these terms interchangeably. Bellman has continued to be extremely prolific in his writings on dynamic programming, which include numerous articles, a book on the application of dynamic programming to control theory [12], and a book on applied dynamic programming [13], written in collaboration with S. Dreyfus.

Other books on dynamic programming have also begun to appear. R. Aris has written a book about the design of chemical reactors [2] and a more general one on discrete dynamic programming [3]. Howard has written about the relationship between dynamic programming and Markov processes [38], Tou, on the optimization of control processes [63], and Roberts, on dynamic programming in chemical engineering [59], a field that seems particularly fertile for dynamic programming applications. Another fruitful field is inventory theory. A book containing a collection of articles on multistage inventory models has appeared recently [62].

4. Optimization Techniques

We conclude this chapter with a brief résumé of standard (single-stage) optimization methods. Once the dynamic programming formulation has been achieved, the optimization may be easier but still remains. The most elementary technique of optimization is exhaustive or total enumeration. This simply means calculating $R(D)$ for all feasible D, and then using the definition of optimality directly to identify the set of optimal solutions.

Enumeration is possible only when there are a finite number of solutions. However, problems having an infinite number of solutions can generally be approximated by problems containing only a finite number of solutions. Even when there are a finite number of solutions, enumeration may be hopeless. In the "traveling salesman" problem, where a salesman has to visit each of n cities and return to his home base, there are $653,837,184,000 = \frac{1}{2}$ (15!) feasible solutions for $n = 16$. Even if a thousand solutions could be evaluated per second on a high-speed computer, it would take over twenty years to enumerate all solutions. Obviously, for problems of this size, methods more efficient than enumeration are required. However, there is often no other choice but to enumerate all feasible solutions. When faced with this unpleasant task, we hope that the number of feasible solutions will not be excessive. Often when there are several variables, enumeration is possible only after a dynamic programming decomposition.

If we are not going to search exhaustively for a global optimum, rules must be provided for selecting a subset of the feasible solutions to evaluate the objective function. In addition, there must be a sufficient condition of optimality that does not depend upon exhaustive search.† Unfortunately, the only universal sufficient condition of optimality is the definition of optimality.

In place of a universal sufficient condition, a condition that is sufficient in special cases and that is necessary in all cases is quite useful.‡ A feasible solution D^0 that satisfies

$$R(D^0) \geq R(D^0 + \Delta D)$$

over all feasible values of the small quantity Δ is defined as a local optimum (maximum). Clearly, the set of (global) optima is contained in the set of local optima. Thus, this condition is necessary for a global optimum. When the local optimum is unique, it is the global optimum. Consequently, for functions with a unique local optimum (unimodal), the definition for a local optimum is a necessary and sufficient condition for a global optimum. How to cope with the problem of more than one local optima has never been resolved, and generally, there is no choice but to enumerate all local optima.

Sequential search procedures are iterative procedures based on the strategy of using results from past evaluations to determine new points to evaluate the objective function. Steepest ascent or gradient methods form an important class of sequential search procedures. The basic idea of steepest ascent is to move from one solution to another, always proceeding in the direction of maximum increase in the objective function. Suppose the objective function has been evaluated at some arbitrary feasible solution D_0, which is not a local optimum. It can be shown that the direction from D_0 in which the objective function rises most rapidly is in the direction given by the gradient of $R(D)$ evaluated at D_0.§ Thus a new solution D_1 along the gradient line of $R(D)$ at D_0 can be determined such that $R(D_1) > R(D_0)$. If D_1 is not an optimum, we evaluate the gradient

---

† A solution that satisfies a sufficient condition of optimality satisfies the definition of optimality.

‡ A solution that satisfies the definition of optimality satisfies a necessary condition.

§ The gradient, when it exists, is defined as $\left(\dfrac{\partial R}{\partial d_1}, \dfrac{\partial R}{\partial d_2}, \ldots, \dfrac{\partial R}{\partial d_n} \right)$.

at D_1, find a new solution D_2 with $R(D_2) > R(D_1)$, and continue in this manner. This procedure will converge to a local maximum. The method of steepest ascent works well even when there are random variables. Furthermore, since the gradient at a particular point can be approximated by evaluating the objective function at points close to the original point, it is not necessary to know $R(D)$ before the steepest ascent analysis is started. There are many variations to the basic idea of steepest ascent. Those interested can refer to Wilde [66] for details.

In the special case of a linear objective function and linear constraints, that is, linear programs, the optimization problem is

$$\max \; CD$$

$$\text{subject to} \; AD \leq B$$

$$D \geq 0$$

where C is an n-component row vector, A is an m by n matrix, and B is an m-component column vector. For linear programs, there is an extremely powerful gradient-type search procedure. From the theory of linear programming, we know that an optimal solution corresponds to an extreme point of the convex set defined by the linear constraints. Linear programming algorithms provide methods (basically solving linear equations) for moving from one extreme point to another adjacent one, always increasing the value of the objective function. When an extreme point is reached which has the property that the objective function cannot be increased by moving to an adjacent extreme point, a global optimum has been found. The importance and power of linear programming is partly due to the large size problems that it can solve. If we use a digital computer, problems with more than a thousand variables can be solved in a reasonable amount of time. Linear programming methods have been extended to the more general area of mathematical programming to handle certain nonlinear functions. There are special algorithms for quadratic objective functions and, more generally, any separable convex function can be approximated by a linear objective function. Nonlinear constraints are more difficult to handle. Rosen's gradient projection method works with any convex set of constraints. There are integer programming algorithms designed to optimize linear objective functions when the variables are constrained to equal natural numbers. There have been several books written on mathematical programming; details regarding theory, computational aspects, and applications may be found in almost all of them. Some of the more outstanding references are Charnes and Cooper [21], Dantzig [24], Graves and Wolfe [32], and Hadley [33, 34].

An alternative to increasing the value of the objective function at each step is to reduce, at each step, the portion of the region of feasibility containing an optimal solution. For example, if with each evaluation of the objective function we could reduce the portion of the region of feasibility containing an optimal solution by $1/a$, $a > 1$, after n evaluations we would know that the optimal solution was contained in a region $(1/a)^n$ the size of the original region. Fibonacci search [13, 66], provides an interesting example of this strategy. It can be applied to any unimodal function of one variable, and it guarantees that no more than a fixed number of evaluations of the objective function need be made to find the optimal solution. In the case of a discrete variable, the number of points that must be searched depends only on the total number of feasible points. When the variable is continuous, the number of points that must be searched depends only on the size of the interval and the degree of accuracy desired. This method can be considered as an optimal search procedure since it minimizes the maximum number of points that must be searched for an arbitrary unimodal function of one variable. It is called Fibonacci search because the number of points examined and the strategy for placing the points are closely related to the Fibonacci sequence $F_{n+2} = F_{n+1} + F_n$. Fibonacci search can be derived using a dynamic programming approach. We shall develop it in detail in Chapter IV.

Unfortunately, there are no optimal search procedures for arbitrary functions of several variables. The method of contour tangents [66] uses an elimination strategy and can be applied to functions of several variables, but it does not give an optimal upper bound on the number of points to be searched.

Finally, an optimal solution may be found with no search at all. An optimal solution for a twice differentiable objective function without constraints may be obtained directly from conditions on the first and second partial derivatives. A necessary condition for D^0 to be a local optimal solution (maximum or minimum) is that all of the first partial derivatives with respect to $R(D)$ vanish at D^0, that is,

$$\frac{\partial R}{\partial d_j^0} = 0, \qquad j = 1, \ldots, n$$

A sufficient condition for a local maximum (minimum) is that the matrix of the quadratic form of the second partial derivatives evaluated at D^0 be negative definite (positive definite). For two variables (d_1, d_2) this sufficient condition for a local maximum reduces to

$$\frac{\partial^2 R}{\partial d_1^2} < 0, \qquad \frac{\partial^2 R}{\partial d_2^2} < 0,$$

$$\frac{\partial^2 R}{\partial d_1^2} \cdot \frac{\partial^2 R}{\partial d_2^2} - \left(\frac{\partial^2 R}{\partial d_1 \, \partial d_2}\right)^2 > 0$$

Furthermore, if $R(D)$ is concave (convex) the necessary conditions are sufficient for a global maximum (minimum).†

---

† $R(D)$ is concave if for all pairs of points (D_1, D_2)
$$R[(1-\alpha)D_1 + \alpha D_2] \geq (1-\alpha)R(D_1) + \alpha R(D_2), \qquad 0 \leq \alpha \leq 1.$$
$R(D)$ is convex if $-R(D)$ is concave.

The conditions given above do not generally apply when there are constraints. However, in this case, Lagrange multipliers may be used to transform the constrained optimization problem into an equivalent unconstrained one. First assume that all of the constraints are equalities, that is, the optimization problem is

$$\max \ R(D)$$
$$\text{subject to } g_i(D) = 0, \qquad i = 1, \ldots, m$$

By considering the new optimization problem

$$\max \ V(D, \Lambda) = R(D) + \sum_{i=1}^{m} \lambda_i g_i(D)$$

as an unconstrained problem, where $\Lambda = (\lambda_1, \ldots, \lambda_m)$ are Lagrange multipliers, we obtain the necessary conditions for (D^0, Λ^0) to be a local optimum

$$\frac{\partial V}{\partial d_j^0} = \frac{\partial R}{\partial d_j^0} + \sum_{i=1}^{m} \lambda_i^0 \frac{\partial g_i}{\partial d_j^0} = 0, \qquad j = 1, \ldots, n$$

and

$$\frac{\partial V}{\partial \lambda_i^0} = g_i(D^0) = 0 \qquad\qquad i = 1, \ldots, m$$

It can be shown that, except in rare circumstances, these conditions are also necessary for (D^0) to be a local optimum for the original constrained problem. When the function $V(D, \Lambda)$ is concave (convex), the above conditions are sufficient as well as necessary for a global maximum (minimum). More general sufficient conditions are rather complicated (see Hancock [35]).

Kuhn and Tucker [44] have extended the classical Lagrangian approach to account for inequality constraints. In the optimization problem,

$$\max \ R(D)$$
$$\text{subject to } g_i(D) \le 0, \qquad i = 1, \ldots, m$$
$$D \ge 0,$$

with Lagrangian function

$$V(D, \Lambda) = R(D) + \sum_{i=1}^{m} \lambda_i g_i(D)$$

the conditions

$$d_j^0 \ge 0, \quad \frac{\partial V}{\partial d_j^0} \le 0, \quad d_j^0 \frac{\partial V}{\partial d_j^0} = 0, \qquad j = 1, \ldots, n$$

and

$$\lambda_i^0 \le 0, \quad \frac{\partial V}{\partial \lambda_i^0} \le 0, \quad \lambda_i^0 \frac{\partial V}{\partial \lambda_i^0} = 0, \qquad i = 1, \ldots, m$$

are necessary for (D^0) to be a local maximum.† When $R(D)$ is concave and $g_i(D)$ form a convex set of constraints, the conditions are sufficient as well as necessary for a global maximum.

There are some analogous conditions for optimizing functions of discrete variables. For example, let U_n be a function of the integro-valued variable n ($n = 1, 2, \ldots$). There is a local maximum at $n = k$ if

$$\Delta U_k = U_{k+1} - U_k < 0 \quad \text{and} \quad \Delta U_{k-1} = U_k - U_{k-1} > 0$$

These conditions are sufficient for a global maximum if

$$\Delta^2 U_n = \Delta(U_{n+1} - U_n) \leq 0, \quad \text{all } n$$

Everett [28] has shown that an objective function of discrete variables subject to constraints can be dealt with by using Lagrange multipliers. His main result is that any set of variables that yields a global maximum to the Lagrange function will yield a global maximum to the original constrained problem for some values of the right-hand sides of the constraints. The only limitation is that some restrictive properties are required on the objective function and the constraint set, to guarantee generation of the solution for all values of the right-hand sides of the constraints. An interesting property of Everett's approach is that sometimes an N-variable problem can be broken into N one-variable problems. This is very much in the spirit of dynamic programming.

---

† In addition, the Kuhn-Tucker Constraint Qualification must be satisfied. In practice, we generally assume that this rather complex condition is satisfied without checking.

II

Basic Theory

1. Multistage Problem Solving

We are all familiar with the approach to problem solving described in this section. When solving a complex problem, we often break it into a series of smaller problems—*decomposition*—and then combine the results from the solutions of the smaller problems to obtain the solution of the whole problem—*composition*. We call this approach *multistage problem solving*. This is in contrast to solving the problem in one step. Of course, if the problem can be solved in one step there is no need to use a multistage approach. But when the problem is complex, we must often resort to the multistage approach. If a suitable decomposition into subproblems can be found, the difficulty of having to determine the whole solution at once will be overcome with the multistage approach.

To be specific, assume some system can be described abstractly by a state vector X_0 and we are to change the system characteristics so that it can be described by a different state vector X_N. How can we find an appropriate transformation T_N to change the system from state X_0 to X_N? Pictorially, we represent the problem using a flow diagram as shown in Figure 1. Or symbolically, using the functional notation of mathematics, we seek a transformation T_N such that $X_N = T_N(X_0)$.

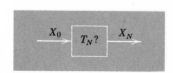

Fig. 1

Suppose we know of some transformation t_N which, when applied to a system in state X_{N-1}, would change the state of the system to X_N as shown in Figure 2. Or functionally, $X_N = t_N(X_{N-1})$.

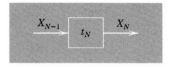

Fig. 2

To solve the original problem we now only need to find a transformation that will change the system from X_0 to X_{N-1}. Suppose T_{N-1} is such a transformation. Then the solution is given in Figure 3. The two boxes

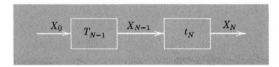

Fig. 3

with respective transformations T_{N-1}, t_N taken in series are equivalent to the single box with transformation T_N. Functionally, the same equivalence is readily established, since

$$X_{N-1} = T_{N-1}(X_0) \quad \text{and} \quad X_N = t_N(X_{N-1})$$

together yield

$$X_N = t_N(T_{N-1}(X_0)) = T_N(X_0)$$

Having achieved a simplification of the problem $X_N = T_N(X_0)$ by breaking it into the two subproblems

1. $X_N = t_N(X_{N-1})$
2. $X_{N-1} = T_{N-1}(X_0)$

we may want to proceed further. The appropriate transformation T_{N-1} may not be apparent. But perhaps T_{N-1} can be found in the same way that we found T_N. Let us introduce another intermediate state X_{N-2} and suppose transformations T_{N-2} and t_{N-1} are known, such that $X_{N-1} = t_{N-1}(X_{N-2})$ and $X_{N-2} = T_{N-2}(X_0)$. Then by applying transformations T_{N-2}, t_{N-1}, and t_N successively to the system in state X_0, we will have succeeded in transforming it to state X_N. Thus

$$X_N = t_N(X_{N-1}) = t_N(t_{N-1}(X_{N-2})) = t_N(t_{N-1}(T_{N-2}(X_0))) = T_N(X_0)$$

The corresponding flow diagram is shown in Figure 4. The original problem has now been broken into three subproblems

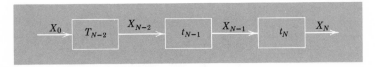

1. $X_N \quad = t_N(X_{N-1})$
2. $X_{N-1} = t_{N-1}(X_{N-2})$
3. $X_{N-2} = T_{N-2}(X_0)$

To arrive at a solution it may eventually be necessary to break the original problem into N subproblems.

$\quad$ 1. $X_N \quad = t_N(X_{N-1})$
$\qquad \vdots$

$N - n.\ \ X_{n+1} = t_{n+1}(X_n)$
$N - n + 1.\ \ X_n \quad = t_n(X_{n-1})$
$\qquad \vdots$

$\quad N.\ X_1 \quad = t_1(X_0)$

Figure 5 shows the corresponding flow diagram.

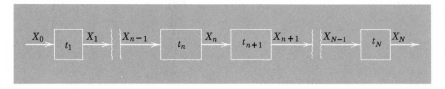

The multistage analysis just described started from the final state X_N and proceeded step by step with the discovery of transformations t_N, $t_{N-1}, \ldots, t_1$, to the initial state X_0. We call this variation of multistage analysis *backward* multistage problem solving. If we want to have the subscripts on the transformations agree with the order in which the transformations are determined, it is only necessary to renumber them in reverse order. To preserve the agreement between the corresponding subscripts on the transformations and states, we renumber the states in reverse order also. Thus X_N becomes the initial state, and X_0 the final state. The renumbered flow diagram of Figure 5 is shown in Figure 6.

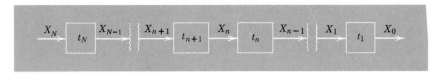

Fig. 6

The corresponding N subproblems are

1. $X_0 \quad = t_1(X_1)$
.
.
.
$n.$ $X_{n-1} = t_n(X_n)$
$n + 1.$ $X_n \quad = t_{n+1}(X_{n+1})$
.
.
.
$N.$ $X_{N-1} = t_N(X_N)$

Their recursive solution yields the desired transformation T_N so that $X_0 = T_N(X_N)$. In fact,

$$T_N = t_1 [\ldots [t_n [t_{n+1} [\ldots [t_N] \ldots]]] \ldots]$$

To see this, substitute $X_1 = t_2(X_2)$ into $X_0 = t_1(X_1)$ to obtain $X_0 = t_1[t_2(X_2)]$. Then substituting for X_2, using $X_2 = t_3(X_3)$, yields

$$X_0 = t_1[t_2(t_3(X_3))]$$

Continuing in this manner recursively the above equation for T_N is obtained.

The determination of t_n is a stage in the step-by-step solution of the whole problem. In fact, finding t_n is the nth stage of an N-stage process. It may be that, physically, the system actually passed through the states $X_{N-1}, \ldots, X_1$ in changing from X_N to X_0, or perhaps the intermediate states are merely artifacts. The really important factor, however, is that by consideration of these intermediate states, by breaking the whole problem into an equivalent series of subproblems by using multistage analysis, the problem becomes solvable.

As an alternative to backward multistage analysis we can start from the initial state X_0 and find a series of transformations leading to the final state X_N. In the forward multistage approach we first decompose into two problems, as shown in Figure 7, with subproblems

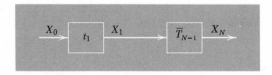

Fig. 7

1. $X_1 = t_1(X_0)$
2. $X_N = \overline{T}_{N-1}(X_1)$

If the forward decomposition is carried out $N - 1$ more times, we eventually reach the flow diagram of Figure 5. Conceptually, the only difference is the order in which the transformations t_n, $n = 1, \ldots, N$ are discovered. However, the direction (forward or backward) of multistage analysis may make a significant difference in the ease of solving the problem. The forward approach seems more natural, but the backward approach frequently leads more easily to the solution. Unfortunately, there appears to be a mental block against working backwards. To quote Polya [57],

There is certainly something in the method that is not superficial. There is a certain psychological difficulty in turning around, in going away from the goal, in working backwards, in not following the direct path to the desired end. When we discover the sequence of appropriate operations, our mind has to proceed in an order which is exactly the reverse of the actual performance. There is some sort of psychological repugnance to this reverse order which may prevent a quite able student from understanding the method if it is not presented carefully.

Multistage analysis is a problem-solving approach rather than a technique. Consequently, its scope of application is quite broad. But it is difficult to delineate a class of problems amenable to this approach. Applications will depend on the ingenuity of the problem solver. In the next two sections we shall illustrate this approach to problems ranging from mathematics to a puzzle suggestive of practical problems in planning and scheduling. In each of these problems, the important concept is the decomposition or multistage analysis, and not the direction of analysis. The forward and backward approaches apply equally as well. As a matter of fact, in the problem of Section 2 it appeared that the backward approach was superior until several students, without having been influenced, previously chose the forward approach and solved the problem rather quickly. We use the backward approach because it is not as familiar as the forward approach. Later, when we deal with multistage optimization problems, the direction of analysis will sometimes be crucial. When it is necessary, a clear distinction will be made.

2. A Puzzle†

A recipe calls for seven ounces of milk, but the cook only has one five-ounce and one eight-ounce cup. How can he measure exactly seven ounces of milk into one of the cups from a large can of milk? No other containers are available.

This is a tricky problem, which requires some deliberation. Try to solve this problem before looking at the solution, keeping in mind the basic idea of multistage analysis.

Clearly, if seven ounces of milk is to be contained in one of the cups, it must be the eight-ounce cup. The problem is to determine how to obtain the final state of seven ounces of milk in the eight-ounce cup.

Suppose the problem were solved and there were seven ounces of milk in the eight-ounce cup. How did it get there? If there were already two ounces of milk in the eight-ounce cup, it would be easy since the last five ounces could be transferred from a full five-ounce cup. Then the problem becomes one of getting two ounces of milk in the eight-ounce cup. How could this be done? Presumably by filling one of the cups and then pouring some out. But if this were to be done using a full eight-ounce cup, six ounces would have to be poured off. That does not seem easy. Perhaps three ounces could be poured from a full five-ounce cup. That is obviously the answer. If the eight-ounce cup contained five ounces of milk (easy enough) and if it were then filled to capacity from a full five-ounce cup, the five-ounce cup would contain exactly two ounces of milk. The problem is solved. All that we need to do is trace our steps back until the eight-ounce cup contains seven ounces of milk. This is shown in Table 1.

By starting at the final state, the key point of getting two ounces of milk in the eight-ounce cup is discovered most easily. If we start with the initial state, it appears that more trial and error is required. Nevertheless, it is perfectly plausible to use forward multistage analysis to solve the problem. In fact, chess players accustomed to planning five moves ahead might see the solution all at once. Multistage analysis, however, makes the problem easier to solve.

This way of using multistage analysis to solve the puzzle is suggestive of an approach to all kinds of planning and scheduling problems, from determining the time that various parts of a meal must be prepared in order to have the whole dinner ready at a given time to scheduling research and development activities for a missile that must be operational

---

† This problem is similar to one given in Polya [57]. In fact, most of the motivation for the first few sections of this Chapter has come from Polya's book.

by a certain date. It is common sense that, when the success of an entire venture depends on the identification and integration of several parts, a step-by-step analysis of each subproblem is essential to the solution of the whole problem.

Table 1

State	Five-Ounce Cup	Eight-Ounce Cup	Transformation
1	0	0	Fill the five-ounce cup and transfer its contents to the eight-ounce cup
2	0	5	Fill the five-ounce cup and from the five-ounce cup fill the eight-ounce cup
3	2	8	Empty the eight-ounce cup and then transfer the contents of the five-ounce cup to it
4	0	2	Fill the five-ounce cup and transfer its contents to the eight-ounce cup.
5	0	7	

3. Mathematical Proof

Suppose we wish to establish the truth or falsity of some statement (mathematical theorem) p_0. Presumably there are some statements related to p_0 whose truth value (true or false) is known. By establishing the logical relationship between p_0 and one of these statements, we can often determine the truth value of p_0.

One plan of attack is to start with p_0 and derive another statement p_1 from p_0. Formally, p_1 is true whenever p_0 is true, or p_0 implies p_1 ($p_0 \rightarrow p_1$). If it is known that p_1 is false, then p_0 is false. However, if the truth value of p_1 is unknown, we can repeat the process. Suppose we finally reach some statement p_n, which is false, after developing the logical relations $p_0 \rightarrow p_1 \rightarrow \ldots \rightarrow p_{n-1} \rightarrow p_n$. Then p_{n-1} must be false. It then follows that p_{n-2} must be false and, finally, that p_0 is false.

Informally translating this mode of proof into our model of multistage analysis, we assume the end result—statement p_0. By working backwards through the intermediate statements $p_1, \ldots, p_{n-1}$, we finally arrive at some false statement p_n, which establishes the falsity of statement p_0.

We can also begin with the negative of p_0, say q_0, a statement that is false whenever p_0 is true, and true whenever p_0 is false. Proceeding as we did in the previous case, we derive statements $q_1, \ldots, q_n$ so that q_1 follows from q_0, q_2 follows from q_1, etc. ($q_0 \to q_1 \to \ldots \to q_{n-1} \to q_n$). Suppose q_n is false, then q_0 is false, so p_0 must be true. Beginning with the final result, p_0 or its negative, is called the backward approach.

In the forward multistage approach we begin with some true statement p_n, and attempt to derive p_0 or q_0 from it. Suppose $p_n \to p_{n-1} \to \ldots \to p_1 \to p_0$, then it follows that p_0 is true. On the other hand, if $p_n \to p_{n-1} \to \ldots \to p_1 \to q_0$, then q_0 is true, so p_0 must be false.

It depends on the particular problem whether the forward or backward approach is more advantageous. However, when adjacent statements are implied by each other, the two modes of proof are essentially equivalent. Suppose p_{i-1} is true (false) whenever p_i is true (false) and p_i is true (false) whenever p_{i-1} is true (false). Symbolically, this relation is expressed as $p_{i-1} \leftrightarrow p_i$. If we begin with p_0 and obtain $p_0 \leftrightarrow p_1 \leftrightarrow \ldots \leftrightarrow p_n$, or begin with p_n and obtain $p_n \leftrightarrow p_{n-1} \leftrightarrow \ldots \leftrightarrow p_0$, the truth value of p_0 is the same as that of p_n.

The example given next, taken from matrix algebra, illustrates the multistage approach to mathematical proof. The same approach is applicable to proving identities in trigonometry and theorems in geometry and in more abstract branches of mathematics.

Prove

$$p_0: \quad I + B(I - AB)^{-1} A = (I - BA)^{-1}$$

where I is an identity matrix, and A and B are square matrices of the same dimension as I.†

Assume this statement is a true equation and multiply both sides of it on the right by $I - BA$. This yields

$$p_1: \quad (I - BA) + B(I - AB)^{-1} A(I - BA) = I$$

Subtracting $I - BA$ from both sides, we obtain

$$p_2: \quad B(I - AB)^{-1} A(I - BA) = BA$$

Multiplying both sides on the left by B^{-1} and then by $(I - AB)$ gives

$$p_3: \quad A(I - BA) = (I - AB)A$$

Expanding yields

$$p_4: \quad AI - ABA = IA - ABA$$

an obvious algebraic identity. This completes the proof of p_0 using the backward multistage approach. Had we started with the statement p_4 and

---

† It is assumed that the matrices B, $I - AB$, and $I - BA$ have inverses (are nonsingular).

reversed the steps given above, p_0 could have been proved as easily by using forward multistage analysis, since each of the previous adjacent statements is implied by the other.

4. A One-Stage Decision System

So far we have only been concerned with multistage problems containing one solution, or if there has been more than one solution, each was as good as any other. The missing element is decision making. Decision making arises when there is more than one feasible solution to a problem. Associated with each solution is a number measuring its return. The decision-making or optimization problem is to find the solution yielding maximum return.

We continue our discussion of the multistage approach and now incorporate decision making in it. We begin by studying the properties of a typical stage of a multistage decision system. A one-stage system is represented in Figure 8 by a box that is characterized by five factors.

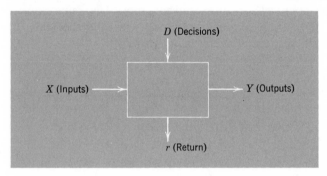

Fig. 8

1. An input state X that gives all all relevant information about inputs to the box (X is called the initial state, as it gives a description of the system at the beginning of the stage).

2. An output state Y that gives all relevant information about outputs from the box (Y is called the final state, as it gives a description of the system at the end of the stage).

3. A decision variable D that controls the operation of the box.

4. A stage return r, a scalar variable that measures the utility of the box, as a single-valued function of inputs, decisions, and outputs, that is

$$r = r(X, D, Y)$$

5. A stage transformation t, a single-valued transformation, sometimes called the stage-coupling function, expressing each component of the output state as a function of the input state and decisions, that is,

$$Y = t(X, D)$$

If, for example, Y contained two components (y_1, y_2) we would have $y_1 = t_1(X, D)$ and $y_2 = t_2(X, D)$. The symbol t is used abstractly to represent the transformations that yield all components of the output state.

The mathematical difference between the input and output states is that the output (Y) is a function of the input (X) and of the decisions. But frequently the difference is artificial. For example, it is immaterial whether we write

$$Y = X - D \quad \text{or} \quad X = Y + D$$

Thus either X or Y can be chosen as the input state. Subsequently, when we want to find the optimal return as a function of the output state, it will be convenient to interchange the roles of inputs and outputs.

Since the stage transformation is single-valued, it can be used to eliminate Y from the stage return. In particular,

$$Y = t(X, D)$$

is substituted into

$$r = r(X, D, Y)$$

to yield

$$r = r(X, D, t(X, D))$$

This says that the only independent variables affecting the stage return are X and D since, given values of X and D, a unique value of Y is specified through t. This leads to a unique value of r. To indicate this dependence we rewrite

$$r = r(X, D, t(X, D))$$

simply as †

$$r = r(X, D)$$

The one-stage initial state optimization problem is to find the maximum stage return *as a function of the input state*. Denoting $f(X)$ as the optimal return, and $D^* = D(X)$ as the optimal decision policy, we have

$$f(X) = r(X, D(X)) = r(X, D^*) = \max_D r(X, D) \geq r(X, D)$$

---

† Mathematical rigor would require us to use a new symbol $g(X, D)$ to distinguish the return function with two arguments from the function with three arguments. However, to preserve the mnemonic symbology of r representing the stage return function, we will use $r = r(X, D)$. This will allow the reader to easily recognize $r(X, D, Y)$, $r(X, D, t(X, D))$, and $r(X, D)$ as alternative expressions for the stage return. This notational device is used frequently, but only when the specific functional forms are of no particular importance.

If X and D are both scalars, the dimensionality of the optimization is one state variable and one decision variable. Generally, the dimensionality is given by an ordered pair of numbers (m, n), where m is the number of components in the state variable and n is the number of components in the decision variable.

If we were free to choose X, it would be considered as a decision variable also. Then

$$f(X^{*}) = \max_{X} f(X) = \max_{X,D} r(X, D)$$

and the dimensionality would be $(o, m + n)$.

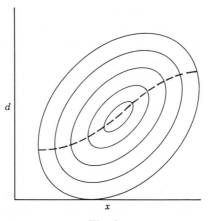

Fig. 9

To clarify the ideas of one-stage optimization, consider a return function $r(x, d)$ in which x and d are scalar variables as shown in Figure 9. The solid lines are contours of constant r increasing towards the center. The dashed line represents the optimal policy $d(x)$, presumably determined from one of the optimization techniques discussed in Chapter I. Figure 10 shows the optimal return as a function of x.

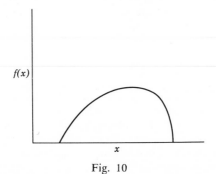

Fig. 10

In an ordinary optimization problem the optimal return is usually a number. However, the optimal return $f(x)$ is a function—a sequence of numbers, one for each value of x. Thus the determination of $f(x)$ is a series of optimization problems, one for each value of x. The idea of determining optimal returns as functions is really the key to dynamic programming.

A minor complication occurs when the optimal return is to be determined as a function of the output (Y). Suppose that it is possible to determine X as a single-valued function of Y and D by "inverting" the transformation

$$Y = t(X, D)$$

to obtain †

$$X = \bar{\imath}(Y, D)$$

Then X can be eliminated from the return function. Thus the stage return can be expressed as a function of only the decisions and outputs as

$$r = r(\bar{\imath}(Y, D), D, Y) = r(Y, D)$$

The one-stage final state optimization problem is to choose D as a function of Y to maximize r. Denoting $f(Y)$ as the optimal return and $D^{*} = D(Y)$ as the optimal policy, we have

$$f(Y) = r(Y, D^{*}) = \max_{D} r(Y, D)$$

If it is neither computationally feasible nor theoretically possible to invert the stage transformation, we can maximize over X and D subject to the stage transformation as a constraint, that is

$$f(Y) = \max_{D,X} r(X, D, Y)$$
$$\text{subject to } Y = t(X, D)$$

Even if the stage transformation is invertible it may not be possible to express all components of X as a function of Y and of D. For example, consider

$$y = \frac{x_1}{x_2 + d}$$

We can solve for either x_1 in terms of x_2, y, and d, or x_2 in terms of x_1, y, and d, but it is not possible to express both input states in terms of the output state and decision variable. Generally, if the optimal return is determined as a function of the output only, all inputs that cannot be eliminated from the inverse of the stage transformation are treated as decision variables.

---

† Formally, if $Y = t(X, D)$ is a one-to-one function on the domain of X, D, there exists a function $\bar{\imath}(Y, D)$ such that $X = \bar{\imath}(Y, D)$.

When the optimal return is determined as a function of the input and output states, there may be no decision making at all. Suppose

$$Y = t(X, D)$$

can be solved for D in terms of X and Y, that is

$$D = \hat{t}(X, Y)$$

Then the optimal return as a function of the input and output states is

$$f(X, Y) = r(X, \hat{t}(X, Y), Y) = r(X, Y)$$

If only some of the components of D can be eliminated by using t, the remaining components are still decision variables.

To present fixed terminology for the various kinds of one-stage optimization problems, we call the determination of $f(X)$ the *initial state* problem, the determination of $f(Y)$ the *final state* problem, and the evaluation of $f(X, Y)$ the *initial-final state* problem. This terminology extends over to multistage decision systems, to which we now turn.

5. Serial Multistage Decision System

A serial multistage system consists of a set of stages joined together in series so that the output of one stage becomes the input to the next (see Figure 11). The backward numbering of stages is used for precisely the same reason as it is used in the multistage analysis of Section 1.

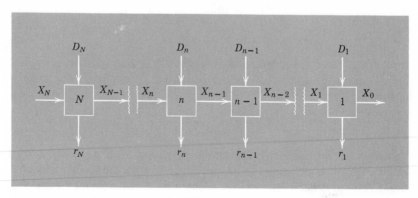

Fig. 11

For the general stage n ($n = 1, 2, \ldots, N$) of the N-stage system, the stage transformation is

$$X_{n-1} = t_n(X_n, D_n)$$

and the stage return is

$$r_n = r_n(X_n, D_n)$$

The elimination of the stage outputs from the return functions follows from the argument given previously. No limitations are placed on the form of the functions t_n and r_n. However, the structure of a serial multistage system implies some important assumptions.

From the transformations, it follows that X_n depends only on the decisions made prior to stage n $(D_{n+1}, \ldots, D_N)$ and X_N. That is,

$$X_n = t_{n+1}(X_{n+1}, D_{n+1}) = t_{n+1}(t_{n+2}(X_{n+2}, D_{n+2}), D_{n+1})$$

$$= t_{n+1}(X_{n+2}, D_{n+2}, D_{n+1}) = t_{n+1}(t_{n+3}(X_{n+3}, D_{n+3}), D_{n+2}, D_{n+1})$$

$$= \ldots = t_{n+1}(X_N, D_N, \ldots, D_{n+1})$$

It then follows, by combining the above equation with the return function, that the return from stage n depends only on the decisions $(D_n, D_{n+1}, \ldots, D_N)$ and X_N, that is,

$$r_n = r_n(X_n, D_n) = r_n(t_{n+1}(X_N, D_N, \ldots, D_{n+1}), D_n)$$

$$= r_n(X_N, D_N, \ldots, D_n)$$

Or, in other words, D_n only affects the return from stages one through n.

The total return R_N from stages one through N is some function of the individual stage returns written as

$$R_N(X_N, X_{N-1}, \ldots, X_1, D_N, D_{N-1}, \ldots, D_1)$$

$$= g[r_N(X_N, D_N), r_{N-1}(X_{N-1}, D_{N-1}), \ldots, r_1(X_1, D_1)]$$

However, as just explained, $(X_{N-1}, \ldots, X_1)$ can be eliminated from the individual stage returns and consequently from the total return. Thus an alternate expression for R_N is

$$R_N(X_N, D_N, D_{N-1}, \ldots, D_1) = g[r_N(X_N, D_N), r_{N-1}(X_N, D_N, D_{N-1}), \ldots,$$
$$r_1(X_N, D_N, \ldots, D_1)]$$

The N-stage initial state optimization problem is to maximize the N-stage return R_N over the variables $D_1, \ldots, D_N$; that is, to find the optimal return as the function of the initial state X_N. Denoting $f_N(X_N)$ as the maximum N-stage return, and $D_n^* = D_n(X_N)$, $X_n^* = t_n(X_N)$ as the optimal decisions and states, we have as alternative expressions for $f_N(X_N)$,

$$\text{I:} \quad f_N(X_N) = g[r_N(X_N, D_N^*), r_{N-1}(X_{N-1}^*, D_{N-1}^*), \ldots, r_1(X_1^*, D_1^*)]$$

$$= \max_{D_N, \ldots, D_1} g[r_N(X_N, D_N), r_{N-1}(X_{N-1}, D_{N-1}), \ldots, r_1(X_1, D_1)]$$

subject to $X_{n-1} = t_n(X_n, D_n), \quad n = 1, \ldots, N$

or II: $f_N(X_N) = g[r_N(X_N, D_N^*), r_{N-1}(X_N, D_N^*, D_{N-1}^*), \ldots,$
$$r_1(X_N, D_N^*, \ldots, D_1^*)]$$

$$= \max_{D_N, \ldots, D_1} g[r_N(X_N, D_N), r_{N-1}(X_N, D_N, D_{N-1}), \ldots,$$
$$r_1(X_N, D_N, \ldots, D_1)]$$

Offhandedly, it seems that the second formulation is preferable, since it contains only N decision variables $(D_N, \ldots, D_1)$ and one state variable X_N. By comparison, Formulation I contains N decision variables N state variables, and N constraints. Since optimization techniques decrease in efficiency as the number of variables increase, it would seem natural to eliminate the intermediate state variables $(X_{N-1}, \ldots, X_1)$ if it were computationally feasible to do so. However, Formulation I frequently can be transformed into N optimization problems, each containing only one decision variable and one state variable. In fact, the intermediate state variables are often introduced artificially. In these cases a problem given in Formulation II is embedded in a larger problem (Formulation I) which, surprisingly enough, is easier to solve.

6. Decomposition—Additive Returns

Our objective is to decompose the problem

$$f_N(X_N) = \max_{D_N, \ldots, D_1} g[r_N(X_N, D_N), r_{N-1}(X_{N-1}, D_{N-1}), \ldots, r_1(X_1, D_1)]$$

subject to $X_{n-1} = t_n(X_n, D_n), \qquad n = 1, \ldots, N$

into N equivalent subproblems each containing only one state variable and one decision variable. Each of the subproblems will be roughly equivalent to a one-stage optimization problem. Instead of solving one optimization problem, in which all of the decisions are interdependent, we shall find the optimal decisions almost one at a time. Our approach is the familiar one of using multistage analysis first to decompose the original problem into N subproblems. Then the solutions from the subproblems are combined to obtain the solution to the original problem.

To achieve this decomposition, a highly restrictive assumption must be made about the function g. Rather than stating this condition now, we will first derive the decomposition for a particular form of g which satisfies the condition. This derivation will provide the insight from which we can deduce a sufficient condition on the form of g for decomposition.

Let

$$g[r_N(X_N, D_N), r_{N-1}(X_{N-1}, D_{N-1}), \ldots, r_1(X_1, D_1)]$$

$$= r_N(X_N, D_N) + r_{N-1}(X_{N-1}, D_{N-1}) + \ldots + r_1(X_1, D_1)$$

Thus

$$f_N(X_N) = \max_{D_N,\ldots,D_1} [r_N(X_N, D_N) + r_{N-1}(X_{N-1}, D_{N-1}) + \ldots + r_1(X_1, D_1)]$$

subject to $X_{n-1} = t_n(X_n, D_n), \qquad n = 1, \ldots, N$

Since

1: the Nth-stage return does not depend on $D_{N-1}, \ldots, D_1$

and

2: for arbitrary real-valued functions $h_1(u_1)$ and $h_2(u_1, u_2)$

$$\max_{u_1, u_2} [h_1(u_1) + h_2(u_1, u_2)] = \max_{u_1} [h_1(u_1) + \max_{u_2} h_2(u_1, u_2)]$$

$$f_N(X_N) = \max_{D_N} [r_N(X_N, D_N) + \max_{D_{N-1}, \ldots, D_1} (r_{N-1}(X_{N-1}, D_{N-1}) + \ldots + r_1(X_1, D_1))]$$

subject to $X_{n-1} = t_n(X_n, D_n), \qquad n = 1, \ldots, N$

Bringing the maximum over $D_{N-1}, \ldots, D_1$ inside the outside parentheses is the crucial step in the decomposition. However, the maximum with respect to D_N is still over $r_{N-1}, \ldots, r_1$, as X_{N-1} depends on D_N through the stage transformation t_N.

From the definition of $f_N(X_N)$ it follows that

$$f_{N-1}(X_{N-1}) = \max_{D_{N-1}, \ldots, D_1} [r_{N-1}(X_{N-1}, D_{N-1}) + \ldots + r_1(X_1, D_1)]$$

Thus

$$f_N(X_N) = \max_{D_N} [r_N(X_N, D_N) + f_{N-1}(X_{N-1})]$$

subject to $X_{N-1} = t_N(X_N, D_N)$

or

$$f_N(X_N) = \max_{D_N} [r_N(X_N, D_N) + f_{N-1}(t_N(X_N, D_N))]$$

Defining

$$Q_N(X_N, D_N) = r_N(X_N, D_N) + f_{N-1}(t_N(X_N, D_N))]$$

the determination of $f_N(X_N)$ and $D_N^* = D_N(X_N)$, given $f_{N-1}(X_{N-1})$, is simply a one-stage initial state optimization problem with state variable X_N, decision variable D_N, and return Q_N. That is,

$$f_N(X_N) = \max_{D_N} Q_N(X_N, D_N).$$

We have simplified the original N-stage problem into two smaller optimization problems

1. $f_{N-1}(X_{N-1}) = \max_{D_{N-1}, \ldots, D_1} [r_{N-1}(X_{N-1}, D_{N-1}) + \ldots + r_1(X_1, D_1)]$

subject to $X_{n-1} = t_n(X_n, D_n), \qquad n = 1, \ldots, N-1$

[an $(N-1)$-stage optimization]

and 2. $\quad f_N(x_N) = \max_{D_N} Q_N(X_N, D_N)$

$$= \max_{D_N} [r_N(X_N, D_N) + f_{N-1}(t_N(X_N, D_N))]$$

(a one-stage optimization)

It is clear that we can proceed further.

In fact, by treating $f_{N-1}(X_{N-1})$ and then $f_{N-2}(X_{N-2}), \ldots, f_2(X_2)$ in the same way as $f_N(X_N)$, we decompose the original problem into N one-stage initial state optimization problems.

1. $f_1(X_1) = \max_{D_1} Q_1(X_1, D_1) = \max_{D_1} r_1(X_1, D_1)$

.
.
.

n. $f_n(X_n) = \max_{D_n} Q_n(X_n, D_n) = \max_{D_n} [r_n(X_n, D_n) + f_{n-1}(t_n(X_n, D_n))]$

.
.
.

N. $f_N(X_N) = \max_{D_N} Q_N(X_N, D_N) = \max_{D_N} [r_N(X_N, D_N) + f_{N-1}(t_N(X_N, D_N))]$

Stating the N problems more compactly, we have †

$$\begin{array}{ll} f_n(X_n) = \max_{D_n} Q_n(X_n, D_n), & n = 1, \ldots, N \\ Q_n(X_n, D_n) = r_n(X_n, D_n), & n = 1 \\ \qquad = r_n(X_n, D_n) + f_{n-1}(t_n(X_n, D_n)), & n = 2, \ldots, N \end{array}$$

The equations in the box represent the usual recursion equations of dynamic programming. Their recursive solution, starting with $n = 1$ and continuing through $n = N$, yields the optimal N-stage return, $f_N(X_N)$, the optimal decision $D_N^* = D_N^*(X_N)$, and the decision functions $D_n = D_n(X_n)$, $n = 1, \ldots, N - 1$. If we want to find the optimal input state X_N^* we simply solve $f_N(X_N^*) = \max_{X_N} f_N(X_N)$.

To find the remaining optimal decisions and states as a function of X_N, we start with

$$X_{N-1}^* = t_N(X_N, D_N^*) = t_N(X_N, D_N(X_N)) = t_N(X_N)$$

and

$$D_{N-1}^* = D_{N-1}(X_{N-1}^*) = D_{N-1}(t_N(X_N, D_N^*)) = D_{N-1}(X_N)$$

---

† An alternate expression for $Q_n(X_n, D_n)$ is

$$Q_n(X_n, D_n) = r_n(X_n, D_n) + f_{n-1}(X_{n-1})$$

subject to $X_{n-1} = t_n(X_n, D_n)$

Frequently when the form of t_n is not important, we write

$$Q_n(X_n, D_n) = r_n(X_n, D_n) + f_{n-1}(X_{n-1})$$

assuming that the constraint is implicity stated.

We then proceed recursively from $n = N - 1, \ldots, 1$ using the relations

$$X_{n-1}^* = t_n(X_n, D_n^*) = t_n(X_N) \quad \text{and} \quad D_{n-1}^* = D_{n-1}(X_{n-1}^*) = D_{n-1}(X_N)$$

7. Terminal Optimization

A special case of the maximization of the sum of stage returns, called terminal optimization, is the maximization of some function of the final output state. That is,

$$f_N(X_N) = \max_{D_N, \ldots, D_1} g(X_0)$$

$$\text{subject to } X_{n-1} = t_n(X_n, D_n), \qquad n = 1, \ldots, N$$

Let

$$r_N(X_N, D_N) = r_{N-1}(X_{N-1}, D_{N-1}) = \ldots = r_2(X_2, D_2) = 0$$

and

$$r_1(X_1, D_1) = g[t_1(X_1, D_1)] = g(X_0)$$

Then,

$$r_N(X_N, D_N) + \ldots + r_1(X_1, D_1) = g(X_0)$$

so

$$f_N(X_N) = \max_{D_N, \ldots, D_1} [r_N(X_N, D_N) + \ldots + r_1(X_1, D_1)]$$

$$\text{subject to } X_{n-1} = t_n(X_n, D_n), \qquad n = 1, \ldots, N$$

Actually a duality exists between the optimization of the sum of stage returns and the terminal optimization problem, since it is also the case that

$$f_N(X_N) = \max_{D_N, \ldots, D_1} \sum_{n=1}^{N} r_n(X_n, D_n)$$

$$\text{subject to } X_{n-1} = t_n(X_n, D_n), \qquad n = 1, \ldots, N$$

can be formulated as a terminal optimization problem. Let

$$y_N = 0 \quad \text{and} \quad y_n = \sum_{k=n+1}^{N} r_k(X_k, D_k), \qquad n = 0, \ldots, N - 1$$

Note that

$$y_0 = \sum_{n=1}^{N} r_n(X_n, D_n) \quad \text{and} \quad y_{n-1} = y_n + r_n(X_n, D_n), \qquad n = 1, \ldots, N$$

Thus

$$f_N(X_N) = \max_{D_N, \ldots, D_1} y_0$$

$$\text{subject to } X_{n-1} = t_n(X_n, D_n)$$

and

$$y_{n-1} = y_n + r_n(X_n, D_n) \qquad n = 1, \ldots, N$$

and we have established the duality. In other words, it is always possible to transform a terminal optimization problem into one of maximizing the sum of stage returns. Conversely, a problem of maximizing the sum of stage returns can be transformed into a terminal optimization problem.

8. A Decision Tree and the Principle of Optimality

Having developed the recursive equations of dynamic programming using a formal and deductive approach, we proceed informally to uncover a simple and intuitive principle upon which the equations are based.

A multistage decision system in which each decision and state variable can take on only a finite number of values can be represented graphically by a "decision tree" (see Figure 12). The circles, called nodes, correspond to the states, and the lines between circles, called arcs, correspond to decisions. Starting from the node at the base of the tree, which denotes the initial state of the system at stage three, there are three possible decisions represented by the three arcs emanating from the node. Associated with each arc is a return and an output. The outputs are shown by the three nodes at the end of these three arcs. These nodes represent the three possible input states to stage two. Stages two and one are interpreted in a similar manner. Feasible solutions correspond to paths (a set of adjoining arcs) between the node at the base of the tree and any node at the top of the tree. The return from a path is the sum of the returns from the arcs included in the path. The objective is to determine a path yielding maximum return.

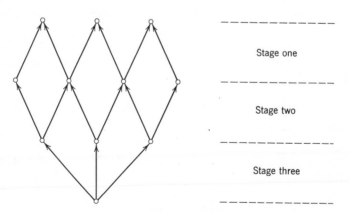

Fig. 12 A Decision Tree

Working backwards to find an optimal path, we start with the four input nodes at stage one. Not knowing, for the moment, which of these nodes is included in an optimal path, we find an arc from each of them that maximizes the return to the top of the tree. Consequently, for each input node at stage one, the optimal return and an optimal arc to the top of the tree is known. This corresponds to the determination of the functions $f_1(X_1)$ and $D_1(X_1)$. In particular, an optimal return from a specific node and the arc which produced that return are specific elements of $f_1(X_1)$ and $D_1(X_1)$. The set of optimal returns and arcs, one for each input node at stage one, corresponds to the functions $f_1(X_1)$ and $D_1(X_1)$ respectively.

Now consider a two-stage system, consisting of stages two and one, which has three input nodes. We seek optimal paths and returns from each of these nodes to the top of the tree. These can be determined by finding arcs that maximize the returns from the arcs combined with *optimal returns* from the output nodes. Once these are known, the same concept can be applied to a three-stage system to determine an optimal path from the base to the top of the tree. The fundamental concept is that we need only consider the *optimal returns* from the output nodes. Or in other words, it is unnecessary to consider returns that are not optimal with respect to the output nodes. After all, if we are to obtain an optimal solution for a system, any portion must be optimal. This is Bellman's [10] "principle of optimality." Stated more succinctly in his words—

An optimal policy has the property that whatever the initial state and decision are, the remaining decisions must constitute an optimal policy with regard to the state resulting from the first decision.

A proof of the principle of optimality (by contradiction) simply states that if the remaining decisions were not optimal then the whole policy could not be optimal.

A mathematical statement of the principle of optimality is the recursion equations of the previous section. Suppose the nodes at stage N were numbered 1, 2, ... and that the variable $X_N = 1, 2, ...$ was used to represent them. Let the arcs emanating from each node at stage N be labeled $A, B, ...$, and be designated by the variable $D_N = A, B, ...$. A particular node-arc combination is specified by assigning values to X_N and D_N, for example, $(X_N, D_N) = (2, A)$. Thus the return from a node-arc combination may be written as $r_N = r_N(X_N, D_N)$, and the node this node-arc combination leads to as $X_{N-1} = t_N(X_N, D_N)$. Let $f_{N-1}(X_{N-1})$ be a function giving the optimal return from each of the input nodes at stage $N - 1$. Then, it follows from the principle of optimality that

$$f_N(X_N) = \max_{D_N} \ [r_N(X_N, D_N) + f_{N-1}(X_{N-1})]$$

For example, for the first input node at stage two,

$$f_2(X_2 = 1) = \max_{D_2 = A, B} \ [r_2(X_2 = 1, D_2) + f_1(X_1)], \qquad X_1 = t_2(X_2, D_2)$$

$$= \max \ [r_2(X_2 = 1, D_2 = A) + f_1(X_1 = 1), \ r_2(X_2 = 1, D_2 = B) + f_1(X_1 = 2)]$$

We have developed the recursive equations of dynamic programming in two ways. We used a constructive derivation—constructing the equations directly from the total return function and constraints for a multistage system. Then we started with the principle of optimality, proved it immediately by contradiction, and then translated it into the recursion equations. The latter is the historical approach, and reveals the insight of Bellman. However, the constructive approach is more useful in providing an understanding of the underlying multistage structure required in dynamic programming.

9. Generalized Decomposition

To generalize the decomposition of

$$\max_{D_N, D_{N-1}, \ldots, D_1} g[r_N(X_N, D_N), \; r_{N-1}(X_{N-1}, D_{N-1}), \ldots, r_1(X_1, D_1)]$$

we must achieve the crucial step of moving the maximization with respect to $D_{N-1}, \ldots, D_1$ inside the Nth stage return. A sufficient condition for achieving this important change in the position of the maximizations has been given by Mitten [51].

First we shall derive Mitten's condition for a two-stage problem.

Let

$$f_2(X_2) = \max_{D_2, D_1} g(r_2(X_2, D_2), \; r_1(X_1, D_1))$$

$$\text{subject to } X_1 = t_2(X_2, D_2)$$

Eliminating X_1, we have

$$f_2(X_2) = \max_{D_2, D_1} g(r_2(X_2, D_2), \; r_1(X_2, D_2, D_1))$$

Let

$$f_2'(X_2) = \max_{D_2} [g(r_2(X_2, D_2), \; \max_{D_1} r_1(X_2, D_2, D_1))]$$

From the definition of a maximum $f_2'(X_2) \leq f_2(X_2)$. We are interested in the cases when equality holds, that is, $f_2'(X_2) = f_2(X_2)$. A sufficient condition for equality is that g be a monotonically nondecreasing function of r_1 for every feasible value of r_2. By the definition of monotonicity, we have, if

$$r_1(X_2, D_2, D_1') \geq r_1(X_2, D_2, D_1'') \quad \text{(with } X_2 \text{ and } D_2 \text{ fixed)}$$

then

$$g(r_2(X_2, D_2), \; r_1(X_2, D_2, D_1')) \geq g(r_2(X_2, D_2), \; r_1(X_2, D_2, D_1''))$$

But for each value of X_2 and D_2

$$r_1(X_2, D_2, D_1^*) = \max_{D_1} r_1(X_2, D_2, D_1) \geq r_1(X_2, D_2, D_1)$$

Hence from the monotonicity, with X_2 and D_2 fixed,

$$g(r_2(X_2, D_2),\ r_1(X_2, D_2, D_1^*)) \geq g(r_2(X_2, D_2),\ r_1(X_2, D_2, D_1))$$

for all values of D_1. In particular, this inequality must hold for the maximum with respect to D_1 of the term on the right-hand side, that is,

$$g(r_2(X_2, D_2),\ r_1(X_2, D_2, D_1^*)) \geq \max_{D_1}\ g(r_2(X_2, D_2),\ r_1(X_2, D_2, D_1))$$

Consequently,

$$f_2'(X_2) = \max_{D_2}\ g(r_2(X_2, D_2),\ r_1(X_2, D_2, D_1^*))$$

$$\geq \max_{D_2} \max_{D_1}\ g(r_2(X_2, D_2),\ r_1(X_2, D_2, D_1)) = f_2(X_2)$$

The given inequality $f_2'(X_2) \leq f_2(X_2)$ together with the derived inequality $f_2'(X_2) \geq f_2(X_2)$ yields the result $f_2'(X_2) = f_2(X_2)$. We have shown that if *g is a monotonically nondecreasing function of r_1 for every r_2 the position of maximization with respect to D_1 can be changed* (as just explained) *with no possibility of missing the optimal solution.*

Another condition is imposed in order to decompose an N-stage problem. We call this condition *separability*. The monotonicity and separability conditions together are sufficient for decomposition. In particular, if

1. Separability
$$g[r_N(X_N, D_N),\ r_{N-1}(X_{N-1}, D_{N-1}), \ldots, r_1(X_1, D_1)]$$

$$= g_1[r_N(X_N, D_N),\ g_2(r_{N-1}(X_{N-1}, D_{N-1}), \ldots, r_1(X_1, D_1))]$$

where g_1 and g_2 are real-valued functions, and

2. Monotonicity
   g_1 is a monotonically nondecreasing function of g_2 for every r_N
then
   3. Decomposition
$$\max_{D_N, D_{N-1}, \ldots, D_1}\ g[r_N(X_N, D_N),\ r_{N-1}(X_{N-1}, D_{N-1}), \ldots, r_1(X_1, D_1)]$$

$$= \max_{D_N}\ g_1[r_N(X_N, D_N),\ \max_{D_{N-1}, \ldots, D_1}\ g_2(r_{N-1}(X_{N-1}, D_{N-1}), \ldots,\ r_1(X_1, D_1))]$$

Given separability and monotonicity, the proof of decomposition for an N-stage is identical to the proof for a two-stage problem. The class of problems that satisfy separability and monotonicity is called decomposable. Note that a two-stage problem with return function

$$g(r_2(X_2, D_2),\ r_1(X_1, D_1))$$

is always separable because $g = g_1$ and $r_1 = g_2$, by definition. However, when there are more than two stages, separability may not be possible. Returning to addition of stage returns where

$$g(r_N, r_{N-1}, \ldots, r_1) = r_N + r_{N-1} + \ldots + r_1$$

and defining

$$g_2(r_{N-1}, \ldots, r_1) = r_{N-1} + \ldots + r_1$$

we have

$$g_1(r_N, g_2(r_{N-1}, \ldots, r_1)) = r_N + g_2(r_{N-1}, \ldots, r_1)$$

Furthermore if

$$r_{N-1}' + \ldots + r_1' \geq r_{N-1}'' + \ldots + r_1''$$

$$r_N + r_{N-1}' + \ldots + r_1' \geq r_N + r_{N-1}'' + \ldots + r_1'', \text{ for all } r_N$$

Thus separability and monotonicity are satisfied, hence problems with additive stage returns always can be decomposed.

There are minor extensions involving the addition of stage returns. If $g(r_N + \ldots + r_1)$ is any monotonically increasing function of $r_N + \ldots + r_1$, for example, $\log(r_N + \ldots + r_1)$, then decomposition is possible. However, this extension is rather trivial. If the objective is to maximize an increasing function of $(r_N + \ldots + r_1)$, it is sufficient to maximize $(r_N + \ldots + r_1)$.

The really interesting question is to identify total return functions not involving the addition of individual stage returns yet satisfying the separability and monotonicity conditions.

To indicate the separability condition, we will consider only total return functions of the form.

$$R_N = r_N(X_N, D_N) \circ r_{N-1}(X_{N-1}, D_{N-1}) \circ \ldots \circ r_1(X_1, D_1)$$
$$= r_N(X_N, D_N) \circ R_{N-1}$$

where

$$R_{N-1} = r_{N-1}(X_{N-1}, D_{N-1}) \circ \ldots \circ r_1(X_1, D_1)$$

We call "o" the *composition operator*. The purpose of the composition operator is to stipulate separability. In other words when we write

$$R_N = r_N \circ R_{N-1}$$

it means that it is possible to express

$$R_N = g(r_N, r_{N-1}, \ldots, r_1) \quad \text{as} \quad R_N = g_1(r_N, g_2(r_{N-1}, \ldots, r_1))$$

We have already discussed the case where "o" stands for addition of stage returns, that is,

$$R_N = r_N(X_N, D_N) + r_{N-1}(X_{N-1}, D_{N-1}) + \ldots + r_1(X_1, D_1)$$

Another useful interpretation is multiplication of stage returns, that is,

$$R_N = r_N(X_N, D_N) \cdot r_{N-1}(X_{N-1}, D_{N-1}) \cdot \ldots \cdot r_1(X_1, D_1)$$

In general, "o" need not have the same interpretation at each stage, for example

$$R_3 = r_3(X_3, D_3) + r_2(X_2, D_2) \cdot r_1(X_1, D_1)$$

Note that in the above case

$$R_2 = r_2(X_2, D_2) \cdot r_1(X_1, D_1)$$

hence

$$R_3 = r_3(X_3, D_3) + R_2$$

However, suppose

$$R_3 = r_3(X_3, D_3) \cdot r_2(X_2, D_2) + r_1(X_1, D_1)$$

If we define

$$R_2 = r_2(X_2, D_2) + r_1(X_1, D_1)$$

$$R_3 \neq r_3(X_3, D_3) \cdot R_2$$

In fact there appears to be no way to define R_2 to obtain separability.

$$R_3 \neq r_3(X_3, D_3) \text{ o } R_2$$

By cumulating returns in the opposite direction (forward), we can overcome this difficulty for the previous problem. Specifically, let

$$R_2 = r_3(X_3, D_3) \cdot r_2(X_2, D_2)$$

and

$$R_3 = r_3(X_3, D_3) \cdot r_2(X_2, D_2) + r_1(X_1, D_1)$$

then

$$R_3 = R_2 + r_1(X_1, D_1)$$

We shall discuss cumulating returns in a forward direction in detail in Section 10.

An example of a return function that is not separable in either direction is

$$R_4 = r_4 + r_3 r_2 + r_1$$

We have shown that monotonicity holds and hence decomposition is possible when stage returns are added. In the case of multiplication of stage returns, let

$$R_N = r_N(X_N, D_N) \cdot r_{N-1}(X_{N-1}, D_{N-1}) \cdot \ldots \cdot r_1(X_1, D_1)$$

and assume $r_n(X_n, D_n)$ is defined so that its range consists of the nonnegative real numbers only. Then if $R'_{N-1} \geq R''_{N-1}$, we have

$$R'_N = r_N(X_N, D_N) \cdot R'_{N-1} \geq r_N(X_N, D_N) \cdot R''_{N-1} = R''_N$$

for all values of r_N, the desired monotonicity property. However, if the range of r_N can be both negative and positive, composition by multiplication is not feasible in the ordinary sense.† For example, let

$$r_1 = d_1, \; r_2 = x_2 d_2, \; g(r_2, r_1) = x_2 d_2 d_1, \; x_2 \geq 0$$

$$\text{and } f_2(x_2) = \max_{\substack{a_1 \leq d_1 \leq b_1 \\ a_2 \leq d_2 \leq b_2}} x_2 d_2 d_1, \; a_1, b_1 > 0, \; a_2, b_2 < 0$$

The solution is obviously $d_1 = a_1$, $d_2 = b_2$, $f_2(x_2) = x_2 b_2 a_1$. However,

$$\max_{a_2 \leq d_2 \leq b_2} [(x_2 d_2) \cdot \max_{a_1 \leq d_1 \leq b_1} d_1] = \max_{a_2 \leq d_2 \leq b_2} x_2 d_2 b_1 = x_2 b_2 b_1$$

and we fail to get the maximum of the original function by optimizing over d_1 first.

Another useful interpretation of the composition operator is maximizing the minimum value of a sequence of functions. Let the measure of total return from N stages be the minimum of the individual stage returns, that is,

$$R_N = \min [r_N(X_N, D_N), \; r_{N-1}(X_{N-1}, D_{N-1}), \ldots, r_1(X_1, D_1)]$$

The optimal return from N stages is defined as

$$f_N(X_N) = \max_{D_N, \ldots, D_1} [\min (r_N(X_N, D_N), r_{N-1}(X_{N-1}, D_{N-1}), \ldots,$$
$$r_1(X_1, D_1))]$$
$$\text{subject to } X_{n-1} = t_n(X_n, D_n), \quad n = 1, \ldots, N$$

Since

$$\min (r_N, R'_{N-1}) \geq \min (r_N, R''_{N-1}) \text{ for all values } r_N, \text{ if } R'_{N-1} > R''_{N-1}$$

decomposition is possible. Thus

$$f_N(X_N) = \max_{D_N} [\min [r_N(X_N, D_N), \max_{D_{N-1}, \ldots, D_1} \min [r_{N-1}(X_{N-1}, D_{N-1}),$$
$$\ldots, r_1(X_1, D_1))]]]]$$

Generally, if the composition operator has the property that with

$$f_{N-1}(X_{N-1}) = \max_{D_{N-1}, \ldots, D_1} [r_{N-1}(X_{N-1}, D_{N-1}) \circ \ldots r_1(X_1, D_1)]$$

$$r_N(X_N, D_N) \circ f_{N-1}(X_{N-1}) \geq r_N(X_N, D_N) \circ [r_{N-1}(X_{N-1}, D_{N-1}) \circ \ldots \circ$$
$$r_1(X_1, D_1)]$$

for all values of r_N and f_{N-1}, decomposition is possible. This condition of monotonicity is slightly weaker than the original. However, it does not appear to broaden the class of problems that can be decomposed.

The derivation of the recursion equations for the general composition operator follows the same approach as in the addition of stage returns. We define

---

† See Exercise 8 for a modified approach.

$$f_N(X_N) = \max_{D_N, \ldots, D_1} [r_N(X_N, D_N) \circ \ldots \circ r_1(X_1, D_1)]$$

subject to $X_{n-1} = t_n(X_n, D_n), \quad n = 1, \ldots, N$

Assuming that the monotonicity property is satisfied, we can bring the maximization with respect to $D_{N-1}, \ldots, D_1$ inside the outer bracket. Thus

$$f_N(X_N) = \max_{D_N} [r_N(X_N, D_N) \circ \max_{D_{N-1}, \ldots, D_1} (r_{N-1}(X_{N-1}, D_{N-1}) \circ \ldots \circ$$
$$r_1(X_1, D_1))]$$

subject to $X_{n-1} = t_n(X_n, D_n), \quad n = 1, \ldots, N$

Since

$$f_{N-1}(X_{N-1}) = \max_{D_{N-1}, \ldots, D_1} [r_{N-1}(X_{N-1}, D_{N-1}) \circ \ldots \circ r_1(X_1, D_1)]$$

we have

$$f_N(X_N) = \max_{D_N} [r_N(X_N, D_N) \circ f_{N-1}(X_{N-1})]$$

subject to $X_{N-1} = t_N(X_N, D_N)$

Defining $Q_N(X_N, D_N) = r_N(X_N, D_N) \circ f_{N-1}(t_N(X_N, D_N))$ the determination of $f_N(X_N)$ is a one-stage optimization, that is,

$$f_N(X_N) = \max_{D_N} Q_N(X_N, D_N)$$

Applying the same decomposition to $f_{N-1}(X_{N-1}), \ldots, f_2(X_2)$, we obtain the recursion equations

$$f_n(X_n) = \max_{D_n} Q_n(X_n, D_n), \qquad n = 1, \ldots, N$$
$$Q_n(X_n, D_n) = r_n(X_n, D_n), \qquad n = 1$$
$$= r_n(X_n, D_n) \circ f_{n-1}(t_n(X_n, D_n)), \qquad n = 2, \ldots, N$$

Unless a particular problem is being analyzed, the recursion equations will be written using the composition operator "o" whose interpretation can be addition, multiplication (under the assumptions given), or any other meaning compatible with the sufficient conditions.

10. Recursive Equations for Final State and Initial-Final State Optimization

The initial-final state optimization problem is to find $f_N(X_N, X_0)$, the optimal N-stage return as a function of the input state of stage N and the output state from stage one. Conceptually, there is no difference between the dynamic programming point of view towards this problem and the initial state problem. The only difference is that we do not eliminate X_0 at stage one of the recursive optimization procedure. In fact, at stage one, we solve a two state, single-stage problem

$$f_1(X_1, X_0) = \max_{D_1} r_1(X_1, D_1, X_0)$$

$$\text{subject to } X_0 = t_1(X_1, D_1)$$

It may be that the constraint can be used to express D_1 as a function of X_0 and X_1, that is,

$$D_1 = \hat{t}_1(X_0, X_1)$$

Then there would be no optimization at stage one, since

$$f_1(X_1, X_0) = r_1(X_1, \hat{t}_1(X_0, X_1), X_0) = r_1(X_1, X_0)$$

After determining $f_1(X_1, X_0)$, the remainder of the recursive analysis proceeds exactly as before, except that at each stage of the analysis, X_0 is carried as an additional state. The recursion equations are

$$f_n(X_n, X_0) = \max_{D_n} [r_n(X_n, D_n) \circ f_{n-1}(t_n(X_n, D_n), X_0)] \qquad n = 2, \dots, N$$

From a theoretical point of view, the addition of another state variable (X_0) at each stage of the analysis causes no problems. However, the calculations involved often increase drastically with the number of state variables.†

The final state optimization problem is to find $f_N(X_0)$, the optimal return as a function of the output state from stage one. One obvious way to proceed is to solve the two state problem for $f_N(X_N, X_0)$ as described above, and then maximize over X_N. Thus

$$f_N(X_0) = \max_{X_N} f_N(X_N, X_0)$$

However, in comparison with the recursive equations for the initial state problem this procedure is unwieldly. If our objective is to determine the optimal return as a function of only one state, why should it be necessary to solve a series of two state problems at each stage of the calculations? What structure makes the initial state and final state optimization problems different?

The underlying structure is the direction of the process, if a direction actually exists. The direction is specified by the stage transformations t_n, which express output states as a function of input states. All states, namely $X_1, \dots, X_{N-1}$, are both input and output states except X_N, which is only an input state, and X_0, which is only an output state. So it is the transformations that distinguish the roles of X_N and X_0 and specify the direction of the process, from input state X_N to output state X_0. Often the direction is arbitrary mathematically. For example, if the transformations are of the form

---

† Computational problems with several state variable are discussed in Chapter IV.

$$X_{n-1} = X_n - D_n, \qquad n = 1, \ldots, N$$

we could write them as

$$X_n = X_{n-1} + D_n, \qquad n = 1, \ldots, N$$

as in Section 4. This, of course, would reverse the direction of the process and interchange the roles of X_N and X_0. In other words, X_0 would be the input state and X_N the output state. Aris et al. [4] have used the term "state inversion" to express the input state as a function of the output state and decision variables. As interpreted here, state inversion can be achieved when

$$X_{n-1} = t_n(X_n, D_n), \qquad n = 1, \ldots, N$$

and can be solved to yield single-valued functions

$$X_n = \bar{t}_n(X_{n-1}, D_n), \qquad n = 1, \ldots, N$$

where $\bar{t}_n$ is the inverse stage transformation.

Depending on the difference between the input and output state dimensionalities, three possible cases can arise concerning the relation between state and decision variables in stage inversion. Let the dimensionality of X_{n-1} and X_n be p and q respectively, and assume that the transformation t_n consists of p independent single-valued relations, each one expressing one of the components of X_{n-1} as a function of X_n and D_n. If all p relations are not independent, we deal with the largest set of independent relations and make a corresponding adjustment in the dimensionality of X_{n-1}. The three cases to be considered are $p = q$, $p < q$, and $p > q$.

1. If $p = q$, the q input state variables can be expressed in terms of the decision variables and p output state variables.

2. If $p < q$, p of the input state variables can be expressed in terms of the decision variables and p output state variables, the remaining $q - p$ input state variables become decision variables.

3. If $p > q$, q of the equations of t_n can be used to express the q input state variables in terms of the decision variables and q of the output state variables; the remaining $p - q$ equations become constraints relating D_n and X_{n-1}.

Once state inversion has been accomplished, the transformations

$$X_n = \bar{t}_n(X_{n-1}, D_n) \qquad n = 1, \ldots, N$$

are substituted into the stage returns

$$r_n = r_n(X_n, D_n, X_{n-1}) \qquad n = 1, \ldots, N$$

to obtain

$$r_n = r_n(\bar{t}_n(X_{n-1}, D_n), D_n, X_{n-1}) = r_n(X_{n-1}, D_n) \qquad n = 1, \ldots, N$$

We can apply recursive optimization to the total return function

$$R_N = r_1(X_0, D_1) \circ r_2(X_1, D_2) \circ \ldots \circ r_N(X_{N-1}, D_N)$$

We begin with r_N as the one-stage return, and compose it successively with r_{N-1}, r_{N-2}, etc. Thus the optimal return from stage N as a function of its output X_{N-1} is

$$f_1(X_{N-1}) = \max_{D_N} r_N(X_{N-1}, D_N)$$

The optimal n-stage return from stages $N, N-1, \ldots, N-n+1$ as a function of the output from stage $N - n + 1$ (X_{N-n}) is

$$f_n(X_{N-n}) = \max_{D_{N-n+1}} [r_{N-n+1}(X_{N-n}, D_{N-n+1}) \circ$$

$$f_{n-1}(t_{N-n+1}(X_{N-n}, D_{N-n+1}))] \qquad n = 2, \ldots, N$$

As shown in Figure 11 (see page 26) this composition proceeds forward, so we refer to it as *forward recursive optimization*. The basic difference between forward and backward recursion is that in forward recursion the analysis proceeds from stage N to stage one, and the optimal returns are found as functions of the stage outputs. In backward recursion the analysis proceeds from stage one to stage N and the optimal returns are found as functions of the stage inputs.

The computational feasibility of forward recursion depends on the feasibility of state inversion. When state inversion is not practical, we are forced to solve the final state problem as an initial-final state problem using backward recursion. After solving the initial-final state problem we optimize over the initial state to obtain the solution of the final state problem.

For most multistage decision problems there is no need to distinguish between initial state versus final state problems and backward recursion versus forward recursion. This is so when the choice between inputs and outputs is arbitrary from a mathematical point of view. In these cases we will construct the transformations so that output states are functions of input states and decisions, and determine the optimal return as a function of the input state to stage N using backward recursion. However, in treating nonserial multistage decisions systems, we will see that the direction of analysis is crucial.

This completes our discussion of the basic theory of dynamic programming for multistage problems with a finite number of stages. All further basic theory that we will consider is just a variation of the concepts given in Chapter II. We are now prepared to recognize when a multistage system can be decomposed into a series of equivalent single stage systems, and from this decomposition obtain the recursive equations of dynamic programming. However, two very important questions remain:

1. How do we transform a general system model into a multistage form?
2. How do we solve the recursive equations in a most efficient way?

The second question concerns the computational aspects of dynamic programming. By studying the computational aspects of various kinds of models formulated as dynamic programs in Chapters III and IV, we hope to answer the first question also. In other words, by taking various models not originally in multistage form and demonstrating how to identify stages, stage returns, decision variables, and state variables, we can answer the first question.

EXERCISES

1. In the problem of Section 2, suppose the small and large cups have capacities of A and B liquid ounces respectively. Show that the possible amounts of liquid we can measure into the large cup are the numbers $kB - nA$ where k and n are integers satisfying $0 \leq kB - nA \leq B$.

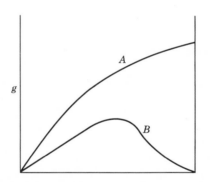

Fig. 13 $r_1(X_2, D_2, D_1)$—X_2 and D_2 are fixed

2. In a one-stage system, what difficulties arise in determining the optimal return as a function of the output when the inverse stage transformation $\bar{t}$ is not single-valued? Does the same difficulty occur in determining the optimal return as a function of the input and output when $\hat{t}$ is not single-valued? How do we overcome these difficulties? In particular, consider

$$r(x, d, y) = x + d + y$$
$$t(x, d) = y = x^2 - d^2$$

and determine the maximum return as a function of the input state, input and output state, and output state.

3. Apply the development of Problem 2 to modify the recursive equation of Section 10 for final state and two state optimization problems when $\bar{t}$ and/or $\hat{t}$ are multivalued functions.

4. Explain graphically the derivation of Mitten's sufficiency condition for a two-stage maximization problem. That is, in Figure 13 explain why in case A recursive optimization will succeed, but in case B it may fail. Why do we say only "may" rather than "will" in case B? In other words, give an example to show that Mitten's condition is not necessary. The easiest way to construct a counterexample to the necessity of the condition is to show contours of g as a function of r_1 and r_2.

5. State and prove Mitten's sufficiency condition for a two-stage minimization problem.

6. Show that

$$\max_{D_2} g(r_2(X_2, D_2), \min_{D_1} r_1(X_2, D_2, D_1)) = \max_{D_2, D_1} g(r_2(X_2, D_2), r_1(X_2, D_2, D_1))$$

when g is a monotonically nonincreasing function of r_1.

7. Use the results of Problem 6 to show that a recursive optimization scheme for

$$\max_{D_n, \ldots, D_1} \prod_{n=1}^{N} r_n(X_n, D_n), \quad r_n(X_n, D_n) \leq 0$$

$$\text{subject to } X_{n-1} = t_n(X_n, D_n) \qquad n = 1, \ldots, N$$

is

$$f_1(X_1) = \min_{D_1} r_1(X_1, D_1)$$

$$f_n(X_n) = \max_{D_n} [r_n(X_n, D_n) \cdot f_{n-1}(X_{n-1})] \qquad n = 2, 4, 6, \ldots, N$$

$$f_n(X_n) = \min_{D_n} [r_n(X_n, D_n) \cdot f_{n-1}(X_{n-1})] \qquad n = 3, 5, 7, \ldots, N-1$$

for N even. Also, develop the recursive equations for N odd.

8. Suppose in Problem 7, r_n can take on both positive and negative values. Show that a recursive optimization scheme can be developed based upon solving two sequences of problems, that is,

$$f_N(X_N) = \max [\max_{D_N} [r_N(X_N, D_N) \cdot f'_{N-1}(X_{N-1})],$$

$$\max_{D_N} [r_N(X_N, D_N) \cdot f''_{N-1}(X_{N-1})]]$$

where

$$f'_{N-1}(X_{N-1}) = \max_{D_{N-1}, \ldots, D_N} \prod_{n=1}^{N-1} r_n(X_n, D_n)$$

and

$$f''_{N-1}(X_{N-1}) = \min_{D_{N-1}, \ldots, D_N} \prod_{n=1}^{N-1} r_n(X_n, D_n)$$

9. Give recursive equations for solving

$$\max_{D_3, D_2, D_1} [r_3(X_3, D_3) \cdot (r_2(X_2, D_2) + r_1(X_1, D_1))]$$

$$\text{subject to } X_{n-1} = t_n(X_n, D_n), \qquad n = 1, 2, 3$$

10. Give recursive equations for solving

$$\max_{D_3, D_2, D_1} \ [r_3(X_3, D_3) + r_2(X_2, D_2) \cdot r_1(X_1, D_1)]$$

subject to $X_{n-1} = t_n(X_n, D_n)$, $n = 1, 2, 3$

11. Give recursive equations for solving

$$\max_{D_3, D_2, D_1} \ [r_3(X_3, D_3) \cdot r_2(X_2, D_2) + r_1(X_1, D_1)]$$

subject to $X_{n-1} = t_n(X_n, D_n)$, $n = 1, 2, 3$

12. In Problems 9, 10, and 11 can forward and backward recursion be used interchangeably? Explain your answer.

III

Basic Computations

1. The General Scheme

Computational aspects of dynamic programming concern the solution of the recursive equations

$$f_n(X_n) = \max_{D_n} Q_n(X_n, D_n) \qquad n = 1, \ldots, N \qquad (1)$$

where

$$Q_n(X_n, D_n) = r_n(X_n, D_n) \qquad n = 1 \qquad (2)$$

and

$$Q_n(X_n, D_n) = r_n(X_n, D_n) \circ f_{n-1}(X_{n-1}) \qquad (3)$$

with

$$X_{n-1} = t_n(X_n, D_n) \qquad n = 2, \ldots, N \qquad (4)$$

The flow chart of Figure 1 illustrates the general scheme of computation. By following the arrows on the solid lines we proceed step by step through the computations. Instructions in the solid rectangular boxes refer to calculations, those in the circles to the setting or adjustment of the index n, and those in the diamond-shaped boxes to binary questions. The dashed rectangular boxes indicate the saving or storing of information obtained from the boxes from which the dashed lines are drawn. Lines from the dashed boxes indicate the use of information in the boxes to which the dashed lines are drawn.

We start with $n = 1$ and calculate $r_1(X_1, D_1)$. Since $n = 1$, $Q_1(X_1, D_1) = r_1(X_1, D_1)$. Equation (1) is then used to obtain $f_1(X_1)$ and $D_1(X_1)$. These are saved for future calculations, but Q_1 and r_1 are no longer needed. Since $n \neq N$, we increase n by 1 ($n = 1 + 1 = 2$) and calculate $r_2(X_2, D_2)$.

For $n = 2$, Q_2 is calculated from equation (3) by appropriately combining r_2 and f_1, f_1 has now served its purpose and may be discarded. The calculations continue similarly for $n = 3, \ldots, N$. Thus we obtain $f_N(X_N)$, the optimal return from the N-stage system, and $D_n(X_n)$, $(n = 1, \ldots, N)$, the optimal nth-stage decision functions of the nth-stage inputs.

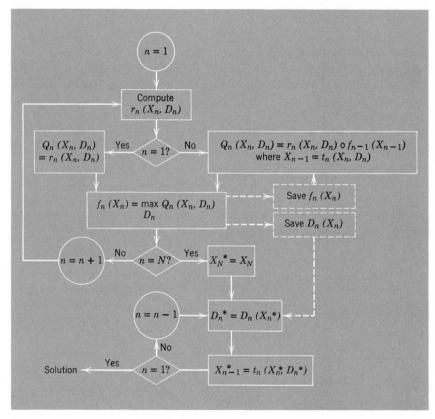

Fig. 1

The next step is to determine the optimal inputs $X_n^*(n = 1, \ldots, N - 1)$ and the optimal decisions $D_n^*(n = 1, \ldots, N)$. We have reached the point in the flow chart where, for the first time, the answer to the question, "Does $n = N$?" is yes. We assume there is a prescribed value of X_N denoted by X_N^*. D_N^* is obtained immediately from the stored function $D_N(X_N)$. Then X_{N-1}^* is calculated from $X_{N-1}^* = t_N(X_N^*, D_N^*)$. Since n is not equal to one, we compute D_{N-1}^* from X_{N-1}^* and the stored function $D_{N-1}(X_{N-1})$. When the answer to the question "Does $n = 1$?" is yes, the optimal solution is obtained.

This flow chart is a general algorithm for optimizing any multistage decision system describable by equations (1) through (4). The characteristics that distinguish problems from one another are:

1. the return functions $r_n(X_n, D_n)$ and transformations $t_n(X_n, D_n)$;
2. the interpretation of the operator "o" which specifies how r_n and f_{n-1} are combined to obtain Q_n;
3. the technique used to maximize $Q_n(X_n, D_n)$ to obtain $f_n(X_n)$ and $D_n(X_n)$.

For certain well-behaved r_n and t_n (for example, differentiable with respect to D_n) and, say, a composition operator of addition, we may be able to determine closed-form expressions for $D_n(X_n)$ and $f_n(X_n)$ analytically. On the other hand, when r_n and t_n are given as tabular data, analytical calculations are not possible. Problems with tabular data are likely to be solved on a digital computer. Computational difficulties may arise when complex problems are solved on a computer.

First we shall study some simple analytical problems, not cluttered with numerous data. This enables us to emphasize formulation of the recursive equations for various objective functions, stage transformations, and composition operators. Then we shall turn to tabular computations. These are required for most practical problems.

2. A Three-Stage Optimization Problem

For our first problem in dynamic programming we consider

$$\text{minimize}\quad d_1{}^2 + d_2{}^2 + d_3{}^2$$

$$\text{subject to } d_1 + d_2 + d_3 \geq k, \quad k > 0, \quad d_1, d_2, d_3 \geq 0$$

To put this problem into the appropriate form of

$$\text{minimize } r_1(x_1, d_1) + r_2(x_2, d_2) + r_3(x_3, d_3)$$

$$\text{subject to } x_{n-1} = t_n(x_n, d_n), \quad n = 1, 2, 3$$

we introduce the state variables (x_0, x_1, x_2, x_3) and replace

$$d_1 + d_2 + d_3 \geq k$$

by $x_3 \geq k$, $x_2 = x_3 - d_3$, $x_1 = x_2 - d_2$ and $x_0 = x_1 - d_1$. This is legitimate, since by adding these four equations, we obtain

$$d_1 + d_2 + d_3 \geq k - x_0$$

In order that $d_1 + d_2 + d_3 \geq k$, it is sufficient that $x_0 = 0$ or equivently $d_1 = x_1$. Since $d_1 = x_1 \geq 0$, we have $d_2 \leq x_2$ and similarly $d_3 \leq x_3$. We can restate the problem as

$$\text{minimize } d_1{}^2 + d_2{}^2 + d_3{}^2$$

$$\text{subject to } x_1 = x_2 - d_2, \quad d_1 = x_1 \geq 0$$

$$x_2 = x_3 - d_3, \quad 0 \leq d_2 \leq x_2$$

$$x_3 \geq k, \quad 0 \leq d_3 \leq x_3$$

This is the appropriate form, since

$$r_n(x_n, d_n) = d_n{}^2$$

$$x_{n-1} = t_n(x_n, d_n) = x_n - d_n \quad n = 1, 2, 3$$

and

$$R_3 = d_3{}^2 + d_2{}^2 + d_1{}^2$$

The remaining restrictions on the decision variables simply limit the feasible combinations of (x_n, d_n) and, in that sense, act to our advantage.

Having determined the appropriate definitions for r_n and t_n, we can state the problem in terms of the recursion equations of dynamic programming:

$$f_1(x_1) = \min_{d_1 = x_1} d_1{}^2,$$

$$f_n(x_n) = \min_{0 \leq d_n \leq x_n} [d_n{}^2 + f_{n-1}(x_n - d_n)], \quad n = 2, 3, \text{ with } x_3 \geq k$$

Before solving the recursion equations, let us reconstruct the steps in the transformation of the original problem to the recursion equations. The difficulty in using dynamic programming, is in the formulation of the equations. Given r_n and t_n, we determine the recursion equations directly from the formula

$$f_n(x_n) = \min_{d_n} [r_n(x_n, d_n) \circ f_{n-1}(t_n(x_n, d_n))]$$

The critical step is the proper interpretation of stages, decisions, returns, and transformations.

We imagine that a nonnegative quantity $x_3, x_3 \geq k$, is divided into three quantities. Each is placed into a separate box marked 3, 2, and 1 respectively. Associated with each box is a decision, the quantity put in the box, and a return, the square of the quantity in the box. Also, the total return is determined by adding the returns from each of the boxes. If we like, we can think of x_3 as an amount of resource to be divided among three projects represented by boxes 3, 2, and 1. The return from the boxes could then be interpreted as the profit from the projects. This, of course, is an allocation model. Several of the problems discussed in Chapters III and IV can be given this interpretation.

We have identified the stages (the boxes), the decisions and returns at each stage, and the way the individual stage returns are combined. We have used all the information in the original problem except that the total quantity placed in all three boxes equals x_3. This constraint determines the relations among stages and consequently among the stage transformations. We imagine that the division of the quantity x_3 is sequential. First, an amount d_3, $0 \leq d_3 \leq x_3$, is placed in box 3. The quantity remaining to be divided between stages two and one is $x_3 - d_3 = x_2$. Likewise, d_2, $0 \leq d_2 \leq x_2$ is placed in box 2, and $x_1 = x_2 - d_2$ remains. This remainder must be allocated to stage one, so $d_1 = x_1$. Figure 2 shows the sequential division of the quantity x_3. Clearly the numbering of boxes and consequently the ordering of stages is arbitrary.

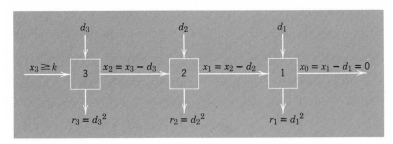

Fig. 2

The solution procedure begins by finding $d_1(x_1)$ and $f_1(x_1)$. In terms of the multistage model, $d_1(x_1)$ is the optimal allocation at stage one as a function of x_1, and $f_1(x_1)$ is the optimal return from stage one that results from an allocation of $d_1(x_1)$. As we have already established that $d_1(x_1) = x_1$, there is no optimization, and $f_1(x_1) = x_1^2$.

The next step is to express the optimal one-stage return as a function of x_2 and d_2. Since

$$x_1 = x_2 - d_2$$

$$f_1(x_1) = (x_2 - d_2)^2$$

the return from stage two is d_2^2. Thus the total return from stages two and one, given that stage one is operated optimally as a function of its input, is

$$Q_2(x_2, d_2) = d_2^2 + (x_2 - d_2)^2$$

The optimal return from two stages as a function of x_2 is

$$f_2(x_2) = \min_{0 \leq d_2 \leq x_2} Q_2(x_2, d_2) = \min_{0 \leq d_2 \leq x_2} [d_2^2 + (x_2 - d_2)^2]$$

Setting the partial derivative of Q_2 with respect to d_2 to zero, we get the necessary condition for a minimum

$$\frac{\partial Q_2}{\partial d_2} = 2d_2 - 2(x_2 - d_2) = 0$$

This condition is also sufficient because the second derivative $(\partial^2 Q_2/\partial d_2^2)$

is positive. The unique solution is $d_2 = x_2/2$ and $f_2(x_2) = x_2^2/2 = (x_3 - d_3)^2/2$. Continuing for $n = 3$, in exactly the same manner

$$f_3(x_3) = \min_{0 \le d_3 \le x_3} \left[d_3^2 + \frac{(x_3 - d_3)^2}{2} \right]$$

By partially differentiating the expression in brackets with respect to d_3, we obtain the solution $d_3 = x_3/3$ which yields $f_3(x_3) = x_3^2/3$. Clearly f_3 is minimum when $x_3 = k$, so we obtain

$$f_3(k) = \frac{k^2}{3}, \quad d_3^* = \frac{k}{3}, \quad x_2^* = k - \frac{k}{3} = \frac{2k}{3}, \quad d_2^* = \frac{x_2^*}{2} = \frac{k}{3}$$

$$\text{and } x_1^* = \frac{2k}{3} - \frac{k}{3} = \frac{k}{3} = d_1^*$$

A great deal of time has been spent on this very simple example because it illustrates the formulation and use of recursive equations. More difficult problems are solved in the same way. The basic step, in transforming the original form of the problem to the recursive equations, is defining the components of the recursive equations. These are: the stages, decisions, states, transformations, returns, and composition between returns. The stages, states, and transformations may not be in the original problem. To identify the stages we must imagine how the problem can be analyzed sequentially. To carry out a stagewise analysis—to determine the decisions one at a time—means that the decisions must be determined as functions of what came before. Thus state variables are introduced which, essentially, summarize the previous decisions compactly.

Transformations are defined to relate the output state of a stage to the input state and decisions. The basic components are then substituted into the general recursion equation

$$f_n(X_n) = \max_{D_n} [r_n(X_n, D_n) \circ f_{n-1}(X_{n-1})]$$

to yield the recursive equations for the particular problem.

In Section 3 we show that the dynamic programming analysis for N stages is an almost trivial extension of the three-stage problem. We shall then consider several variations of this problem to illustrate different return functions, transformations, and composition operators.

3. Generalization to N Stages

In the problem just considered we actually solved

$$\min \sum_{n=1}^{N} d_n^2$$

$$\text{subject to } \sum_{n=1}^{N} d_n \geq k, \qquad d_n \geq 0$$

for the three particular cases $N = 1, 2, 3$. The results obtained yield a consistent pattern (see Table 1).

Table 1

N	$d_N(x_N)$	$f_N(x_N)$
1	x_1	$x_1{}^2$
2	$x_2/2$	$x_2{}^2/2$
3	$x_3/3$	$x_3{}^2/3$

In view of these results it would be plausible to guess that for any positive integer n, $d_n(x_n) = x_n/n$ and $f_n(x_n) = x_n{}^2/n$.

We proceed by induction assuming $f_n(x_n) = x_n{}^2/n$, and $d_n(x_n) = x_n/n$. Thus

$$f_{n+1}(x_{n+1}) = \min_{0 \leq d_{n+1} \leq x_{n+1}} \left[d_{n+1}^2 + \frac{(x_{n+1} - d_{n+1})^2}{n} \right]$$

The condition for a minimum

$$d_{n+1} - \frac{x_{n+1} - d_{n+1}}{n} = 0$$

is satisfied only by $d_{n+1} = x_{n+1}/n + 1$, which yields $f_{n+1}(x_{n+1}) = x_{n+1}^2/ n + 1$, and the induction is complete. We have proved that the minimum of the sum of squares of N variables whose sum is equal to or greater than a constant k is k^2/N.

4. $r(d_n) = d_n{}^p$

Again extending our results, we consider

$$\min \sum_{n=1}^{N} d_n{}^p, \qquad p > 1$$

$$\text{subject to } \sum_{n=1}^{N} d_n \geq k, \qquad d_n \geq 0$$

For the particular case $p = 2$, we have already shown that $d_n(x_n) = x_n/n$ and $f_n(x_n) = x_n{}^2/n$. Although it is difficult to generalize from one special case, a plausible guess might be $d_n(x_n) = x_n/n$ and $f_n(x_n) = x_n{}^p/n$, $p > 1$. We restrict ourselves to $p > 1$, because in the obvious case $p = 1$, $f_n(x_n) = x_n$, and the conjecture is not true. Furthermore, at $p = 1$, $d_n{}^p$ changes from a concave to a convex function as p increases.

Let us check our conjecture for an arbitrary $p > 1$, in the special cases $n = 1$ and 2. If it is true for $n = 1$, we will have part of the ingredients needed for an inductive proof. Furthermore, if it is true for $n = 2$, we will have considerably more confidence in undertaking a general proof.

The recursive equations are the same as those of Section 3 except that the return $r_n = d_n{}^2$ is replaced by $r_n = d_n{}^p$. For $n = 1$,

$$f_1(x_1) = \min_{d_1 = x_1} d_1{}^p$$

and our conjecture is true, since $d_1(x_1) = x_1$ and $f_1(x_1) = x_1{}^p$. Thus

$$f_2(x_2) = \min_{0 \le d_2 \le x_2} [d_2{}^p + (x_2 - d_2)^p]$$

The necessary condition for a minimum is

$$pd_2{}^{p-1} - p(x_2 - d_2)^{p-1} = 0$$

This condition is also sufficient since, as in all of the previous cases, the second derivative is always positive. Hence,

$$d_2(x_2) = x_2/2 \quad \text{and} \quad f_2(x_2) = x_2{}^p/2^{p-1}$$

Part of our conjecture has been disproved; a general proof certainly would have failed. In the special case $p = 2$, $n^{p-1} = n$, and the exponent $p - 1$ disappears. In fact a bit of checking would have revealed that $d_n = x_n/n$ and $f_n = x_n{}^p/n$ are inconsistent except for $p = 2$. Nevertheless, our work has not been futile. We now have substantial evidence that $d_n(x_n) = x_n/n$ and $f_n(x_n) = x_n{}^p/n^{p-1}$.[†]

We assume this new conjecture to be true for all real $p \ge 1$ and positive integers n (we have the special cases $n = 1, 2$, for all p, and $p = 1, 2$, for all n) and proceed by induction on n. Thus

$$f_{n+1}(x_{n+1}) = \min_{0 \le d_{n+1} \le x_{n+1}} \left[d_{n+1}^p + \frac{(x_{n+1} - d_{n+1})^p}{n^{p-1}} \right]$$

The solution is

$$d_{n+1}(x_{n+1}) = \frac{x_{n+1}}{n+1} \quad \text{and} \quad f_{n+1}(x_{n+1}) = \frac{x_{n+1}^p}{(n+1)^{p-1}}$$

The induction is complete and we have established the solution for $p \ge 1$ and for any number of stages.

5. $r(d_n)$—an Arbitrary Monotonically Increasing Convex Function

The results obtained in the last case tempt us to consider a further generalization. As we mentioned in the last section, $d_n{}^p$ is convex for all real $p \ge 1$. The set of functions, $d_n{}^p, p \ge 1$, contains an infinite number

---

[†] This is also true for $p = 1$.

of elements, all of which are monotonically increasing convex functions.

Shouldn't we expect our previous results to hold for any $r(d_n)$ which is convex and monotonically increasing? So far, in every case we have considered $d_n^* = x_N/N = k/N$. Thus for the problem†

$$\min \sum_{n=1}^{N} r(d_n), \qquad \sum_{n=1}^{N} d_n \geq k, \quad d_n \geq 0$$

where $r(d_n)$ is convex ‡ and monotone-increasing, we guess that $d_n^* = x_N/N$.

Once again the solution procedure is basically the same. The only difference is the new return function. As usual, we start the recursive analysis with $n = 1$, so

$$f_1(x_1) = \min_{d_1 = x_1} r(d_1)$$

Thus

$$d_1(x_1) = x_1 \quad \text{and} \quad f_1(x_1) = r(x_1)$$

which agrees with our conjecture. We proceed immediately to the induction on n, assuming that $f_n(x_n) = nr(x_n/n)$. Thus

$$f_{n+1}(x_{n+1}) = \min_{0 \leq d_{n+1} \leq x_{n+1}} \left[r(d_{n+1}) + nr\left(\frac{x_{n+1} - d_{n+1}}{n}\right) \right]$$

The term in the outermost brackets is convex with respect to d_{n+1}, since each of the two individual terms is convex by hypothesis. Thus,

$$r'(d_{n+1}) - r'\left(\frac{x_{n+1} - d_{n+1}}{n}\right) = 0$$

where $r' = \partial r/\partial d$, is a sufficient condition for a minimum. Clearly the arguments of both of the terms must be equal, so

$$d_{n+1} = \frac{x_{n+1} - d_{n+1}}{n} \quad \text{or} \quad d_{n+1}(x_{n+1}) = \frac{x_{n+1}}{n+1}$$

Substituting this value of d_{n+1} in the equation for f_{n+1} yields

$$f_{n+1}(x_{n+1}) = (n+1)r\left(\frac{x_{n+1}}{n+1}\right)$$

We have made the assumption that $r(d_n)$ is monotonically increasing to preserve the analogy with the previous cases. Because $r(d_n)$ is monotonically increasing, the minimum of $f_N(x_N) = Nr(x_N/N)$ occurs at $x_N = k$.

---

† The notation $r(d_n)$ is used to indicate that $r_n(d_n) = r_m(d_m)$ for all m and n.
‡ $r(d)$ is convex if for all (d_A, d_B) and $0 < \alpha < 1$

$$r(\alpha d_A + (1 - \alpha) d_B) \leq \alpha r(d_A) + (1 - \alpha) r(d_B)$$

The properties of convex functions needed here are:
1. The necessary condition for a minimum is also sufficient for a convex function.
2. The sum of convex functions is convex.

Thus $d_n{}^* = k/N$, $n = 1, \ldots, N$, as in the other cases. By relaxing this assumption, we would determine an optimal x_N, denoted by $x_N{}^*$, from

$$f_N(x_N{}^*) = \min_{x_N \geq k} Nr\left(\frac{x_N}{N}\right) = Nr\left(\frac{x_N{}^*}{N}\right)$$

and then $\qquad\qquad d_n{}^* = \dfrac{x_N{}^*}{N}, \qquad n = 1, \ldots, N$

6. Lagrange Multipliers and the Kuhn-Tucker Conditions

An alternative procedure for solving the problem of Section 5 is that of Lagrange multipliers using the Kuhn-Tucker conditions.† The Lagrange function is

$$V(d_1, \ldots, d_N, \lambda) = \sum_{n=1}^{N} r(d_n) + \lambda\left(\sum_{n=1}^{N} d_n - k\right)$$

Since the return function is convex and the constraint is linear, the Kuhn-Tucker conditions are necessary and sufficient for a global minimum. They are

$$\textstyle\sum d_n \geq k, \qquad \lambda(\sum d_n - k) = 0, \qquad\qquad \lambda \leq 0$$

$$d_n \geq 0, \qquad d_n(r'(d_n) + \lambda) = 0, \qquad r'(d_n) + \lambda \geq 0, \qquad n = 1, \ldots, N.$$

The unique solution to these equations is, of course,

$$d_n = k/N, \qquad n = 1, \ldots, N$$

All decision variables are determined simultaneously from the Kuhn-Tucker conditions. The advantage of dynamic programming is that the decisions are found one at a time. The disadvantage is that each decision must be found by first determining a decision function. For the previous example, both approaches yield the solution without any difficulty, and can be classed as equal alternatives.

However, when the return functions are not so well-behaved, there is a distinct advantage to solving a series of one-variable problems. For example, if $r(d_n)$ was concave and monotone-increasing for all n, the Kuhn-Tucker conditions would only be necessary for a local minimum. There are several solutions that satisfy the necessary conditions:

1. $d_j = k$, $d_i = 0$, $i \neq j$
2. $d_j = d_p = k/2$, $d_i = 0$, $i \neq j, p$
   .
   .
   .
N. $d_i = k/N$, all i

---

† Chapter I, pp. 12, 13.

The global minimum is the first, but there is no way of telling this from the Kuhn-Tucker conditions. When we use dynamic programming the solution for the concave case is no more difficult than that for convex case.† This is so because the dynamic programming analysis only requires the solution of a series of one-variable problems. The identification of global maxima from the set of solutions containing global maxima, local maxima, and inflection points, whether the global maxima occur at interior or boundary points, is certainly least difficult when there is only one variable. Thus we have an example of dynamic programming overriding the almost insurmountable difficulty of local optima.

Dynamic programming does not preclude the use of the Kuhn-Tucker conditions. The comparison is between using the Kuhn-Tucker directly on the whole problem and decomposing the problem by dynamic programming, and then solving a series of subproblems. Frequently the subproblems are constrained optimization problems, which can be solved efficiently by the Kuhn-Tucker conditions.

There are also a large number of problems solvable by the Kuhn-Tucker conditions that cannot be decomposed by dynamic programming, and problems that can be formulated as dynamic programs for which the Kuhn-Tucker conditions do not apply. The main limitations of dynamic programming are the separability and monotonicity conditions given in Chapter II.

The Kuhn-Tucker conditions apply only to differentiable functions. Furthermore, they are not viable when the Lagrange function is theoretically differentiable, but so complex that the derivatives cannot be calculated analytically. And even when the Lagrange function can be differentiated, the resulting equations might be very difficult to solve. Unfortunately, there is a wide variety of problems that have these characteristics. The minimization of maximum return problem of Section 7 is not differentiable. Many practical problems contain functions of discrete variables which, of course, are not differentiable. These problems will be studied later in this chapter.

We shall return to Lagrange multipliers later. As will be seen in Chapter IV, they are important in conjunction with discrete variable problems containing more than one constraint.

7. Minimization of Maximum Return

When we wish to minimize the cumulative effect from individual returns, an alternative criterion to minimizing the sum of the returns is to minimize the maximum individual return. The rationale for this criterion

---

† See Exercise 4 for a slightly different version.

is that best overall results may be attained when the worst individual result (say error) is smallest. It is particularly useful in control theory when often the objective is to minimize the maximum amount that a system deviates from prescribed behavior.

To study how optimization problems with the criterion of minimization of maximum return can be solved using a dynamic programming approach, we consider

$$\min_{d_N, \ldots, d_1} \quad [\max \; (r(d_N), \ldots, r(d_1))]$$

$$\text{subject to} \quad \sum_{n=1}^{N} d_n \geq k, \qquad d_n \geq 0$$

The only assumption made on $r(d_n)$ is that it be monotonically increasing. Convexity and differentiability are not stipulated as they were in the previous case.

By analogy with the last example our basic recursion equation is

$$f_n(x_n) = \min_{0 \leq d_n \leq x_n} [r(d_n) \circ f_{n-1}(x_n - d_n)]$$

The measure of return from n stages is the maximum of the individual stage returns, that is,

$$\max \; (r(d_n), \; r(d_{n-1}), \ldots, r(d_1))$$

If stages $n - 1, \ldots, 1$ are optimal with respect to the state x_{n-1}, then $r(d_{n-1}), \ldots, r(d_1)$ can be replaced by $f_{n-1}(x_{n-1})$. Consequently $r(d_n) \circ f_{n-1}(x_{n-1}) = \max \; (r(d_n), \; f_{n-1}(x_{n-1}))$ and

$$f_n(x_n) = \min_{0 \leq d_n \leq x_n} [\max \; (r(d_n), \; f_{n-1}(x_n - d_n))], \qquad n = 2, \ldots, N$$

In the special case $n = 1$

$$f_1(x_1) = r(x_1)$$

Substituting $r(x_2 - d_2)$ for $f_1(x_2 - d_2)$ in the recursion equation for $n = 2$, we obtain

$$f_2(x_2) = \min_{0 \leq d_2 \leq x_2} [\max \; (r(d_2), \; r(x_2 - d_2))]$$

Clearly the maximum of the term in brackets is minimum when $r(d_2) = r(x_2 - d_2)$ (see Figure 3). Thus $d_2(x_2) = x_2/2$ and $f_2(x_2) = r(x_2/2)$. Proceeding by induction, we assume $d_n(x_n) = x_n/n$ and $f_n(x_n) = r(x_n/n)$. Thus

$$f_{n+1}(x_{n+1}) = \min_{0 \leq d_{n+1} \leq x_{n+1}} \left[\max \left(r(d_{n+1}), \; r\left(\frac{x_{n+1} - d_{n+1}}{n}\right) \right) \right]$$

Again the minimum occurs where $d_{n+1}(x_{n+1})$ is chosen, so that the two terms in brackets are equal. But, since r is an increasing function, their arguments must be equal. Thus

$$d_{n+1} = \frac{x_{n+1} - d_{n+1}}{n}$$

which yields

$$d_{n+1} = \frac{x_{n+1}}{n+1} \quad \text{and} \quad f_{n+1}(x_{n+1}) = r\left(\frac{x_{n+1}}{n+1}\right)$$

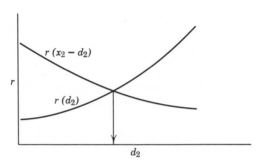

Fig. 3

The optimal N-stage return is $r(x_N/N)$, and since r is monotonically increasing, $x_N{}^* = k$ and $d_n{}^* = k/N$, as in the previous cases. However, it is certainly not true that the criteria of minimization of the sum of returns and minimization of maximum return yield the same decisions in all cases. For example, if $r(d_n)$ were concave and monotonically increasing, the optimal decisions are $d_n{}^* = k/N$ for minimization of maximum return, but $d_j = k$ and $d_i = 0$ ($i \neq j$) for minimization of the sum of returns.

The dynamic programming approach is particularly important for problems of minimization of maximum return because there are so few other methods. When we were dealing with total return equal to the sum of stage returns, it would have been feasible to differentiate the total-return function to establish necessary conditions for a minimum. But to minimize the maximum return we must either compare all of the stage returns simultaneously for all feasible decision combinations (enumeration) or compare them two at a time (dynamic programming). No one will doubt the computational advantage of the two-at-a-time comparison.

8. A Multiplicative Constraint

We have made several changes and generalizations in the objective function from the first simple problem of Section 2. To continue studying formulation and use of dynamic programming models, we consider a multiplicative constraint.

The problem is

$$\min \sum_{n=1}^{N} r(d_n)$$

$$\text{subject to} \quad \prod_{n=1}^{N} d_n \geq k, \qquad k > 0,$$

$$d_n \geq 0$$

where $r(d_n)$ is convex and monotone-increasing. Actually, an assumption as strong as convexity is not needed for this analysis, but we retain it to preserve the similarity between this problem and the one of Section 5.

To replace $\Pi \, d_n \geq k$ by N equations of the form $y_{n-1} = t_n(y_n, d_n)$ we consider a quantity $y_N \geq k$ divided sequentially into N quantities $d_N, \ldots,$ d_1 so that $\Pi \, d_n = y_N$. The quantity d_N is placed in stage N, yielding a return $r(d_N)$ and an amount $y_{N-1} = y_N/d_N$ to be divided among the remaining $N-1$ stages. Proceeding with the sequential division of the remaining quantities, we obtain

$$y_{n-1} = \frac{y_n}{d_n}, \qquad n = 2, \ldots, N$$

and $$d_1 = y_1$$

Thus the recursion equations are

$$f_1(y_1) = r(y_1)$$

$$f_n(y_n) = \min_{d_n \geq 0} \left[r(d_n) + f_{n-1}\left(\frac{y_n}{d_n}\right) \right], \qquad n = 2, \ldots, N$$

Substituting $f_1(y_1) = r(y_2/d_2)$ into the recursion equation for $n = 2$, we obtain

$$f_2(y_2) = \min_{d_2 \geq 0} \left[r(d_2) + r\left(\frac{y_2}{d_2}\right) \right]$$

The values of d_2 for which a minimum is attained are solutions of the equation

$$r'(d_2) - \frac{y_2}{d_2{}^2} \, r'\left(\frac{y_2}{d_2}\right) = 0$$

Thus $$d_2 = y_2^{\frac{1}{2}} \quad \text{and} \quad f_2(y_2) = 2r(y_2^{\frac{1}{2}})$$

Proceeding by induction, we obtain

$$d_n = k^{1/N}, \qquad n = 1, \ldots, N$$

and $Nr(k^{1/N})$ as the minimum total return.

9. Two Constraints: Additive and Multiplicative

It is interesting to consider the dynamic programming analysis for the case of both additive and multiplicative constraints, that is,

$$\min \sum_{n=1}^{N} r(d_n)$$

$$\text{subject to } \sum_{n=1}^{N} d_n \geq k_1, \qquad k_1 > 0$$

$$\prod_{n=1}^{N} d_n \geq k_2, \qquad k_2 > 0$$

$$d_n \geq 0$$

where $r(d_n)$ is convex and monotone-increasing. Here we assume the simultaneous, stagewise division of two quantities (x_N, y_N), $x_N \geq k_1$ $y_N \geq k_2$ so that

$$x_{n-1} = x_n - d_n$$

$$y_{n-1} = \frac{y_n}{d_n} \qquad n = 2, \ldots, N$$

When considering the additive and multiplicative constraints separately, we made $\Sigma d_n = x_N$ and $\Pi d_n = y_N$, consequently $d_1 = x_1$ and $d_1 = y_1$. In this case it would be inconvenient to do so, since this would mean $x_1 = y_1$, which would impose further constraints upon x_n and y_n at the remaining stages. Instead, we require $\Sigma d_n \geq x_N$ and $\Pi d_n \geq y_N$ which implies $d_1 \geq x_1$ and $d_1 \geq y_1$ but imposes no relations between x_1 and y_1.

For the first time we encounter recursion equations that are functions of two state variables, namely

$$f_n(x_n, y_n) = \min_{d_n \geq 0} \left[r(d_n) + f_{n-1} \left(x_n - d_n, \frac{y_n}{d_n} \right) \right], \qquad n = 2, \ldots, N$$

The recursive analysis is started with

$$f_1(x_1, y_1) = \min_{d_1} r(d_1), \qquad d_1 \geq \max (x_1, y_1)$$

Thus
$$f_1(x_1, y_1) = r(x_1), \qquad x_1 \geq y_1$$
$$= r(y_1), \qquad y_1 \geq x_1$$

Two possibilities must be now examined for the optimal two-stage return.

(i) $f_2(x_2, y_2) = \min\limits_{d_2 \geq 0} [r(d_2) + r(x_2 - d_2)], \qquad x_2 - d_2 \geq \dfrac{y_2}{d_2}$

(ii) $f_2(x_2, y_2) = \min\limits_{d_2 \geq 0} \left[r(d_2) + r\left(\dfrac{y_2}{d_2}\right)\right], \qquad \dfrac{y_2}{d_2} \geq x_2 - d_2$

Cases (i) and (ii) are merely the two-stage recursion equations for the problems with the additive constraints only and multiplicative constraints only, respectively. Thus the solutions are

(i) $$d_2 = \frac{x_2}{2}, \quad f_2(x_2, y_2) = 2r\left(\frac{x_2}{2}\right)$$

(ii) $$d_2 = y_2^{1/2}, \quad f_2(x_2, y_2) = 2r(y_2^{1/2})$$

Their respective regions of applicability are, for (i) $x_2^2 \geq 4y_2$, and for

(ii) $x_2^2 \leq 4y_2$.

Before we attempt to guess an induction hypothesis, it would be worthwhile to continue the analysis for one more stage. The optimal three-stage returns are

(i) $f_3(x_3, y_3) = \min\limits_{d_3 \geq 0} \left[r(d_3) + 2r\left(\dfrac{x_3 - d_3}{2}\right)\right], \qquad (x_3 - d_3)^2 \geq \dfrac{4y_3}{d_3}$

(ii) $f_3(x_3, y_3) = \min\limits_{d_3 \geq 0} \left[r(d_3) + 2r\left(\left(\dfrac{y_3}{d_3}\right)^{1/2}\right)\right], \qquad \dfrac{4y_3}{d_3} \geq (x_3 - d_3)^2$

Once again, the analysis of Section 5 gives the solution for case (i); similarly Section 8 yields the answer for case (ii).

(i) $$d_3 = \frac{x_3}{3}, \quad f_3(x_3, y_3) = 3r\left(\frac{x_3}{3}\right), \qquad x_3^3 \geq 27y_3$$

(ii) $$d_3 = y_3^{1/3}, \quad f_3(x_3, y_3) = 3r(y_3^{1/3}), \qquad 27y_3 \geq x_3^3$$

It now seems appropriate to try the induction hypothesis

(i) $$d_n = \frac{x_n}{n}, \quad f_n(x_n, y_n) = nr\left(\frac{x_n}{n}\right), \qquad x_n^n \geq n^n y_n$$

(ii) $$d_n = y_n^{1/n}, \quad f_n(x_n, y_n) = nr(y_n^{1/n}), \qquad n^n y_n \geq x_n^n$$

This leads to the recursive equations for the $(n + 1)$-stage optimal return.

(i) $f_{n+1}(x_{n+1}, y_{n+1}) = \min\limits_{d_{n+1} \geq 0} \left[r(d_{n+1}) + nr\left(\dfrac{x_{n+1} - d_{n+1}}{n}\right)\right]$

$$(x_{n+1} - d_{n+1})^n \geq \frac{n^n y_{n+1}}{d_{n+1}}$$

(ii) $$f_{n+1}(x_{n+1}, y_{n+1}) = \min_{d_{n+1} \geq 0} \left[r(d_{n+1}) + nr\left(\left(\frac{y_{n+1}}{d_{n+1}} \right)^{1/n} \right) \right]$$

$$\frac{n^n y_{n+1}}{d_{n+1}} \geq (x_{n+1} - d_{n+1})^n$$

The solution of these equations validates our induction hypothesis. Consequently, for $k_1 \geq Nk_2^{1/N}$, $d_n = k_1/N$ with minimum total return of $Nr(k_1/N)$ and for $Nk_2^{1/N} \geq k_1$, $d_n = k_2^{1/N}$ with minimum total return of $Nr(k_2^{1/N})$.

This completes the set of examples. Our objective has been to study formulation and to some extent solution of the recursive equations of dynamic programming.

To recapitulate, we began with the problem of minimizing the sum of three quadratic returns, subject to linear and nonnegativity constraints. We showed how to identify stages, returns, states, and the stage transformations. This formulation led to a set of recursive equations, which were solved recursively, using differential calculus. From the results of the three variable problems, we were able to induce the solution for an arbitrary number of variables. Subsequently, the objective function was generalized to the sum of N convex functions. The modifications required in the formulation and solution of the recursive equations were very slight indeed. To illustrate the use of a different composition operator for combining individual stage returns, we considered the minimization of maximum return from N convex functions. It was no longer possible to use differential calculus to solve the recursion equations, but by a direct comparison of the return from stage n with the optimal return from $n - 1$ stages, we could very easily determine the minimum of maximum return from n stages. Finally, a nonlinear (multiplicative) constraint was introduced. All that was necessary was to modify the stage transformations in the formulation with the linear constraint. The problem with both linear and nonlinear constraints required a two state variable per stage formulation, one state variable for the linear transformation and another for the nonlinear. However, the additional state variable caused only a slight increase in the complexity of the computations.

These examples were chosen strictly for pedagogical purposes. Our objective was to emphasize the formulation of dynamic programming models according to various assumptions. We indicated that the examples could be interpreted as allocation models. But certainly they are too simple to represent real-world models. Nevertheless, this simplicity was deliberate. The formulation of many practical models is basically the same as that for the simple models—only the solution techniques are more complicated. Problems in which closed-form expressions cannot be obtained for the returns and decisions often present certain computational difficulties that require special methods of solution. These purely computational devices will be studied later.

Some general principles that have been illustrated in these examples, such as the relation between the number of constraints and state variables and sensitivity, will be discussed in Sections 10 and 11.

10. Constraints and State Variables

The problems of Sections 2 to 8 each had one constraint relating all of the decision variables and one state variable per stage. When a second constraint was added (Section 9), a two state variable dynamic programming formulation was required. Generally, a state variable is needed, at each stage, for each constraint that relates state and decision variables. Assuming that the ith constraint, $i = 1, \ldots, M$, can be represented at the nth stage by the stage transformations

$$x_{n-1,i} = t_{ni}(x_{ni}, d_n), \qquad i = 1, \ldots, M$$

then the optimal return from n stages will be a function of $(x_{n1}, \ldots, x_{nM})$ and be written as $f_n(x_{n1}, \ldots, x_{nM})$. For example, consider

$$\min \sum_{n=1}^{N} r(d_n)$$

$$\text{subject to} \sum_{n=1}^{N} g_i(d_n) \geq k_i, \qquad i = 1, \ldots, M$$

$$d_n \geq 0, \qquad n = 1, \ldots, N.$$

The nth stage transformation relating the state and decision variables are

$$x_{n-1,i} = x_{ni} - g_i(d_n), \qquad n = 1, \ldots, N$$

and the recursion equation for the optimal nth stage return is

$$f_n(x_{n1}, \ldots, x_{nM}) = \min_{d_n \geq 0} [r(d_n) + f_{n-1}(x_{n1} - g_1(d_n), \ldots, x_{nM} - g_M(d_n))]$$

This illustrates the very different role of a constraint relating all of the decision variables and a constraint (such as nonnegativity) restricting the feasible region for a single decision variable. The latter type or constraint merely serves to reduce the region of feasibility over which an optimization is performed at one of the stages. The former increases the dimensionality of the space in which the original problem is embedded to achieve a dynamic programming formulation, that is, increases the number of state variables.

It is not always the case that a state variable is required at each stage for each constraint. Suppose the decision variables and constraints were

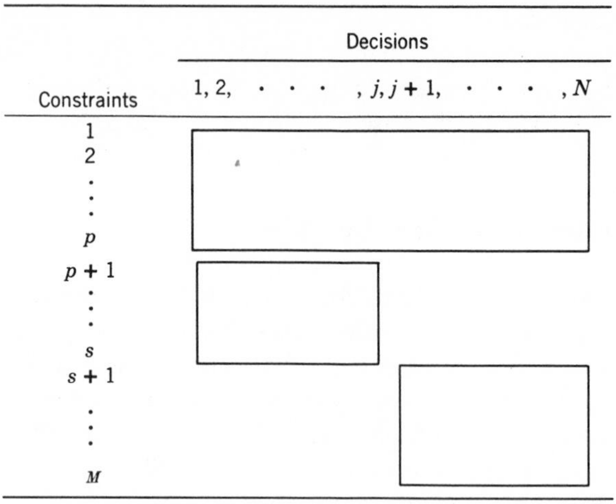

Fig. 4

numbered so that the first p constraints contained all of the decision variables, constraints $p + 1$ through s included only decision variables one through j, and the remaining $M - s$ constraints contained the remaining decision variables $j + 1$ through N (see Figure 4). In particular, consider

$$\min \sum_{n=1}^{N} r(d_n)$$

$$\text{subject to} \sum_{n=1}^{N} g_i(d_n) \geq k_i, \quad i = 1, \ldots, p$$

$$\sum_{n=1}^{j} g_i(d_n) \geq k_i, \quad i = p + 1, \ldots, s$$

$$\sum_{n=j+1}^{N} g_i(d_n) \geq k_i, \quad i = s + 1, \ldots, M$$

$$d_n \geq 0, \quad n = 1, \ldots, N$$

Naturally, if constraints $(1, \ldots, p)$ did not exist, there would be two independent problems

(i) $$\min \sum_{n=1}^{j} r(d_n)$$

$$\text{subject to} \sum_{n=1}^{j} g_i(d_n) \geq k_i, \quad i = p + 1, \ldots, s$$

$$d_n \geq 0, \quad n = 1, \ldots, j$$

(ii)
$$\min \sum_{n=j+1}^{N} r(d_n)$$

subject to $\sum_{n=j+1}^{N} g_i(d_n) \geq k_i, \qquad i = s+1, \ldots, M$

$$d_n \geq 0, \qquad n = j+1, \ldots, N$$

In this sense, (i) and (ii) can be considered as two subsystems joined together by system constraints one through p. Although the two subsystems cannot be optimized independently, we are able through a dynamic programming formulation to treat the subsystems as if they were almost independent.

Since $(d_1, \ldots, d_j)$ do not affect constraints $s+1, \ldots, M$, they can be chosen independently of these constraints. Similarly, once $(d_1, \ldots, d_j)$ have been chosen, the remaining decision variables, $(d_{j+1}, \ldots, d_N)$ can be chosen independently of constraints $p+1, \ldots, s$. By choosing the decision variables sequentially, we can ignore the state variables associated with constraints $s+1, \ldots, M$ in the first j stages of analysis, and the state variables for constraints $p+1, \ldots, s$ can be omitted in the optimization of stages $j+1, \ldots, N$. Thus the recursion equations for stages one through j will have only s state variables and for stages $j+1$ through N, only $p+M-s$ state variables. That is,

$$f_n(x_{n1}, \ldots, x_{np}, x_{n,p+1}, \ldots, x_{ns})$$

$$= \min_{d_n \geq 0} [r(d_n) + f_{n-1}(x_{n1} - g_1(d_n), \ldots, x_{np} - g_p(d_n), x_{n,p+1}$$

$$- g_{p+1}(d_n), \ldots, x_{ns} - g_s(d_n))], \qquad n = 1, \ldots, j$$

$$f_n(x_{n1}, \ldots, x_{np}, x_{n,s+1}, \ldots, x_{nM})$$

$$= \min_{d_n \geq 0} [r(d_n) + f_{n-1}(x_{n1} - g_1(d_n), \ldots, x_{np} - g_p(d_n), x_{n,s+1}$$

$$- g_{s+1}(d_n), \ldots, x_{nM} - g_M(d_n))], \qquad n = j+1, \ldots, N$$

We have developed a rough relationship between the member of constraints and dimensionality (the number of state variables). Each constraint need not contribute an additional state variable to the dynamic programming formulation. Dimensionality can be a real computational burden in dynamic programming analyses. But if we take advantage of the structure of the problem, the dimensionality need not be as large as might seem apparent at first glance.

---

† For an application of this idea to linear programming problems with a "block diagonal" structure, see Nemhauser [55].

11. Sensitivity Analysis

A desirable property of an optimization scheme is that it be flexible enough to handle changes in system parameters without having to re-solve the problem. The investigation of how the optimal decisions and return change with respect to changes in the system parameters is called *sensitivity analysis*. The capability of doing certain kinds of sensitivity analysis is automatically built into a dynamic programming formulation.

The embedding of the original problem into the larger space containing the state variables and the subsequent determination of the solution as a function of the state variables means that the optimal return and decisions are known for all feasible values of the state variables. The state variables at stage N are the inputs to the system. Consequently when $f_N(X_N)$ and $D_N^*(X_N), \ldots, D_1^*(X_N)$ are determined, we have the optimal return and decisions for all possible inputs. Then, if the inputs can be chosen, an additional optimization is performed to determine the optimal inputs. That is,

$$f_N(X_N^*) = \max_{X_N} f_N(X_N)$$

where X_N^* is the optimal input, $f_N(X_N^*)$ is the optimal return, and $D_N^*(X_N^*), \ldots, D_1^*(X_N^*)$ are the optimal decisions. This was illustrated in the examples of Sections 2 to 9. In each of these problems the optimal N-stage return was determined as a function of the variable input x_N. Subsequently, x_N was chosen to optimize $f_N(x_N)$, subject to the condition that x_N be equal to or greater than a specified input k. Of course, if it was meaningful, an optimal value of k could have been chosen simultaneously.

A second kind of sensitivity concerns the number of stages. For a particular system input X, one might want to know how the optimal return varies as a function of the number of stages. Because of the recursive nature of dynamic programming calculations, this information is provided in the course of analysis. That is, if our original objective was to determine $f_N(X)$, we must have previously determined $f_{N-1}(X), \ldots,$ $f_1(X)$ in the dynamic programming calculations. The optimal number of stages given the input X, written N^*, is defined as

$$f_N^*(X) = \max_N f_N(X)$$

The previous examples illustrate the idea of determining the sequence $f_1(X), f_2(X), \ldots, f_N(X)$ so that information about how the optimal return varies with the number of stages was provided. Fortunately, in each of these simple examples, we were able, by induction, to go almost immediately from $f_1(X)$ to the general form of $f_N(X)$. Generally, the sequence must be calculated term by term. Also, the determination of an optimal number of stages was of no interest in the examples since, in every case, the minimum return was monotone-decreasing with the number of stages. Sensitivity analysis on the number of stages may readily be combined with sensitivity on the state variables, to provide a more general description of optimal system behavior. In this way we can find the optimal input to a two-stage process, three-stage process, and so on.

12. Tabular Computations

The term tabular computations is used to describe dynamic programming analyses in which the optimal decision functions and optimal return functions are given in discrete form in lists or tables. In other words, for each feasible value of X_n, $n = 1, \ldots, N$, there is an entry in a table (for example, Table 2) containing values of $D_n(X_n)$ and $f_n(X_n)$.

Table 2   OPTIMAL nTH STAGE DECISION FUNCTIONS AND RETURNS

List of Feasible Values for State Variable X_n	Associated Optimal Decision Variable $D_n(X_n)$	Associated Optimal Return $f_n(X_n)$
$X_n = 1$ (first value)	$D_n(X_n = 1)$	$f_n(X_n = 1)$
.	.	.
.	.	.
.	.	.
$X_n = k$	$D_n(X_n = k)$	$f_n(X_n = k)$
.	.	.
.	.	.
.	.	.
$X_n = K_n$ (last value)	$D_n(X_n = K_n)$	$f_n(X_n = K_n)$

Naturally, it is only possible to give this information in a table when there are a finite number of feasible values for X_n. But tabular representation of continuous data is possible if we make discrete approximations. The feasible values of X_n are assigned integer numbers from 1 to K_n; the order is completely arbitrary. For $X_n = k$ $(k = 1, \ldots, K_n)$, $D_n(X_n = k)$ is the value of D_n that maximizes

$$r_n(X_n = k, D_n) \circ f_{n-1}(t_n(X_n = k, D_n)) = Q_n(X_n = k, D_n)$$

and $f_n(X_n = k)$ is the maximum value of the above expression.

Compared with the "closed-form" solutions obtained previously, tables are a rather cumbersome way of recording the optimal decision and return functions. This statement is certainly true for manual calculations. But even when computations are done digitally on a computer, closed-form solutions are more compact. For example, to record $d_n = x_n/n$ in a table for all integer values of x_n between 1 and 10,000 requires 10,000 entries. On the other hand, if $d_n(x_n)$ were known to be a polynomial of degree no higher than four, for example, $d_n = a_0 + a_1 x_n + a_2 x_n^2 + a_3 x_n^3 + a_4 x_n^4$, only the coefficients $(0, 1/n, 0, 0, 0)$ would have to be recorded to represent $d_n = x_n/n$.

The need for tabular representation of the optimal functions arises when the return and/or stage transformations are irregular and are themselves given in tabular form. The term "irregular" is used to convey the idea of being not expressible in neat or easily manipulated mathematical form. Even if the individual stage returns and transformations are well behaved, the multistage returns are frequently irregular. This is not surprising since the n-stage return is a composite function of n return functions and n stage transformations.

13. Flow Charts for Tabular Computations

The flow chart of Figure 1 can be made a bit more specific for tabular computations. Figure 5 shows this revised flow chart. It conveys the basic idea of discrete or tabular computations, namely that r_n, Q_n, and f_n are computed separately for each value of X_n. The feasible values of X_n are numbered 1 through K_n using the notation $X_n = k$, $k = 1, \ldots, K_n$. For each value of k, $r_n(X_n, D_n)$, $Q_n(X_n, D_n)$, and $f_n(X_n)$ are calculated successively. The tables of $f_n(X_n)$ and $D_n(X_n)$ are saved for future calculations. However, once $f_n(X_n = K_n)$ has been computed, $f_{n-1}(X_{n-1})$ is no longer needed, and the table $f_{n-1}(X_{n-1})$ is replaced by $f_n(X_n)$. Thus one optimal return table is used to calculate the next, and it is necessary only to reserve storage space for two optimal return tables, $f_n(X_n)$ and $f_{n-1}(X_{n-1})$, at a time. Assuming that K_s and K_t are the largest and second largest of $(K_1, \ldots, K_N)$, we need only reserve $K_s + K_t$ storage spaces for the optimal returns. However, for storage of the optimal decision functions, we must reserve space for N optimal decision function tables, since $D_n(X_n)$, $n = 1, \ldots, N-1$, are needed after $D_N(X_N)$ has been determined. Each of these tables contains K_n entries, so $\sum\limits_{n=1}^{N} K_n$ spaces are reserved for the optimal decision functions. In total, to store the optimal return and decision functions, the number of storage spaces required is $K_s + K_t + \sum\limits_{n=1}^{N} K_n$ or, if $K_n = K$ for all n, $(N+2)K$, a linear function of N.

The calculations are basically done in two parts; first, the calculation of $f_N(X_N)$ and $D_1(X_1), \ldots, D_N(X_N)$, and second, the tracing of the optimal policy $D_N^*, \ldots, D_1^*$. Each part is repetitive and cyclic with two loops, one for k and the other for n. In the calculation of the optimal return and decision functions, k is the index for the inner loop, that is, for each n, $n = 1, \ldots, N$, the optimal return and decision functions are computed for $k = 1, \ldots, K_n$. In the tracing of the optimal policy the positions of n and k are interchanged, so for each k, the optimal policies are traced for $n = N, \ldots, 1$.

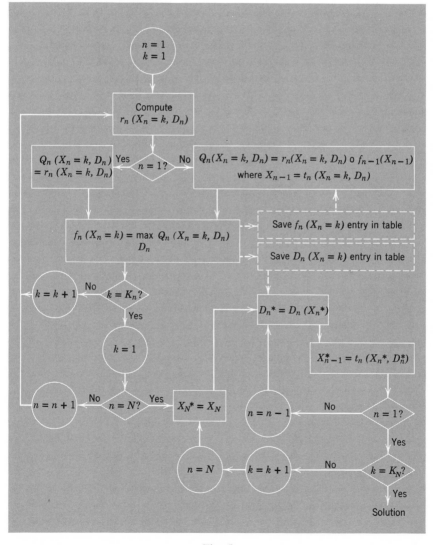

Fig. 5

Often, when calculations are done discretely for each value of the state variable X_n, the same discrete calculations must be done for the decision variable D_n. In the worst situations—unfortunately they are common—exhaustive search or total enumeration of the decision variables is required. Let the feasible values of D_n be numbered 1 through J_n with $D_n = j$ corresponding to the jth value of D_n, $j = 1, \ldots, J_n$. The determination of $f_n(X_n = k)$ from $Q_n(X_n = k, D_n = j)$ by exhaustive search simply means that Q_n is calculated for all J_n values of D_n, and the

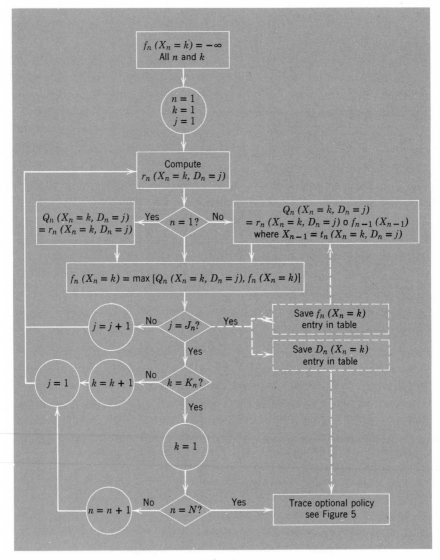

Fig. 6

maximum of Q_n is chosen as f_n. Although this is not a very sophisticated or pleasant way to determine an optimal solution, it is frequently the most efficient alternative. In fact, the only other choice might be direct exhaustive search on all feasible combinations of $(D_1, \ldots, D_N)$. The savings achieved by using exhaustive search on the recursion equations rather than direct exhaustive search in unusually enormous, as we shall see after reference to an example.

Figure 6 shows a flow chart for the optimization of the recursion equations by exhaustive search. It is an enlargement of the part of the flow chart of Figure 5 concerned with the computation of the optimal returns and decisions. The part for the tracing of the optimal policy is identical to that part of Figure 5, so it is not included here. There are three loops in the cyclic computations of the optimal returns. In the innermost loop for particular values of n and k, Q_n is calculated for all J_n values of D_n, and the maximum of Q_n is taken as $f_n(X_n = k)$. Then the index j is set back to 1, and the calculations are repeated for the next value of k ($k = k + 1$). After the calculations have been made for all values of k for a particular value of n, both k and j are set back to one and n is increased by one. This is continued through $n = N$. Storage requirements for the optimal returns and decision functions are the same no matter whether D_n is examined exhaustively or some more elegant method is used for optimization.

The flow chart in Figure 6 is the basis for a computer program. The program can be quite general; to apply it to a particular problem, input data specifying the functions r_n and t_n, the interpretation of the composition operator and the values of J_n, K_n, and N are required.

14. An Example: One State Variable and Irregular Returns and Transformations

This example shows how tabular computations are organized and provides some clues to the number of computations involved when the recursion equations are solved by enumeration. There are three stages with one state variable and one decision variable per stage. The objective is to maximize the sum of the stage returns. The stage returns and transformations are highly irregular, as can be seen from the data given in Tables 3 and 4.

The recursive analysis begins with stage one and simply involves setting $Q_1(x_1, d_1) = r_1(x_1, d_1)$, and for each value of x_1, maximizing Q_1 over d_1 to obtain $f_1(x_1)$. For example, $f_1(x_1 = 3) = \max (3, 5, 4, 3) = 5$. Then from Table 4 we see that $d_1(x_1 = 3) = 2$, and from Table 3 $t_1(x_1 = 3, d_1 = 2) = 3 = x_0(x_1 = 3)$ The tabular computations for stage one are summarized in Table 5.

Table 3　STAGE TRANSFORMATIONS　$x_{n-1} = t_n(x_n, d_n)$

		Stage 3						Stage 2						Stage 1			
		d_3						d_2						d_1			
		1	2	3	4			1	2	3	4			1	2	3	4
	1	3	2	1	4		1	–	2	5	1		1	1	2	1	–
	2	4	3	3	4		2	3	4	3	–		2	4	3	2	–
x_3	3	3	1	2	4	x_2	3	4	5	4	–	x_1	3	5	3	4	2
	4	2	4	2	1		4	3	4	2	3		4	–	4	3	4
													5	–	–	5	5
		x_2						x_1						x_0			

(—indicates that the corresponding combination of (x_n, d_n) is not feasible. When calculations are done on a digital computer, it is convenient to consider them as feasible, but assign them very large negative returns, for example, −10,000.)

Table 4　STAGE RETURNS　$r_n = r_n(x_n, d_n)$

		Stage 3						Stage 2						Stage 1			
		d_3						d_2						d_1			
		1	2	3	4			1	2	3	4			1	2	3	4
	1	3	4	1	4		1	–	1	5	4		1	2	1	3	–
	2	2	4	3	3		2	5	4	2	–		2	4	3	2	–
x_3	3	3	4	5	4	x_2	3	2	3	3	–	x_1	3	3	5	4	3
	4	4	2	3	2		4	3	5	4	2		4	–	4	3	5
													5	–	–	4	3
		r_3						r_2						r_1			

Table 5　ONE-STAGE RECURSION ANALYSIS

	$Q_1(x_1, d_1)$						
	d_1						
x_1	1	2	3	4	$f_1(x_1)$	$d_1(x_1)$	$x_0(x_1)$
1	2	1	3	–	3	3	1
2	4	3	2	–	4	1	4
3*	3	5	4	3	5	2*	3*
4	–	4	3	5	5	4	4
5	–	–	4	3	4	3	5

To evaluate the efficiency of the recursive analysis we shall compute the total number of additions and logical comparisons made at each stage, and then compare this with the number of additions and logical comparisons required in direct exhaustive search. Even though the additions and logical comparisons are not the total number of computations, they do provide a reasonable estimate for comparing different approaches, since they give a rather accurate measure of the magnitude of calculations needed to calculate the optimal return. To compute $f_1(x_1)$, the only calculations needed are the comparisons of the $Q_1(x_1, d_1)$ entries across each row to determine the row maximum. Assuming that the two numbers are compared at a time (as would be the case in logical operations on a digital computer), we see that there are three comparisons per row or 15 in all.

Turning to the two-stage recursion analysis we see that $Q_2(x_2, d_2) = r_2(x_2, d_2) + f_1(x_1)$. The r_2 values are in Table 4, and the f_1 values are in Table 5. The appropriate value of $f_1(x_1)$ added to $r_2(x_2, d_2)$ is the value of $f_1(x_1)$ such that $x_1 = t_2(x_2, d_2)$. For example, $x_2 = 2$ and $d_2 = 1$ imply $t_2(x_2 = 2, d_2 = 1) = (x_1 = 3)$, (from Table 3), and $f_1(x_1 = 3) = 5$ (from Table 5). Thus $Q_2(x_2 = 2, d_2 = 1) = 5 + 5 = 10$. There are 16 of these additions to determine Q_2, and then 12 logical comparisons to find $f_2(x_2)$. We assume an addition and comparison is made even when the (x_2, d_2) combination is infeasible. The stage two computations are given in Table 6.

Table 7 shows the three-stage recursion analysis. It is constructed in exactly the same manner as Table 6. Once again there are 16 additions and 12 comparisons to find the optimal returns.

The $f_3(x_3)$ column of Table 7 gives the optimal returns for all feasible values of x_3. Assuming that only the maximum of these returns is of interest, we determine $f_3(x_3^*) = 15$, $x_3^* = 3$, by making three additional comparisons. To trace the optimal set of decisions, given $x_3^* = 3$, we find from Table 7 that $d_3^* = 3$ and $x_2^* = 2$. Turning back to Table 6 with $x_2^* = 2$ yields $d_2^* = 1$ and $x_1^* = 3$. Then from Table 5, $d_1^* = 2$ and $x_0^* = 3$. The optimal decisions and states are starred in Tables 5, 6, and 7. Note that when there are alternative maxima, they are shown by multiple entries in the $d_n(x_n)$ and/or $x_{n-1}(x_n)$ columns. So alternative optimal solutions can be readily generated when they exist. Many other nonexhaustive search procedures do not possess this flexibility.

The total number of additions and logical comparisons required to determine $f_3(x_3^*)$ is summarized in Table 8.

Because the stage returns and transformations are so irregular, direct exhaustive search would have been the only alternative to the recursion analysis. Since there are four possible values for each of three decision variables, there are $4^3 = 64$ solutions (including the few infeasible solutions) for each value of the input (x_3). Hence there are $4^4 = 256$ com-

Table 6 TWO-STAGE RECURSION ANALYSIS

x_2	$Q_2(x_2, d_2)$ d_2				$f_2(x_2)$	$d_2(x_2)$	$x_1(x_2)$
	1	2	3	4			
1	—	$1+4=5$	$5+4=9$	$4+3=7$	9	3	5
2*	$5+5=10$	$4+5=9$	$2+5=7$	—	10	1*	3*
3	$2+5=7$	$3+4=7$	$3+5=8$	—	8	3	4
4	$3+5=8$	$5+5=10$	$4+4=8$	$2+5=7$	10	2	4

Table 7 THREE-STAGE RECURSION ANALYSIS

x_3	$Q_3(x_3, d_3)$ d_3				$f_3(x_3)$	$d_3(x_3)$	$x_2(x_3)$
	1	2	3	4			
1	$3+8 = 11$	$4+10 = 14$	$1+9\ = 10$	$4+10 = 14$	14	2,4	2,4
2	$2+10 = 12$	$4+8 = 12$	$3+8\ = 11$	$3+10 = 13$	13	4	4
3*	$3+8 = 11$	$4+9\ = 13$	$5+10 = 15$	$4+10 = 14$	15	3*	2*
4	$4+10 = 14$	$2+10 = 12$	$3+10 = 13$	$2+9\ = 11$	14	1	2

75

Table 8

Stage	Additions	Comparisons	Total
1	0	15	15
2	16	12	28
3	16	12	28
optimal input	0	3	3
Total	32	42	74

binations of (x_3, d_3, d_2, d_1). Two additions are required to compute the return from a feasible solution, so altogether there are $2 \cdot 256 = 512$ additions, an increase of 1,600% over the number required in the recursion analysis. To select an optimal solution from the 256 combinations we require 255 comparisons, a 600% increase over the number needed in the recursion analysis. These particular differences are small. In general they are much greater, on both an absolute and relative scale, when the number of stages and decision variables are larger. A more general analysis of the number of computations required in recursion analysis, as compared with direct enumeration, follows.

15. Recursion Analysis versus Direct Exhaustive Search

For those skeptics who remain unimpressed by the comparative advantage of recursive analysis in the previous illustration we provide more general evidence. Consider an optimization problem with the same irregular form as the illustration, with N stages and K_n and J_n values for the state and decision variables respectively at stage n, $n = 1, \ldots, N$.

Since a feasible solution is specified by a particular value of the vector $(x_N, d_N, \ldots, d_1)$, there are $K_N \prod_{n=1}^{N} J_n$ feasible solutions. To determine the return from each by enumeration we require the addition of N numbers. Hence, if they are added two at a time, there are $(N - 1) K_N \prod_{n=1}^{N} J_n$ additions. Then to choose a maximum from these, we have $K_N \prod_{n=1}^{N} J_n - 1$ comparisons.

On the other hand, recursion analysis requires an addition for each combination of (x_n, d_n) at stages two through N, or $\sum_{n=2}^{N} K_n J_n$ additions. For each value of the state variable at all stages there are $J_n - 1$ comparisons, and at the last stage there are an additional $K_N - 1$ comparisons to determine the maximum of $f_N(x_N)$—a total of $\sum\limits_{n=1}^{N} K_n(J_n - 1) + K_N - 1$ comparisons. Notice that the additions and comparisons grow exponentially with N for direct search and roughly linearly with N in dynamic programming. Yet $(K_1, \ldots, K_{N-1})$ do not appear in the number of calculations required using direct search, so if they are very large relative to $(K_N, J_1, \ldots, J_N)$, dynamic programming might not be so favorable.

To make the comparisons more obvious and striking let $J = K_m = J_n$, for all m and n. Then the number of additions plus comparisons for direct search is $NJ^{N+1} - 1$, and for dynamic programming $(2N - 1)J^2 - (N - 1)J - 1$. Table 9 (a, b, c) shows the absolute and relative size of these numbers for some appropriate values of N and J.

Table 9 NUMBER OF ADDITIONS AND COMPARISONS

(a) Direct search $= NJ^{N+1} - 1$ (NJ^{N+1} for large values)

N	J			
	2	10	100	1000
2	15	2×10^3	2×10^6	2×10^9
3	47	3×10^4	3×10^8	3×10^{12}
5	319	5×10^6	5×10^{12}	5×10^{18}
10	2×10^4	10^{12}	10^{23}	10^{34}
50	5×10^{16}	5×10^{52}	5×10^{103}	5×10^{154}

(b) Dynamic Programming $= (2N - 1)J^2 - (N - 1)J - 1$
(approximate for large J)

N	J			
	2	10	100	1000
2	9	289	3×10^4	3×10^6
3	15	479	5×10^4	5×10^6
5	27	959	9×10^4	9×10^6
10	66	1809	1.9×10^5	1.9×10^7
50	346	9409	10^6	10^8

(c) Relative Number $= NJ^{N+1}/[(2N-1)J^2 - (N-1)J - 1]$
(approximate)

N	J			
	2	10	100	1000
2	1.7	7	70	100
3	3.1	60	6×10^3	6×10^5
5	12	5×10^3	5×10^7	5×10^{11}
10	300	5×10^8	5×10^{17}	5×10^{26}
50	1.3×10^{14}	5×10^{48}	5×10^{97}	5×10^{146}

It is indeed obvious that for large N and/or J, particularly for large N, the savings achieved by dynamic programming are enormous, even when we allow for an inordinately large amount of time for the subsidiary calculations in dynamic programming. Savings is not really the appropriate term. It is more a matter of whether the computations can be done at all. Suppose we have a large digital computer that is capable of doing ten thousand additions or logical comparisons per second, and assume that a maximum of one hundred hours of computer time is available. At present rates of, say, $600/hour, it is hard to imagine a single problem on which we might invest more than one hundred hours. In one hundred hours 3.6×10^9 additions and comparisons could be done, so direct enumeration would only be possible in about half the cases in Table 9. The extreme case $N = 50$, $J = 1000$ would require under 3 hours by dynamic programming,† and a more modest case $N = 10$, $J = 100$, less than 20 seconds. If we put it another way, the case $N = 50$, $J = 10$ would require 10^{48} seconds by direct enumeration, but the age of the earth is postulated to be something less than 10^{17} seconds. There is no denying that recursion analysis, together with high-speed digital computers, brings many problems into the range of computability. Alone neither would suffice.

Why does the recursion analysis reduce the number of computations so considerably? To answer this, we must reflect on ͵the basic concept of dynamic programming—the principle of optimality. Paraphrasing it, we may say that if there are J inputs to the nth stage of an N-stage process, only the optimal returns and decisions from each of these input states are relevant to the optimization of the N-stage process. If we assume there is a unique optimal set of decisions from each of these input states, only J out of, say, J^n, of the decision combinations $(d_1, \ldots, d_n)$ remain as candidates for the optimal decisions $(d_1^*, \ldots, d_n^*)$. Thus after n stages

---

† In fact, this case takes about 2½ hours on the IBM 7094.

of recursion analysis, $(J^n - J)J^{N-n}$ out of J^N decision policies $(d_1, \ldots, d_N)$ may be dropped as candidates for optimality even though they have not been evaluated completely.

16. Discrete Variable Optimization

Models of optimization often have constraints limiting the domain of the variables to discrete points, usually the natural numbers. Economic models of production, inventory, and distribution have this characteristic when the variables are, for example, the number of items to be produced. Integer-valued variables can also be used to represent logical variables and to express logical relations. For example, the logical statement $p \vee q$ (either p is true, or q is true, or both are true) can be expressed algebraically using variables whose values are zero or one. Let

$$p = 0 \text{ if and only if } p \text{ is false}$$

$$q = 0 \text{ if and only if } q \text{ is false}$$

$$p = 1 \text{ if and only if } p \text{ is true}$$

$$q = 1 \text{ if and only if } q \text{ is true}$$

then $\qquad p + q \geq 1$ is equivalent to $p \vee q$

Mixed algebraic-logical statements can be transformed into entirely algebraic relations using zero-one variables. Consider a model with constraints $x + y \leq 10$ and $y \leq 0$ when $x < 5$. Let us introduce a zero-one variable z, such that when $x < 5, z = 0$. This can be achieved with the equation $z(5 - x) \leq 0$. Note that $z(5 - x) \leq 0$ is satisfied by z equals zero or one when $x \geq 5$. Now when $z = 0$, we require $y \leq 0$, which can be expressed as $y(1 - z) \leq 0$. Note when $y \leq 0$, z can be zero or one. The values of z which satisfy $z = 0, 1$, $z(5 - x) \leq 0$, $y(1 - z) \leq 0$ are summarized in Table 10. Consequently, $x + y \leq 10$, $z(5 - x) \leq 0$, $y(1 - z) \leq 0$, $z = 0, 1$ is one algebraic way of stating the original constraints.

Table 10

	Feasible z	
	y	
x	≤ 0	> 0
< 5	0	–
≥ 5	0,1	1

Although models with integer-valued variables are quite useful in representing real-world phenomena algebraically, generally they are not as easy to solve as their continuous counterparts. Properties that provide regularity are often destroyed when the domain of a function is limited to integers. One is tempted to optimize over the continuous domain and round off the results to the nearest integers. Although this sometimes works, there is no guarantee that rounding off will yield an optimum or even feasible integer solution, as we shall see in the following example.

17. An Example of Integer Optimization

Consider

$$\min \sum_{n=1}^{4} (a_n d_n + b_n d_n^2), \qquad A = (a_1, a_2, a_3, a_4) = (5, 4, 3, 2)$$

$$B = (b_1, b_2, b_3, b_4) = (2, 3, 4, 5)$$

$$C = (c_1, c_2, c_3, c_4) = (1, 2, 3, 4)$$

$$\text{subject to} \sum_{n=1}^{4} c_n d_n \geq 10, \qquad d_n = 0, 1, 2, \ldots$$

Ignoring the integer constraints, we see that the problem is of the type considered in section 5—the minimization of a separable convex function subject to a linear constraint. Because it lacks symmetry this problem requires more computations than that of Section 5, but is, however, readily solved by dynamic programming, Lagrange multipliers, or most easily by a quadratic programming algorithm. The optimal solution is $(d_1^*, d_2^*, d_3^*, d_4^*) = (0, 0.64, 1.09, 1.36)$. If we take into account the integer constraint, this solution is not feasible.

A straightforward four-stage tabular recursion analysis yields the optimal integer solution. We introduce state variables $(x_4 = 10, x_3, x_2, x_1)$ with $x_3 = x_4 - 4d_4$, $x_2 = x_3 - 3d_3$, $x_1 = x_2 - 2d_2$, and $d_1 \geq x_1$. Since $r_n(d_n)$ is increasing with d_n for all n, it follows from

$$d_1 + 2d_2 + 3d_3 + 4d_4 \geq 10$$

that it is satisfactory to take $d_1 = 0, 1, \ldots, 10$, $d_2 = 0, 1, \ldots, 5$, $d_3 = 0, 1, \ldots, 4$, $d_4 = 0, 1, \ldots, 3$ as the feasible region for the decision variables. Then, from the above definitions, the feasible regions of the state variables are $x_3 = 10, 6, 2, \leq 0,$† $x_2 = 10, 7, 6, 4, 3, 2, 1, \leq 0,$ and $x_1 = 10, 8, 7, 6, 5, 4, 3, 2, 1, \leq 0$. At the first stage

$$f_1(x_1) = \min_{d_1 \geq x_1} r_1(x_1, d_1) = \min_{d_1 \geq x_1} (5d_1 + 2d_1^2)$$

---

† ≤ 0, stands for all nonpositive integers.

Since r_1 is increasing with d_1, $d_1 = x_1$ for $x_1 = 0, 1, \ldots, 10$, so

$$f_1(x_1) = 5x_1 + 2x_1{}^2, \qquad x_1 = 0, 1, \ldots, 10$$

and $d_1 = f_1(x_1) = 0$, for $x_1 \leq 0$, as shown in Table 11. With x_2 as the

Table 11   ONE-STAGE RECURSION ANALYSIS

x_1	≤ 0	1*	2	3	4	5	6	7	8	10
$d_1(x_1)$	0	1*	2	3	4	5	6	7	8	10
$f_1(x_1)$	0	7	18	33	52	75	102	133	168	250

input to the two-stage system, and $x_1 = x_2 - 2d_2$, the optimal two-stage return is

$$f_2(x_2) = \min_{d_2 = 0, 1, \ldots, 5} Q_2(x_2, d_2),$$

$$Q_2(x_2, d_2) = 4d_2 + 3d_2{}^2 + f_1(x_2 - 2d_2)$$

The calculations of $d_2(x_2)$ and $f_2(x_2)$ are given in Table 12. Note the irregularities of $f_2(x_2)$ and $d_2(x_2)$ as compared with the continuous case in which they are quadratic and linear functions respectively. However, there is one important regularity to be observed; for every value of x_2, $Q_2(x_2, d_2)$ is a unimodal function of d_2 (that is, has only one peak). More will be said about this important property.

The three-stage analysis is given in Table 13, with the optimal three-stage return determined from

$$f_3(x_3) = \min_{d_3 = 0, 1, 2, 3, 4} Q_3(x_3, d_3), \qquad Q_3(x_3, d_3) = 3d_3 + 4d_3{}^2 + f_2(x_3 - 3d_3)$$

Note that $Q_3(x_3, d_3)$ is a unimodal function of d_3.

The four-stage recursion equation is

$$f_4(x_4 = 10) = \min_{d_4 = 0, 1, 2, 3, 4} Q_4(x_4, d_4),$$

$$Q_4(x_4, d_4) = 2d_4 + 5d_4{}^2 + f_3(x_4 - 4d_4)$$

The four-stage calculations are given in Table 14. From Table 14, $x_4{}^* = 10$, $f_4(x_4{}^*) = 28$, $d_4{}^* = 1$, $x_3{}^* = 6$. Tracing the optimal solution back through stage one yields $d_4{}^* = d_3{}^* = d_2{}^* = d_1{}^* = 1$. The optimal noninteger solution was (0, 0.64, 1.09, 1.36). Rounding it to the nearest integer solution yields (0, 1, 1, 1) which is not feasible. The closest feasible integer solution to (0, 0.64, 1.09, 1.36) is (0, 1, 1, 2) with return equal to 38. By taking this solution as the optimal integer solution, we would have a 35% error in the optimal return.

Actually some of the calculations done were unnecessary. In particular, it was not necessary to carry out an exhaustive search of $Q_n(x_n, d_n)$ over

Table 12   TWO-STAGE RECURSION ANALYSIS

| x_2 | $Q_2(x_2, d_2)$ | | | | | | $f_2(x_2)$ | $d_2(x_2)$ | $x_1(x_2)$ |
| | d_2 | | | | | | | | |
	0	1	2	3	4	5			
0	0 + 0	7 + 0	20 + 0	39 + 0	64 + 0	95 + 0	0	0	0
$\leq$ 1	0 + 7	7 + 0	20 + 0	39 + 0	64 + 0	95 + 0	7	0, 1	0, −1
2	0 + 18	7 + 0	20 + 0	39 + 0	64 + 0	95 + 0	7	1	0
3*	0 + 33	7 + 7	20 + 0	39 + 0	64 + 0	95 + 0	14	1*	1*
4	0 + 52	7 + 18	20 + 18	39 + 0	64 + 0	95 + 0	20	2	0
6	0 + 102	7 + 52	20 + 33	39 + 0	64 + 0	95 + 0	38	2	2
7	0 + 133	7 + 75	20 + 102	39 + 7	64 + 0	95 + 0	46	3	1
10	0 + 250	7 + 168		39 + 52	64 + 18	95 + 0	82	4	2

Table 13 THREE-STAGE RECURSION ANALYSIS

x_3	$Q_3(x_3, d_3)$					$f_3(x_3)$	$d_3(x_3)$	$x_2(x_3)$
	d_3							
	0	1	2	3	4			
≤ 0	$0+0$	$7+0$	$22+0$	$45+0$	$76+0$	0	0	0
2	$0+7$	$7+0$	$22+0$	$45+0$	$76+0$	7	0, 1	2, −1
6*	$0+38$	$7+14$	$22+0$	$45+0$	$76+0$	21	1*	3*
10	$0+82$	$7+46$	$22+20$	$45+7$	$76+0$	42	2	4

Table 14   FOUR-STAGE RECURSION ANALYSIS

	$Q_4(x_4, d_4)$						
	d_4						
x_4	0	1	2	3	$f_4(x_4)$	$d_4(x_4)$	$x_3(x_4)$
10	$0+42$	$7+21$	$24+7$	$51+0$	28*	1*	6*

all values of d_n. Because Q_n is a unimodal function of d_n in every case (we could have proved this in advance), a powerful selective search procedure could have been used to determine the minimum. Admittedly, it would not have made much difference in this problem, since in no case were there more than five feasible values of d_n. But suppose there were 10,000 feasible values of d_n. If it were necessary to calculate only, say, 20 values of Q_n rather than 10,000, there would be an enormous reduction in the total number of computations. This achievement, as well as other devices for reducing computations, will be given in Chapter IV.

EXERCISES

1. Determine

$$\max \ d_1{}^2 + d_2{}^2 + d_3{}^2$$
$$\text{subject to } d_1 + d_2 + d_3 \leq k, \qquad d_1, d_2, d_3 \geq 0$$

2. Extend the results of Problem 1 to

$$\max \ \sum_{n=1}^{N} d_n{}^2$$

$$\text{subject to } \sum_{n=1}^{N} d_n \leq k$$

$$d_n \geq 0, \qquad n = 1, \ldots, N$$

3. Extend the results of Problem 2 to

$$\max \ \sum_{n=1}^{N} d_n{}^p, \qquad p \geq 1$$

subject to the constraints of Problem 2.

4. Extend the results of Problem 3 to

$$\max \ \sum_{n=1}^{N} r(d_n),$$

$r(d_n)$ an arbitrary monotonically increasing convex function, subject to the constraints of Problem 2.

5. Determine

$$\max \ \sum_{n=1}^{N} r(d_n),$$

$r(d_n)$, an arbitrary monotone increasing convex function,

$$\text{subject to} \ \prod_{n=1}^{N} d_n \leq k, \qquad d_n \geq 0$$

6. Determine

$$\min \ \sum_{n=1}^{N} d_n{}^p$$

$$\text{subject to} \ \sum_{n=1}^{N} d_n{}^q \geq k$$

$$d_n \geq 0, \qquad n = 1, \ldots, N$$

for (a) $p > q$, (b) $p = q$, (c) $p < q$.

7. Determine

$$\max \ \prod_{n=1}^{N} d_n$$

$$\text{subject to} \ \sum_{n=1}^{N} d_n = k, \qquad d_n \geq 0$$

8. Determine

$$\max \ \sum_{n=1}^{4} (4d_n - nd_n{}^2)$$

$$\text{subject to} \ \sum_{n=1}^{4} d_n = k, \qquad d_n \geq 0$$

9. There are k machines available; each can do two jobs. If d of them do the first job, they produce a return of $3d$, and if d of them do the second job, they produce a return of $2.5d$. The machines are subject to attrition so that after doing the first job only $\frac{1}{3}d$ out of d remain available for further work, and for the second job only $\frac{2}{3}d$ out of d remain available for further work. The process is repeated with the remaining machines for two more stages. Find the number of machines we should allocate to each job at each stage in order to maximize profit. Assume that any nonnegative real number of machines of those available can be assigned at each stage.

10. Assume that at time 0 we have k lb of a certain chemical. At each of n subsequent periods, $n = 1, \ldots, N$, if we sell d_n lb of the chemical, we obtain a monetary return $r(d_n)$, and if we use z_n lb of the chemical for production in period n, the yield is az_n lb of the same chemical at the end of the period $a > 1$. Determine the amount of chemical sold and used for production in each of the N periods to maximize profit assuming:

(a) $r(d_n) = bd_n, \qquad b > 0$

(b) $r(d_n) = b_1 d_n + b_2 d_n{}^2, \qquad b_1, b_2, > 0$

(c) $r(d_n)$ is convex and monotonically increasing with $r(0) = 0$.

(d) $r(d_n)$ is strictly concave and monotonically increasing with $r(0) = 0$. Determine only the structure of the optimal solution for case (d).

11. In an inventory system, demand for a single item is constant at the rate R over the time interval $(0, T)$. The item is to be replenished N times over this period. The cost of carrying the item is c_1 (dollars/unit-time). There is no cost of ordering and shortages are not permitted. Determine the times t_n, $n = 1, \ldots, N$, when orders should arrive so that carrying costs are minimized. Then assume an ordering cost of the form $c_2 N$, and determine the optimal number of orders.

12. A company is planning its production schedule for the next 4 months. Monthly demands, which must be met, are as follows:

Month	January	February	March	April
Demand	1500	1000	800	1200

The cost of changing production from month to month is the difference between the productions squared. Any excess production during the month does not carry over to the next month, and in fact there is a cost incurred equal to the square of the excess. Determine monthly productions to minimize the cost of changing production and the cost of excess production. Assume that production during the previous December was 1200 units.

13. $N + 1$ houses are to be located along a street of length L, (as shown). The first and last houses are at the ends of the street, and the houses are assumed to be of infinitesimal width. The amount of disturbance a home owner receives

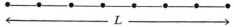

is a function of the distance he is from his two neighbors. In particular, the curve of Figure 7 has been established as a measure of disturbance. Assume that the disturbance to a home owner is the sum of the disturbances from each of his adjacent neighbors. Find the locations of the houses so that total disturbance along the street will be minimum.

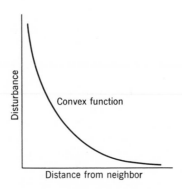

Fig. 7

14. M jobs are to be scheduled on two machines, A and B. Each job is processed first on machine A and then on machine B. The processing times for the ith job on machines A and B respectively are a_i and b_i. Show that to minimize the processing time for all M jobs the following rules should be applied:

1. If the $\min\limits_{i} (a_i, b_i) = a_k$, process job k first on both machines.

2. If the $\min\limits_{i} (a_i, b_i) = b_k$, process job k last on both machines.

3. Delete job k and apply Rules 1 and 2 again. Ties may be broken arbitrarily.†

15. A warehouse can store V units of a particular item. In each of N months, $n = 1, \ldots, N$, d_n units are sold at a price of p_n dollars per unit and $d_n{}'$ are bought at a price of c_n dollars per unit (selling precedes buying).

Assuming that months are numbered backwards, show that the optimal return from the last n months is

$$f_n(x_n) = a_n + b_n x_n$$

where x_n is the stock on hand at the beginning of month n. Then establish the optimality of the following decision policy

1. if $p_n \geq c_n$, and
 (a) $b_{n-1} \geq c_n$,   then $d_n = x_n$, $d_n{}' = V$
 (b) $b_{n-1} \leq c_n$,   then $d_n = x_n$, $d_n{}' = 0$
2. if $c_n \geq p_n$, and
 (a) $b_{n-1} \geq c_n$,   then $d_n = 0$, $d_n{}' = V - x_n$
 (b) $b_{n-1} \leq p_n$,   then $d_n = x_n$, $d_n{}' = 0$
 (c) $p_n \leq b_{n-1} \leq c_n$, then $d_n = 0$, $d_n{}' = 0$‡

16. Solve the "warehouse problem" with the data given in the table following. Assume an initial stock of five units and a warehouse capacity of ten units.

Month	January	February	March	April	May	June	July	August
c_n	107	105	105	105	101	95	90	90
p_n	110	110	104	103	102	100	103	105

17. It is desired to separate four different particle sizes of coal by means of industrial screening equipment. The equipment operates in the following manner. The raw feed which contains all four sizes is placed on a vibrating screen, the largest particles (size 3) are retained on the screen, but the small particles (sizes 0, 1, 2) pass onto the next screen. However, the amount of smaller particles passing through the screen depends upon the degree and time of vibration. The process continues in this manner, passing through 3 screens, which produce 4 products. The material retained on each screen is removed

---

† Bellman and Dreyfus [13] give the dynamic programming derivation of these rules. The original derivation, by an alternate approach, is given by Johnson [39].

‡ Bellman and Dreyfus [13] have derived these rules using dynamic programming. An alternate approach to this problem, known as the "warehouse problem," is a linear programming formulation.

for sale. The last product is obtained from the material passing through the third screen. A diagram of the process is given in Figure 8. The amount of the undersize material that is passed onto the next screen is given by:

amount passed to next screen $= \alpha$ (amount that entered the screen)

where $0 \leq \alpha \leq 1$, and depends upon the degree and time of vibration. The

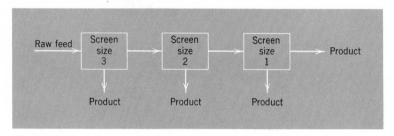

Fig. 8

cost of separation for each screen depends on α, and on the total amount of material entering the screen. This relationship is given as follows:

separation cost for the ith screen
$$= (\text{amount of material entering the } i\text{th screen}) k_i ln (1 - \alpha_i)$$

where k_i is a negative constant. The feed contains

$$\begin{array}{ll}
1 \text{ ton of size } 3 & \text{material (largest)} \\
3 & 2 \\
4 & 1 \\
2 & 0 \qquad \text{(smallest)}
\end{array}$$

The product removed from screen 3 is sold at $1 per ton

$$\begin{array}{ll}
2 & \$3 \\
1 & \$5
\end{array}$$

The product passing through screen 1 is sold at $8 per ton. The k_i's are as follows:

$$k_3 = -1.5$$
$$k_2 = -1.0$$
$$k_1 = -0.5$$

Determine the composition of the product removed for sale at each stage and the α's to maximize profit.†

18. Determine

$$\max \sum_{n=1}^{N} u_n \cdot v_n$$

---

† For a more detailed study of separation problems by dynamic programming see Mitten and Nemhauser [53].

$$\text{subject to} \quad \sum_{n=1}^{N} u_n = k_1$$

$$\sum_{n=1}^{N} v_n = k_2$$

19. Determine

$$\max \prod_{n=1}^{N} d_n$$

$$\text{subject to} \quad \sum_{n=1}^{N} d_n = 1$$

$$d_n \geq 0, \quad d_{n+1} \geq a d_n, \quad n = 1, \ldots, N-1$$

20. Determine

$$\max \sum_{n=1}^{N} r(d_n),$$

$r(d_n)$ an arbitrary monotone increasing convex function,

$$\text{subject to} \quad \sum_{n=1}^{N} d_n \leq k_1$$

$$\prod_{n=1}^{N} d_n \leq k_2$$

$$d_n \geq 0$$

21. Formulate as a dynamic program

$$\min [\max r_n(d_n)], \quad n = 1, \ldots, N$$

$$\text{subject to} \quad \sum_{n=1}^{N} d_n = k$$

$$d_n \geq 0$$

22. Use the results of Problem 21 to solve the following prolbem. Slobovia has 4 districts (A, B, C, D) with populations as shown in the following table. Assume that each district can be assigned any nonnegative *integer* number of representatives with the requirement that the total number of representatives assigned is 11. Find an optimal allocation of representatives so that the maximum discrepancy, in *representatives per person*, from ideal representation will be minimum. Ideal representation is defined so that each citizen in Slobovia would have equal representation.† The ideal case is given in the following table.

---

† For the application of this concept to the actual problem of allocation of representatives to the U.S. House of Representatives, see Burt and Harris [18].

District	Population	Ideal Rep.	Ideal Rep./Person
A	120	1.20	0.01
B	155	1.55	0.01
C	360	3.60	0.01
D	465	4.65	0.01
Total	1100	11	

23. A company has 6 salesman and 3 market areas (A, B, C). It is desired to determine the number of salesmen to allocate to each market area to maximize profit. The following table gives the profit from each market area as a function of the number of salesmen allocated.

Market Area	Number of Salesmen						
	0	1	2	3	4	5	6
A	38	41	48	58	66	72	83
B	40	42	50	60	66	75	82
C	60	64	68	78	90	102	109

24. A student has final examinations in 3 courses (X, Y, Z). (Assume each course counts for the same number of credits.) He has 12 hours available for study (the remainder of his time has been previously committed to more profitable pursuits). He feels that it would be best to break the 12 hours up into three blocks of 4 hours each, and to devote each 4-hour block to one particular course. His estimates of his grades based on various numbers of hours devoted to studying each course are:

Course	Number of Hours			
	0	4	8	12
X	F	D	D	B
Y	D	D	B	A
Z	F	D	B	B

Assuming a 4-point grading procedure (that is, $A = 4$, $B = 3$, $C = 2$, $D = 1$, $F = 0$), how many hours should he devote to each subject to maximize his total points this semester? Give two dynamic programming formulations for the problem.

25. In Problem 9 find the solution with $k = 8$ and when only an integer number of machines can be assigned.

26. A company that produces autopilots for aircraft can produce 0, 1, or 2 autopilots per month. The company is planning its production schedule for the next 3 months: February, March, and April. At the beginning of February it will have 1 autopilot in inventory. During February, March, and April it anticipates sales of 1, 2, and 0 autopilots, respectively. At the end of April the company wants to have 1 autopilot in inventory. Production and inventory costs are given in the table following, where inventory costs refer to beginning of the month inventory.

Production (autopilots/month)	0	1	2	
Total cost (in $1000)	15	20	35	
Inventory (no. of autopilots in stock)	0	1	2	3
Total inventory cost (in $1000/month)	2	5	9	15

What production schedule for the next 3 months will minimize the sum of production and inventory costs?

27. A company is planning its production schedule for the next 5 months. Its product is produced at the rate of one batch per month. However, two and only two batch sizes are possible: 500 items and 1000 items. The 500-item batch costs $500 to produce, and the 1000-item batch costs $800. Monthly demands, which must be met, are shown in the following table.

Month	February	March	April	May	June
Demand	1500	1000	500	500	1500

At the end of each month, an inventory charge of $0.20 per item is charged against every item in stock at that time. The inventory level at the end of January will be 1500, and the desired inventory level at the end of June is zero. What production schedule will minimize the sum of inventory and production costs?

28. A system is composed of N different types of components in series, and each type of component may be duplicated in parallel one or more times to increase the reliability. The number of components of the nth type in parallel is d_n, with cost $c_n d_n$, and probability of successful operation $1 - (\frac{1}{2})^{d_n}$. Assume the different types of components operate independently, and determine the optimum values of d_n such that P, the probability of successful operation of the entire system, exceeds 0.7 with $N = 4$ and $(c_1, c_2, c_3, c_4) = (3, 2, 1, 0.5)$. Then maximize P subject to total cost equal to or less than 20.†

29. In the "knapsack" problem we are given a set of N items, $n = 1, \ldots, N$, with corresponding weights per unit w_n, and values per unit p_n. Formulate the problem of finding the integer quantity of each item to be placed in the knapsack such that the total weight in the knapsack does not exceed W and the total value is maximized. In particular, consider the following data $W = 19$, and

Item	1	2	3	4
Weight/unit	1	3	4	6
Value/unit	1	5	7	11

† For a detailed dynamic programming analysis of this kind of problem, see Kettelle [41].

IV

Computational Refinements

1. Introduction

In tabular dynamic programming calculations, at each stage, for each feasible value of the state variables, the return is computed for every feasible value of the decision variables. Then, for each feasible value of the state variables, an optimal value for the decision variables is recorded to trace the optimal solution. It is not hard to imagine problems, with a large number of stages and/or state variables, that cannot be solved even on a high-speed digital computer.

The methods discussed in this chapter are designed to reduce computation time. This can be achieved at several levels. Since an optimization is performed for each value of the state variables, it is obvious that each optimization should be done efficiently. It may be possible to optimize Q_n for a fixed value of X_n without searching over all feasible values of D_n. There are numerous efficient search procedures; many are available as computer subroutines. An excellent exposition of search methods is contained in Wilde [66].

A particularly useful and interesting procedure for finding the optimum of a unimodal function of one variable is Fibonacci search. Under the criterion of minimizing the maximum number of function evaluations required to find the optimum, Fibonacci search is the best one-dimensional search procedure. It can be derived from a dynamic programming approach, and is the subject of Section 2.

Computational refinements more closely related to dynamic programming are associated with the state variables. There are two basic strategies. The first is to reduce the number of feasible values of a state variable. The second, when there is more than one state variable, is to eliminate some state variables altogether.

The role of the state variable is very different from the role of the decision variable, so a fundamentally different approach must be taken to reduce the number of values of the state variable. To delineate, as sharply as possible, the different roles of these two kinds of variables, consider the basic recursion equation

$$f_n(X_n) = \max_{D_n} Q_n(X_n, D_n)$$

$$Q_n(X_n, D_n) = r_n(X_n, D_n) \circ f_{n-1}(X_{n-1})$$

Since we are interested in the maximum values of $Q_n(X_n, D_n)$ only as a function of X_n, it is justifiable and certainly advisable to calculate $Q_n(X_n, D_n)$ for as few values of D_n as possible, provided that these few calculations yield the maximum.

On the other hand, the recursion equation stipulates that f_n must be calculated for all feasible values of X_n, since the optimal return function $f_n(X_n)$ is used in its entirety to calculate $f_{n+1}(X_{n+1})$. We are well aware that $f_n(X_n = A) > f_n(X_n = B)$ gives no indication whatsoever about the optimality or even preferability of $X_n = A$, or $X_n = B$. In fact, it is not until the optimal return has been calculated from the whole process that we can begin to determine the optimal values for intermediate state variables X_n, $n = N - 1, \ldots, 1$. The problem is simply that to determine the optimal states and decisions $f_N(X_N)$ must be known. But to calculate $f_n(X_n)$ we must know $f_{n-1}(X_{n-1})$ for all feasible values of X_{n-1}. Under certain circumstances the *coarse grid approach* (Section 5) can be used to determine the optimal decisions without having to determine the optimal return for all feasible values of the state variable.

If it appears difficult to reduce the number of values of a state variable, it seems to be against the grain of dynamic programming altogether to eliminate state variables. The state variable is the basic element that allows us to treat optimization problems recursively. However, there are computational procedures for reducing the number of state variables. When we solve a problem on a computer, an extremely important benefit from state variable elimination is storage reduction. The optimal decision functions $D_n(X_n)$ that must be recorded to trace the optimal policy will, of course, have fewer entries when there are fewer state variables.

In most cases the computational refinements associated with state variable reduction yield only approximate solutions, and in some circumstances may not work at all. The two main procedures, *Lagrange multipliers* and the *one-at-a-time* method, are illustrated with examples that point out both success and failure. To show the magnitude of success and the implications of failure, the examples are also worked in detail with the full number of state variables.

2. Fibonacci Search

We have used the term "unimodal function" to stand for a function having a single peak. But to develop the Fibonacci search procedure for optimizing functions of one variable, we must define a unimodal function of one variable precisely. For the sake of simplicity, we restrict ourselves to a function defined on a discrete set of points. Similar arguments apply to continuous functions [66]. Figure 1 illustrates an arbitrary unimodal discrete function $Q(d)$. The values of d, not necessarily equally spaced, are numbered with the positive integers from 1 to k. There is a single peak (maximum) at d^*, which could be anywhere between 1 and k, including the endpoints.

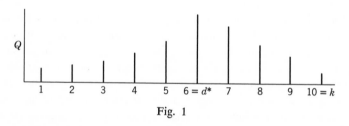

Fig. 1

$Q(d)$ is unimodal (with respect to finding a maximum) if there is a value of d^* such that for all $(d_1, d_2) \leq d^*$ with $d_1 < d_2$, $Q(d_1) < Q(d_2)$, and for all $(d_1, d_2) \geq d^*$ with $d_1 < d_2$, $Q(d_1) > Q(d_2)$. This simply says that for two points on the same side of d^*, the one closer to d^* yields the

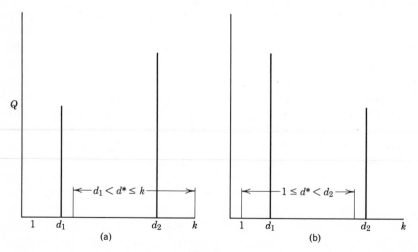

Fig. 2

higher value of Q. For $Q(d)$ to be unimodal with respect to locating a minimum, all of the inequalities on $Q(d)$ are reversed.

Using this definition, we see that if we evaluate a unimodal function at any two points, say d_1 and d_2, $d_2 > d_1$, and obtain $Q(d_2) > Q(d_1)$ then $d_1 < d^* \leq k$ (see Figure 2a). Suppose $1 \leq d^* \leq d_1$; then $(d_1, d_2) \geq d^*$ and $Q(d_1) < Q(d_2)$ contradicts the definition of unimodality. Similarly, if $Q(d_1) > Q(d_2)$, then $1 \leq d^* < d_2$ (see Figure 2b).

Thus if we compare the values of the function at any two points, a finite number of points can be excluded from optimality. Clearly by making successive evaluations and comparisons, we do not need to carry out an exhaustive search to find the optimal solution. The problem is to design the search procedure so that the number of evaluations is minimal. Depending upon where d^* lies, search procedures generally require different numbers of evaluations. Under the assumption of complete uncertainty regarding the value of d^*, a reasonable measure of effectiveness is to minimize the maximum number of evaluations. Another way of stating this is to let k_n be the maximum number of points in the domain so that the optimum point always may be determined with no more than n evaluations. A number k_n can be assigned to each search procedure. Let f_n equal the maximum over-all search procedures of k_n. Fibonacci search attains the number f_n and in this sense is optimal.

Let us calculate f_n directly for some small value of n, and then attempt to construct a general rule. When we have only one evaluation of the function Q ($n = 1$), it is clear that no comparisons can be made. So for this trivial case the domain of the function cannot contain more than one point. Hence $f_1 = 1$. For $n = 2$, with two evaluations and a comparison, we can certainly find the optimum of a function defined on two points, but obviously not for a function defined on three points. Therefore $f_2 = 2$.

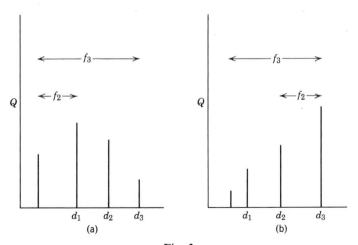

(a)   (b)

Fig. 3

The first interesting case is $n = 3$ (see Figure 3). What is the maximum number of points in the domain $1 \leq d \leq k$ of the unimodal function $Q(d)$ so that the optimum can be found with three evaluations and two comparisons? Let the first two evaluations be at d_1 and d_2, $d_2 > d_1$. If $Q(d_1) > Q(d_2)$ then $1 \leq d^* < d_2$ (Figure 3a). The third and last evaluation is at d_3, $1 \leq d_3 < d_2$. Since $1 \leq d_1 < d_2$, there are two evaluations in the region $1 \leq d < d_2$, namely d_1 and d_3. But $f_2 = 2$. Thus, the maximum number of points contained in this region, when we want to find the optimum without further evaluations, is two. If the region $1 \leq d < d_2$ is to contain no more than two points, these obviously must be $d = 1, 2$, thus $d_2 < 4$. By a similar argument, if $Q(d_2) > Q(d_1)$, the maximum number of points in the region $d_1 < d \leq k_3$ is also two. From $d_1 < d_2$ and $d_2 < 4$ it follows that $d_1 < 3$, and thus $k_3 < 5$. Hence the maximum of k_3 is 4, achieved by setting $d_1 = 2$ and $d_2 = 3$. With three evaluations, the maximum can always be found on an interval of four points by making the first two evaluations at the second and third points and the third evaluation at the first or fourth point. Hence $f_3 = 4$.

A general strategy is beginning to emerge, although the tactics are by no means established. That is, if there is to be a total of n evaluations, the interval remaining after the first two evaluations must contain no more than f_{n-1} points, and the point already evaluated in this region must be placed optimally with respect to the search of the region containing f_{n-1} points. More generally stated, this means that an optimal first decision (the first two points at which the function is to be evaluated) in an n-point search must be placed optimally with respect to the resulting $(n-1)$-point search. In other words, the dynamic programming principle of optimality must apply, if the search is to be done optimally.

Let us apply this strategy to the case $n = 4$ (Figure 4). Depending on the outcomes of the first two evaluations at d_1 and d_2, the remaining region is either $1 \leq d^* < d_2$ or $d_1 < d^* \leq k$. Each of these regions can

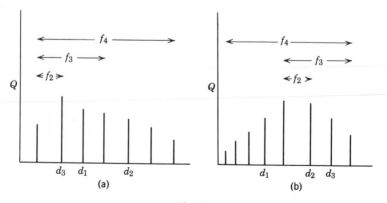

(a)   (b)

Fig. 4

contain no more than four points since $f_3 = 4$. And the point already evaluated in the interval (either d_1 or d_2) must be the second or third point, since in an optimal search of a four-point region the first two evaluations must be at the second and third points. From $1 \leq d^* < d_2$ it follows that $d_2 < 6$ and $d_1 = 2$ or 3. To maximize k_4 and not exceed the four-point constraint on the region $d_1 < d^* \leq k_4$, we set $d_1 = 3$; consequently f_4 = maximum of $k_4 = 7$. Furthermore, d_2 must be the second or third point in the interval $3 < d \leq 7$ ($d_2 = 5, 6$), and as stated previously, $d_2 < 6$; hence $d_2 = 5$. By combining portions of both parts of Figure 4, as shown in Figure 5, we see that $f_4 = f_3 + f_2 + 1$, $d_1 = f_2 + 1$, and $d_2 = f_3 + 1$. Note that the same relationships were also true for $n = 3$, that is, $f_3 = f_2 + f_1 + 1$, $d_1 = f_1 + 1$, $d_2 = f_2 + 1$.

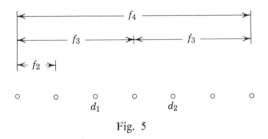

Fig. 5

We proceed by induction with the hypothesis $f_n = f_{n-1} + f_{n-2} + 1$, $d_1 = f_{n-2} + 1$, $d_2 = f_{n-1} + 1$. In the case of $n + 1$ evaluations (see Figure 6), the regions $1 \leq d^* < d_2$ and $d_1 < d^* \leq k_{n+1}$ must not contain more

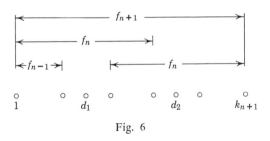

Fig. 6

than f_n points each; that is, $d_2 < f_n + 2$ and $k_{n+1} - d_1 < f_n + 1$. If we assume that $1 \leq d^* < d_2$ is the region under consideration, the first two evaluations in it must be made at $f_{n-2} + 1$ and $f_{n-1} + 1$. This implies that the first of the $n + 1$ evaluations (d_1) is at $f_{n-2} + 1$ or $f_{n-1} + 1$. From $k_{n+1} < f_n + 1 + d_1$ it follows that $k_{n+1} < \max (f_n + f_{n-1} + 2, f_n + f_{n-2} + 2)$. Since f_n is obviously an increasing sequence, $f_{n+1} = \max k_{n+1} = f_n + f_{n-1} + 1$, and $d_1 = f_{n-1} + 1$. To complete the proof d_2 must be the $(f_{n-2} + 1)$th or the $(f_{n-1} + 1)$th point in the region $d_1 < d^* \leq k_{n+1}$, and satisfy $d_2 < f_n + 2$. Since $d_1 = f_{n-1} + 1$, $d_2 = 2f_{n-1} + 2$, or $d_2 = f_{n-1} + f_{n-2} + 2 = f_n + 1$. The latter value of d_2 satisfies $d_2 < f_n + 2$, but the former does not. Hence $d_2 = f_n + 1$.

To summarize our results, we see that the optimum value of a unimodal function defined on f_n points can be determined by evaluating the function at n points, where

$$f_n = f_{n-1} + f_{n-2} + 1, \qquad n \geq 2$$

$$f_1 = 1, \quad f_2 = 2$$

The first two evaluations are made at the $(f_{n-2} + 1)$th and $(f_{n-1} + 1)$th points. This reduces the region under consideration to f_{n-1} points, with an evaluation already made at one of the appropriate points in this interval.

Table 1

n	f_n	d_1	d_2
1	1	1	–
2	2	1	2
3	4	2	3
4	7	3	5
5	12	5	8
6	20	8	13
7	33	13	21
8	54	21	34
9	88	34	55
10	143	55	89
11	232	89	144
12	376	144	233
13	609	233	377
14	986	377	610
15	1596	610	987
16	2583	987	1597
17	4180	1597	2584
18	6764	2584	4181
19	10945	4181	6765
20	17710	6765	10946

For a continuous unimodal function of one variable the results are very similar. Let the domain of the function be all real numbers in the interval $0 \leq d \leq k_n$, and suppose that it is desired to determine the maximum within a unit interval with n evaluations. Let f_n be the maximum value of k_n for which this can be achieved. Then

$$f_n = f_{n-1} + f_{n-2}, \quad n \geq 2,$$

$$f_1 = 1, \quad f_2 = 2$$

Table 1 gives f_n and the points of the first two evaluations as a function of n (in the discrete case) for n up to 20. For a function defined on 1500 points, only 1% of its values need be determined to find the optimum. When the original region does not contain a number of points corresponding to some f_n, the number of evaluations required is generally equal to the n corresponding to the first value of f_n greater than the number of points in the region. To preserve symmetry, we may add ficticious points with very low returns so that the total number of points corresponds exactly to the first value of f_n greater than the number of points in the region.

This search procedure is called Fibonacci search because of its relationship to the sequence generated by the difference equation $y_n = y_{n-1} + y_{n-2}$ studied by the Italian mathematician Fibonacci several centuries ago.

3. Convexity and Fibonacci Search

The two major limitations of Fibonacci search are that it works only for functions of one variable and the function must be unimodal. However, return functions of one variable are unimodal in many practical situations. Strictly convex functions are always unimodal with respect to finding a minimum, and strictly concave functions are always unimodal with respect to finding a maximum. To show the former is true recall that $Q(d)$ is strictly convex if for all (d_1, d_2) and $0 < \alpha < 1$

$$Q(\alpha d_1 + (1 - \alpha)d_2) < \alpha Q(d_1) + (1 - \alpha)Q(d_2)$$

Let $d_1 < d_2 < d^*$ and $d_2 = \alpha d_1 + (1 - \alpha)d^*$, with $Q(d^*) \leq Q(d)$ for all d. Then from the convexity property

$$Q(d_2) < \alpha Q(d_1) + (1 - \alpha)Q(d^*)$$

But Q attains a unique minimum at d^*, so

$$(1 - \alpha)Q(d^*) < (1 - \alpha)Q(d_1)$$

Combining the two above inequalities, we have

$$Q(d_2) < \alpha Q(d_1) + (1 - \alpha)Q(d_1) = Q(d_1)$$

So if $Q(d)$ is strictly convex, it is unimodal.

Often in multistage optimization problems the objective is to minimize the sum of stage returns, where each stage return is convex. The convexity of the individual stage returns is sufficient to establish the convexity, and hence unimodality, of the multistage optimal returns. To be specific, let $r_n(x_n, d_n)$ be the nth stage return $(n = 1, \ldots, N)$, where $r_n(x_n, d_n)$ is convex in both x_n and d_n. We want to show that

$$f_n(x_n) = \min_{d_n} Q_n(x_n, d_n)$$

where $Q_n(x_n, d_n) = r_n(x_n, d_n) + f_{n-1}(x_{n-1})$

is a convex function of x_n, $n = 1, \ldots, N$. For if $f_n(x_n)$ is convex, it follows that $Q_{n+1}(x_{n+1}, d_{n+1})$ is convex, since the sum of convex functions is convex. Thus Fibonacci search may be used to minimize Q_{n+1}.

Observe that if we show that $f_1(x_1)$ is convex, where

$$f_1(x_1) = \min_{d_1} Q_1(x_1, d_1)$$

$$Q_1(x_1, d_1) = r_1(x_1, d_1)$$

a straightforward induction will establish the convexity of $f_n(x_n)$. So the burden of proof rests on showing that $f_1(x_1)$ is convex. Or in other words (suppressing the stage subscripts), we show that if $Q(x, d)$ is a convex function of x and d, then

$$f(x) = \min_d Q(x, d)$$

is a convex function of x. Let

$$f(x_1) = Q(x_1, d_1) = \min_d Q(x_1, d)$$

and $$f(x_2) = Q(x_2, d_2) = \min_d Q(x_2, d)$$

Thus from the above definitions

$$\alpha f(x_1) + (1 - \alpha)f(x_2) = \alpha Q(x_1, d_1) + (1 - \alpha)Q(x_2, d_2)$$

Let

$$x = \alpha x_1 + (1 - \alpha)x_2$$

and $$d = \alpha d_1 + (1 - \alpha)d_2, \qquad 0 < \alpha < 1$$

Since $Q(x, d)$ is a convex function with respect to x and d, we have

$$\alpha Q(x_1, d_1) + (1 - \alpha)Q(x_2, d_2) \geq Q(x, d)$$

But

$$f(x) = \min_d Q(x, d) \leq Q(x, d)$$

Hence $$f(x) \leq \alpha f(x_1) + (1 - \alpha) f(x_2)$$

and the convexity property is established. We shall use this result in section 4.

4. An Illustration of Fibonacci Search

To illustrate Fibonacci search we return to the example of Chapter III, Section 17 with one apparently innocent change. The constraint $\sum_{n=1}^{4} c_n d_n$ ≥ 10 is replaced by $\sum_{n=1}^{4} c_n d_n \geq 10{,}000$. Thus the entire problem is to find nonnegative integer values of the variables d_n to minimize

$$\sum_{n=1}^{4} (a_n d_n + b_n d_n^2), \quad A = (5, 4, 3, 2)$$

$$B = (2, 3, 4, 5)$$

$$\text{subject to } \sum_{n=1}^{4} c_n d_n \geq 10{,}000 \quad C = (1, 2, 3, 4)$$

$$d_n = 0, 1, 2, \ldots$$

The change in the value of the right-hand side of the constraint is computationally quite burdensome. For instead of having to consider less than eleven values of x_n $(0, \ldots, 10)$ and the corresponding number of values of d_n for each value of x_n, we must consider roughly a thousand times as many values of x_n and, for each value of x_n, about a thousand times as many values of d_n. Fibonacci search can, in part, although by no means entirely, alleviate this purely computational difficulty. For each value of x_n, only a small fraction of the multistage returns $Q_n(x_n, d_n)$ need be computed to determine $f_n(x_n)$, if we use Fibonacci search. It is valid for this problem since the stage returns are convex.

To illustrate Fibonacci search, we will determine one value of $f_n(x_n)$, namely $f_2(x_2 = 10{,}000)$. The equation to be solved is

$$f_2(x_2 = 10{,}000) = \min_{d_2 = 0, 1, \ldots, 5000} [Q_2(x_2 = 10{,}000, d_2)]$$

where

$$Q_2(x_2 = 10{,}000, d_2) = r_2(d_2) + f_1(x_1)$$

The one-stage computations (which are of the same nature as those in Section 17) yield

$$f_1(x_1) = 5x_1 + 2x_1^2, \quad x_1 = 0, 1, \ldots, 10{,}000$$

$$= 5(x_2 - 2d_2) + 2(x_2 - 2d_2)^2$$

Thus

$$Q_2(x_2, d_2) = 4d_2 + 3d_2^2 + 5(x_2 - 2d_2) + 2(x_2 - 2d_2)^2$$

and

$$Q_2(x_2 = 10,000, d_2) = 4d_2 + 3d_2{}^2 + 5(10,000 - 2d_2) + 2(10,000 - 2d_2)^2$$

$$= 11d_2{}^2 - 80,006\, d_2 + \text{constant}$$

Ignoring the constant and subscripts, we see that our objective is to minimize the unimodal function

$$Q(d) = 11d^2 - 80,006\, d$$

defined on the 5001 points $d = (0, 1, \ldots, 5000)$.

We must apologize for an example really unworthy of Fibonacci search. Because there is a closed-form expression for $Q(d)$, obviously d^* is most easily determined from

$$Q(d^*) < Q(d^* + 1)$$

$$Q(d^*) < Q(d^* - 1)$$

This yields

$$11(d^*)^2 - 80,006\, d^* < 11(d^* + 1)^2 - 80,006(d^* + 1)$$

$$11(d^*)^2 - 80,006\, d^* < 11(d^* - 1)^2 - 80,006(d^* - 1)$$

which is satisfied only by $d^* = 3637$. But in most circumstances, it is not possible to obtain a closed-form expression for $Q(d)$.

Turning to the Fibonacci search, we find that there are 5001 points in the domain of the function. In accordance with Table 1, we must evaluate the function at eighteen points to determine the minimum, since $4180 = f_{17} < 5001 < f_{18} = 6764$. To start with a number of points equal to f_{18}, we introduce fictitious points $d = 5001, \ldots, 6763$. These fictitious points are assigned very high returns, so when compared with values of $Q(d)$ at real points, they never yield a lower value of $Q(d)$.

The calculations are given in Table 2. The last two columns show the interval remaining under consideration for optimality after the corresponding evaluation and comparison has been made. The number of decimal places given for $Q(d)$ varies according to the accuracy needed for comparison.

All of the directions needed to perform the calculations in the proper sequence are given in Table 1. To start the calculations, we enter Table 1 with $n = 18$, and find that the first two points ($n = 1$ and 2, in Table 2) at which to evaluate $Q(d)$ are the 2584th ($d = 2583$) and the 4181st ($d = 4180$). Since $Q(4180) < Q(2583)$, we conclude that $2584 \le d^* \le 6763$. The next point at which $Q(d)$ is to be evaluated is found in Table 1 with $n = 17$. For an interval containing 4180 points ($2584 \le d \le 6763$ contains exactly this number of points) the function is to be evaluated at the 1597th and 2584th points. The 2584th point is $d = 5167$ (a fictitious point), and the 1577th point is $d = 4180$, which has already been evaluated. Thus $Q(4180) < Q(5167)$ and $2584 \leq d^* \leq 5000$ (5166). We continue with $n = 18, 17, \ldots, 1$ of Table 1 to build $n = 1, 2, \ldots, 18$ of

Table 2

			$a \leq d^* \leq b$	
n	d	$-Q(d) \cdot 10^{-7}$	a	b
1	2583	12.59	0	5000 (6763)
2	4180	14.22	2584	5000 (6763)
3	5167	very low	2584	5000 (5166)
4	3570	14.543	2584	4179
5	3193	14.33	3194	4179
6	3808	14.52	3194	3802
7	3426	14.499	3427	3802
8	3659	14.54709	3571	3802
9	3714	14.540	3571	3713
10	3625	14.54749	3571	3658
11	3604	14.546	3605	3658
12	3638	14.5476344	3626	3658
13	3646	14.54754	3626	3645
14	3633	14.547622	3634	3645
15	3641	14.547616	3634	3640
16	3636	14.5476360	3634	3637
17	3635	14.5476335	3636	3637
18	3637	14.5476363	3637	3637

Table 2. For each value of n, Table 1 gives two points at which $Q(d)$ is to be calculated, one new point and one point already calculated for a prior value of n. After evaluating the function eighteen times, we determine $d^* = 3637$, and $Q(d^*) = -[14.5476363] \cdot 10^7$.

No doubt, Fibonacci search requires substantially fewer evaluations of Q than exhaustive search. In this particular example there are 18 out of 5001 evaluations, or 0.36% of the total. For the entire example, $f_n(x_n)$ must be calculated about 40,000 times. Using the calculation of $f_2(x_2 = 10,000)$ as a guide, we estimate 7.2×10^5 calculations of Q rather than 2×10^8 calculations of Q for the entire example.† This saving is enormous, but it may not be good enough. The 40,000 calculations of $f_n(x_n)$ and the resultant storage-retrieval problems may be prohibitive anyway.

---

† Actually this estimate is a bit higher for both Fibonacci and exhaustive search, because for smaller values of x a correspondingly smaller number of evaluations of Q are required, but the orders of magnitude are reasonable.

Clearly, to reduce computations further, we must reduce the number of values of the state variable. A technique for doing this is discussed in Section 5. We will then have the ingredients for handling the entire example of Section 4 with a reasonable number of calculations.

5. Coarse Grid Approach

The coarse grid approach is used to reduce the number of feasible values of each state variable. It is based on the notion of solving a series of problems, beginning with only a few widely spaced values for each state variable. The solution to the first problem yields an approximation to the true solution. Based on this approximation some previously feasible values of state and decision variables can be eliminated. In the new and smaller feasible region, finer spacing is used on the state and decision variables to obtain a better approximation to the true solution. This procedure continues until the desired accuracy is attained. However, one must be aware of pitfalls that can lead to entirely erroneous results in some situations.

To be specific, suppose we are to determine the optimum of a function of one variable $Q(d)$, whose domain is $d = 0, \Delta, 2\Delta, \ldots, k\Delta$. The spacing between successive values of d is denoted by Δ, and called the grid size. The grid size, together with the length of the interval (L), specifies the number of points (P) on which the function is defined, specifically

$$P = \frac{L}{\Delta} + 1$$

Thus for a fixed L, P is inversely proportional to Δ. By making the grid coarser, that is, by changing the spacing from Δ to a larger value δ there

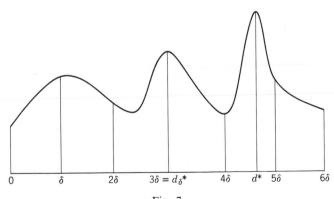

$$0 \qquad \delta \qquad 2\delta \qquad 3\delta = d_\delta{}^* \qquad 4\delta \qquad d^* \; 5\delta \qquad 6\delta$$

Fig. 7

is a corresponding decrease in P. For example, if $\delta = 10\Delta$, there is roughly a tenfold decrease in P since

$$\frac{P_\delta}{P_\Delta} = \frac{L/10\Delta + 1}{L/\Delta + 1} = \frac{1 + 10\Delta/L}{10 + 10\Delta/L} \cong 0.1$$

for small values of Δ/L. Suppose on the new grid $0, \delta, 2\delta, \ldots, k\delta/10$, we determine the maximum of $Q(d)$ to be d_δ^*. Then if $Q(d)$ is unimodal, we conclude that $d_\delta^* - \delta < d_\Delta^* < d_\delta^* + \delta$. If $Q(d)$ is not unimodal, the conclusion may be invalid, since the grid may not have been fine enough to detect a steep, narrow peak (see Figure 7). Although unimodality is a sufficient condition from which the conclusion $d_\delta^* - \delta < d_\Delta^* < d_\delta^* + \delta$ can be drawn, it is not a necessary one. That is, even if there are several peaks, $d_\delta^* - \delta < d_\Delta^* < d^* + \delta$ is a valid conclusion, provided that the grid has been fine enough to detect the relevant peaks.

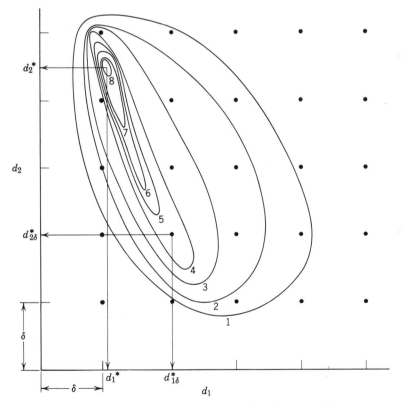

Fig. 8 Contours of Constant Q with a Narrow Ridge

The condition of the grid fineness is the necessary, and therefore, important one, since the unimodality condition is not sufficient for functions of more than one variable. Figure 8 gives an example of this for a function of two variables. Contour lines of constant $Q(d_1, d_2)$ are shown on a graph of d_1 versus d_2. There is a single peak at d_1^*, d_2^*, but this peak is located along a very narrow ridge. So when the function is evaluated using the course grid, $d_1 = 0, \delta, 2\delta, \ldots$, $d_2 = 0, \delta, 2\delta, \ldots$, the ridge is undetected. Thus the conclusion that (d_1^*, d_2^*) is in the region defined by

$$d_{1\delta}^* - \delta < d_1^* < d_{1\delta}^* + \delta$$
$$d_{2\delta}^* - \delta < d_2^* < d_{2\delta}^* + \delta$$

may be false even for a unimodal function. The danger of the coarse grid approach is that the optimum may be missed because of a narrow ridge. However, functions with quite narrow ridges are not very common. If one is willing to take the risk of missing a narrow ridge, the coarse grid approach can be of considerable computational help. One can, to a certain extent, control the risk by choosing an appropriate grid size. But there is a conflicting objective; the coarser the initial grid, the fewer the computations, but the greater the chance of missing a narrow ridge.

To see how the computations decrease as the coarseness of the grid increases, suppose we want the maximum of $Q(d)$, $0 \leq d \leq 20,000$ on the grid $d = 0, 1, \ldots, 20,000$. If we start with the initial grid, there are 20,001 points at which the function is to be evaluated. By increasing the initial grid size to $d = 0, 100, 200, \ldots, 20,000$ and evaluating the function at 201 points, the interval of optimality is reduced to a length of 200. Then another 201 evaluations of the function will yield the integer solution. But the number of computations can be reduced still further by starting with a very coarse grid $d = 0, 1000, 2000, \ldots, 20,000$. The first 21 evaluations reduce the length of the interval under consideration to 2000, and thus three more sets of 21 evaluations each yield the optimal integer solution, provided that a narrow peak has not been missed. Generally, when there is a grid spacing of L/θ, an interval of length $2L$ is reduced to an interval of length $L_1 = 2L/\theta$ with $2\theta + 1$ evaluations. Then, by taking a grid spacing of L/θ^2, another $2\theta + 1$ evaluations reduce the length of the interval to $L_2 = 2L/\theta^2$. To achieve a reduction to an interval of length $L^* = 2L/M$, with successive grid spacings of $L/\theta, L/\theta^2, \ldots, L/\theta^k$ requires $k[2\theta + 1]$ evaluations where k is the smallest integer greater than $(lnM/ln\theta)$. As θ gets smaller, $k[2\theta + 1]$ decreases. However, the limiting practical value of θ must still be determined by a judgment on the probability of missing a narrow peak.

In dynamic programming the main benefit of a coarse grid on the decision vairables is that it produces a corresponding coarse grid on the state variables. In the relation

$$X_{n-1} = t_n(X_n, D_n)$$

the number of feasible values of X_{n-1} is roughly proportional to the num- of feasible values of D_n. By reducing the number of feasible values of

X_{n-1}, we evaluate $f_{n-1}(X_{n-1})$ fewer times. The successive grids used in a dynamic programming analysis depend on the number of values tolerable for the state variables and the accuracy required.

In the problem

$$\min \sum_{n=1}^{4} (a_n d_n + b_n d_n^2), \qquad A = (2, 3, 4, 5)$$
$$B = (5, 4, 3, 2)$$

$$\text{subject to} \sum_{n=1}^{4} c_n d_n \geq 10{,}000, \qquad C = (1, 2, 3, 4)$$

$$d_n = 0, 1, 2, \ldots$$

the integer constraints specify the desired grid,

$$d_1 = 0, 1, 2, \ldots, 10{,}000$$
$$d_2 = 0, 1, 2, \ldots, 5000$$
$$d_3 = 0, 1, 2, \ldots, 3334$$
$$d_4 = 0, 1, 2, \ldots, 2500$$

Within this grid there are approximately 2×10^{14} combinations of (d_1, d_2, d_3, d_4) satisfying $\sum\limits_{n=1}^{4} c_n d_n \geq 10{,}000$.

Only a small fraction of the calculations needed to evaluate 2×10^{14} solutions exhaustively are required using dynamic programming. However, this number is quite extensive. Each of the optimal return functions

$$f_1(x_1) = \min_{d_1 \geq x_1} 2d_1^2 + 5d_1$$
$$f_2(x_2) = \min_{d_2} (3d_2^2 + 4d_2 + f_1(x_2 - 2d_2))$$
$$f_3(x_3) = \min_{d_3} (4d_3^2 + 3d_3 + f_2(x_3 - 3d_3))$$

must be evaluated at more than 2500 points, and the corresponding values of the optimal decision functions $d_1(x_1)$, $d_2(x_2)$, $d_3(x_3)$ must be stored to retrace the optimal solution. Specifically, there are 2501 feasible values for x_3 (0, 4, 8, . . . , 10,000), roughly twice as many for x_2, and four times as many for x_1. The computation of

$$f_4(x_4) = \min_{d_4} (5d_4^2 + 2d_4 + f_3(x_4 - 4d_4))$$

is not so tedious, since x_4 is equal to 10,000. But for all four steps there are about 17,500 values for the state variables. Certainly we would want to coarsen the grid for hand computations and perhaps even for digital computer computations if cost economy were a factor.

We begin with a very coarse grid (δ_1)

$$d_1 = 0, 1000, 2000, \ldots, 10,000$$

$$d_2 = 0, 500, 1000, \ldots, 5000$$

$$d_3 = 0, 333, 667, \ldots, 3333$$

$$d_4 = 0, 250, 500, \ldots, 2500$$

On this grid (x_1, x_2, x_3) are defined on only eleven points each (0, 1000, 2000, ..., 10,000). The computations for this problem are roughly equivalent to the problem of Chapter III, Section 17 which has the same objective function as this problem and constraints

$$\sum_{n=1}^{4} c_n d_n \geq 10 \qquad d_n = 0, 1, 2, \ldots$$

since replacing d_n by $1000 d_n$ in these constraints makes the two sets of constraints almost equivalent.

A summary of the computations on this very coarse grid for the one-, two-, three-, and four-stage analyses are given in Tables 3, 4, 5, and 6 respectively. The optimal solution on this first grid (δ_1) is denoted by $d_n^*(\delta_1)$, and marked with stars in the tables. We have $d_1^*(\delta_1) = d_2^*(\delta_1) = d_3^*(\delta_1) = d_4^*(\delta_1) = 1000$, so

$$0 < d_1^* < 2000$$

$$500 < d_2^* < 1500$$

$$667 < d_3^* < 1333$$

$$750 < d_4^* < 1250$$

Table 3

$x_1 = d_1(x_1)$	$f_1(x_1) \cdot 10^{-6}$
0	0
*1000	*2.005
2000	8.01
3000	18.015
4000	32.02
5000	50.025
6000	72.03
7000	98.035
8000	128.04
9000	162.045
10000	200.05

Table 4

x_2	$f_2(x_2) \cdot 10^{-6}$	$d_2(x_2)$	$x_1(x_2)$
0	0	0	0
1000	0.752	500	0
2000	2.757	500	1000
*3000	*5.009	*1000	*1000
4000	8.761	1500	1000
5000	14.013	2000	1000
6000	20.018	2000	2000
7000	26.770	2500	2000
8000	35.022	3000	2000
9000	44.774	3500	2000
10000	54.779	3500	3000

Table 5

x_3	$f_3(x_3) \cdot 10^{-6}$	$d_3(x_3)$	$x_2(x_3)$
0	0	0	0
1000	0.445	333	0
2000	1.198	333	1000
3000	2.532	667	1000
4000	4.537	667	2000
5000	6.760	1000	2000
*6000	*9.012	*1000	*3000
7000	12.124	1333	3000
8000	15.878	1333	4000
9000	19.878	1667	4000
10000	24.767	2000	4000

Table 6

x_4	$f_4(x_4) \cdot 10^{-6}$	$d_4(x_4)$	$x_3(x_4)$
*10000	*14.014	*1000	*6000

In this new region, we choose the grid (δ_2)

$$d_1 = 0, 100, 200, \ldots, 2000$$
$$d_2 = 500, 550, 600, \ldots, 1500$$
$$d_3 = 667, 700, 733, \ldots, 1333$$
$$d_4 = 750, 775, 800, \ldots, 1250$$

This leads to the grid on the state variables

$$x_1 = 0, 100, 200, \ldots, 2000$$
$$x_2 = 1000, 1100, 1200, \ldots, 5000$$
$$x_3 = 5000, 5100, 5200, \ldots, 7000$$
$$x_4 = 10,000$$

Therefore $f_n(x_n)$ has to be calculated only $21 + 41 + 21 + 1 = 84$ times. The solution on this grid (calculations are not shown) is $d_1^*(\delta_2) = 700$, $d_2^*(\delta_2) = 900$, $d_3^*(\delta_2) = 1033$, $d_4^*(\delta_2) = 1100$. Thus

$$600 < d_1^* < 800$$
$$850 < d_2^* < 950$$
$$1000 < d_3^* < 1067$$
$$1075 < d_4^* < 1125$$

We use one more intermediate grid (δ_3) on the decision variables

$$d_1 = 600, 610, 620, \ldots, 800$$
$$d_2 = 850, 855, 860, \ldots, 950$$
$$d_3 = 1000, 1003.3, 1006.7, \ldots, 1067$$
$$d_4 = 1075, 1077.5, 1080, \ldots, 1125$$

and thus the state variable grid

$$x_1 = 600, 610, 620, \ldots, 800$$
$$x_2 = 2300, 2310, 2320, \ldots, 2700$$
$$x_3 = 5500, 5510, 5520, \ldots, 5700$$
$$x_4 = 10,000$$

We have found it computationally convenient to have the same grid spacing for x_1, x_2, x_3. To achieve this, we need a different grid for each of the decision variables, because of the different coefficients in the constraint $\sum_{n=1}^{4} c_n d_n \geq 10,000$.

The solution on the grid δ_3 yields the result

$$680 < d_1^* < 700$$
$$910 < d_2^* < 920$$
$$1026.7 < d_3^* < 1033.3$$
$$1095.0 < d_4^* < 1100.0$$

An integer grid is then placed over this region, and from it we obtain the optimal integer solution $d_1^* = 686$, $d_2^* = 914$, $d_3^* = 1030$, $d_4^* = 1099$, with optimal return $13 \cdot 742359 \cdot 10^6$.

We obtained this result using four successive grids, each grid (except the final grid) ten times as fine as the previous one. In the four problems, the function $f_n(x_n)$ was calculated 34, 84, 84, and 68 times respectively, a total of 270 times. On the other hand, if the integer grid had been used initially, $f_n(x_n)$ would have been calculated about 17,500 times, and each time $f_n(x_n)$ is calculated, an optimization problem must be solved. More important is that the coarse grid reduces the memory requirement for the decision functions. Using the integer grid directly, 17,500 storage places would have been reserved for $d_n(x_n)$. With the coarse grid, the decision functions obtained from one grid can be discarded before the calculations are started on the next grid, so only 84 storage places are needed for the optimal decision functions.

The computational advantages of the coarse grid approach are enormous. Yet if the grid is too coarse, the advantages may be eliminated by an incorrect answer. Local exploration, on a very fine grid around the final solution, may be used to test the validity of the solution. In the illustration the optimal solution given is correct. We ascertained this by comparing the integer solution with the solution obtained analytically by assuming the variables to be continuous, and then by checking all solutions near the optimum without integer constraints. This procedure is valid for this problem since the continuous and integer solutions are almost identical. However, generally the optimal integer solution may not even be close to the optimal solution without integer constraints.

We have begun to encounter formidable computational problems with discrete dynamic programming calculations. Unfortunately, these computational problems grow exponentially as the number of state variables per stage increase from one. The remainder of this chapter will be devoted to problems with multidimensional state variables.

6. Several State Variables

For tabular computations a distinction is made between problems with one and more than one state variable per stage because of the great difference in the number of calculations involved and the special methods needed to alleviate this computational burden. In fact, unless state variable reduction methods are adopted, the number of calculations increases by an order of magnitude for each additional state variable. The reason for this is quite simple. The number of feasible values of the state variable increases exponentially with the number of state variables. Since there is a computation of an optimal return and decision function for each value of the state variable, the total number of computations increase exponentially. For example, at stage n let the state variable consist of p components, $X_n = (x_{n1}, \ldots, x_{np})$ with K_i feasible values of x_{ni}. Then the number of feasible values of X_n and $f_n(X_n)$ is $\prod_{i=1}^{p} K_i$ or, if $K_i = K$, the number is K^p.

By imagining how the optimal functions are recorded, we observe a more dramatic illustration of this increase. When there is one state variable, we assume that the optimal return and decision functions are contained in a table—a table of the kind shown in the examples of the past few sections, containing a list of the feasible values of the state variable and the corresponding optimal returns and decisions. When there are two state variables, in order to have a complete record of the optimal functions, we must have a "table" containing the optimal functions for all values of the first state variable for each of the second state variable. Thus a set of tables or a "book" is required to tabulate the optimal functions. When a third state variable is introduced, the optimal functions must be tabulated for all combinations of the first two state variables for each value of the third state variable. Thus a set of books or a "bookcase" is required. The listing of the optimal functions of four state variables requires a set of bookcases or a "library," and five state variables, a set of libraries. Even if we can afford all of these libraries, there is still the nasty problem of locating the proper information.

We have ignored the dependence of storage requirements on the number of decision variables per stage, but the effect is insignificant when compared with the effect of the number of state variables. The number of entries in the lists of optimal functions increases linearly with the number of decision variables. For an s-component decision variable there are $s + 1$ tabulations of optimal functions for each value of X_n, consisting of a single tabulation of $f_n(X_n)$ and s tabulations of $D_n(X_n)$. Furthermore the amount of data recorded is independent of the number of feasible values of each component of D_n.

To estimate total storage requirements for optimal decision and return functions, recall that $D_n(X_n)$, $n = 1, \ldots, N$ is saved until the optimal policy is traced, but $f_n(X_n)$ is saved only until $f_{n+1}(X_{n+1})$ has been computed. Thus storage space must be available for all N functions $D_n(X_n)$ but for only two consecutive functions $f_n(X_n)$. Assume there are N stages, p

state variables per stage, each having K feasible values and s decision variables per stage. Then the total storage requirements for optimal functions is $N(s + 2)K^p$. The factor that has the most significant influence on the total storage requirement is the number of state variables per stage, p.

Our apparent obsession with the storage requirements for optimal functions rather than the actual number of calculations is based on our ultimate concern with the actual time required to solve problems on a digital computer. For problems small enough to be solved manually, the storage requirement is not important, and the actual number of computations is a better measure of the time required. But for small problems there is really no need to worry about the time for manual computations anyway. With the general availability of computers, a problem somewhat too long for manual calculations can be run on a computer in almost no time. But for solving very large problems, tactics that reduce the time required using a digital computer can be vitally important.

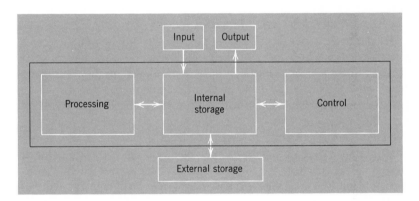

Fig. 9

To appreciate the storage problem we must have at least a little understanding of how a digital computer operates.† Figure 9 is a schematic diagram of a digital computer. The storage unit contains instructions used by the control unit and data to be used by the processing unit. The control unit directs the operations of the computer. The actual calculations are done in the processing or arithmetic unit.

Basically, there are two time-consuming processes in the computer—the calculations in the processing unit and the transfer of information to and from the storage units. Thus the time for the total operation depends almost entirely on speed of calculation and transfer of information.

A large scientific computer contains several kinds of storage mechan-

---

† Those interested in more details can refer to McCracken [48], or any of several other books on computers and computer programming.

isms. The most general distinction is between internal and external storage. From internal storage there are direct links to the processing and control units, but all communication to and from external storage must go through internal storage.

The most advanced internal-storage mechanisms, such as magnetic core, give rapid access to data and instructions. The times to locate and transfer information to and from the processing unit are comparable to unit calculation times. However, economic considerations limit the amount of high-speed memory included in any computer system. For example, machines in the IBM 7090 class contain about 30,000 to 40,000 rapid-access storage locations. The trend is toward larger high-speed memories. Systems containing 100,000 rapid-access storage locations are becoming available.

To augment the very-high-speed memories, there are cheaper forms of internal storage, such as the magnetic drum. However, these memory systems are thousands of times slower than the rapid-access memories. When storage requirements for data and instructions exceed the rapid access memory, a bottleneck forms.

This bottleneck can become acute when the amount of data and instructions exceeds the entire capacity of internal storage and it becomes necessary to use external storage. External storage mechanisms are very cheap and are usually available in virtually unlimited amounts. The most common form is magnetic tape. But retrieval of information from tape can be a million times as slow as that from rapid-access memory.

Judicious programming can partially alleviate delays caused by transfer of data from external to internal storage, since it is possible for these transfers to be carried out while other operations are going on in the processing unit. Nevertheless, when there is a great deal of data to be transferred from auxiliary to internal storage, the transfer time can exceed the time required in the internal units, and this causes a serious bottleneck. The easiest remedy may be switching to a machine with more internal storage—if there is one. Although computers frequently have two or three types of internal storage, even large digital computers are designed for an average problem. Many problems require storage exceeding the internal space of even the largest computers.

For example, consider the solution of a dynamic program with ten stages, one decision variable and four state variables per stage, each state variable having one hundred feasible values. The total storage requirement for optimal return and decision functions alone is $10(1 + 2) \cdot (100)^4 = 3 \cdot 10^9$ storage cells. To this must be added memory space for initial data on returns and transformations, for other intermediate results, and for the program of instructions. This total storage requirement would obviously exceed the rapid-access memory of any computer system envisioned in the near future.

The problem is really not quite so severe. Since the optimal decision functions are not used until the optimal policy is traced, sophisticated programming will allow them to be stored externally with almost no penalty. In particular, by reserving internal storage space for only the optimal decision function currently being computed $(D_n(X_n))$ and for $f_n(X_n)$ and $f_{n-1}(X_{n-1})$, we find that the internal storage requirement for optimal functions is reduced to $3K^p$. For the numbers just given this would reduce storage requirements by a factor of ten, but would probably not be decisive. It is possible to reduce storage requirements to K^p by reserving internal memory space only for $f_{n-1}(x_{n-1})$. Putting $D_n(X_n)$ and $f_n(X_n)$ into external storage immediately will probably not cause a large delay. It is absolutely crucial to keep $f_{n-1}(X_{n-1})$ in internal memory because when computing $f_n(X_n)$, we cannot anticipate in advance the sequence in which the values of $f_{n-1}(X_{n-1})$ will be needed. However, K^p may exceed internal storage capacity, as in the above example.

Methods must be found that require less storage. Even methods that reduce storage requirements at the expense of increasing the number of computations might be highly desirable. At some point we might be willing to trade one transfer from internal to external storage for a million calculations, as the latter would take less time. Note how the computer has influenced our idea of what constitutes a desirable method of calculation. The concept of the number of calculations being paramount is replaced by another in which routineness and storage requirements have an important role in determining the efficiency of a method. Dynamic programming calculations are certainly routine enough, but may not always satisfy the restrictions on storage space.

The most obvious way to reduce storage requirements is to reduce the number of state variables. In the storage formula $N(s + 2)K^p$, where p is the number of state variables, reduction of p from 4 to 2, in the case $N = 10$, $s = 1$, $k = 1000$, would be decisive. In fact, it would be so decisive that we might be willing to solve thousands of problems with $p = 2$ rather than solve one with $p = 4$. Most state variable reduction methods have originated with Bellman [10, 12, 13] and his colleagues at the Rand Corporation.

Some illustrations of the straightforward dynamic programming solution of multi-state-variable problems will be given. Later, these examples will be solved by the special methods designed to reduce computation time. The illustrations have been chosen to explain these computational ploys and to show their advantages and limitations. But to appreciate their advantages one must imagine much larger problems being solved on a computer.

The illustrations are problems containing two state variables generated by adding another constraint to the problem of Chapter III, Section 17. The additional constraint can be one relating the variables of the original problem, or new variables. In the former case, there is one decision variables and two state variables per stage; the latter requires two state and two decision variables per stage. Both cases will be exemplified.

7. Two State Variables and One Decision Variable

Our objective is to minimize, over the variables (d_1, d_2, d_3, d_4) defined on the nonnegative integers, the function

$$\sum_{n=1}^{4} a_n d_n + b_n d_n^2, \qquad A = (5, 4, 3, 2)$$
$$B = (2, 3, 4, 5)$$

subject to the constraints $\displaystyle\sum_{n=1}^{4} c_n d_n \geq 10, \qquad C = (1, 2, 3, 4)$

$$\sum_{n=1}^{4} c_n' d_n \geq 8, 9, \qquad C' = (2, 1, 2, 1)$$

In effect we will be solving two problems by setting the right-hand side of the second constraint equal to both 8 and 9. But very little additional effort is required to solve the problem for two values at once rather than just one. As we shall see later, there is a good reason to solve the problem for both values.

We already solved this problem with the second constraint omitted (Chapter III, Section 17). If the solution for that case had satisfied the second constraint, it would have been optimal for this problem too. But $d_1 = d_2 = d_3 = d_4 = 1$, the optimal solution without the second constraint, does not satisfy $\Sigma c_n' d_n \geq 8$ or 9. Thus the problem must be re-solved.

For the new constraint we introduce the state variable $y = (y_1, y_2, y_3, y_4)$ with the relations

$$y_4 = 8, 9, \quad y_3 = y_4 - d_4, \qquad d_4 = 0, 1, \ldots, 9$$

Setting the maximum feasible value of d_4 equal to 9 is satisfactory, since r_4 is an increasing function, and $\Sigma c_n' d_n \geq 9$ and $\Sigma c_n d_n \geq 10$ are satisfied by any nonnegative combination of (d_1, d_2, d_3) with $d_4 = 9$. The feasible values of y_3 are †

$$y_3 = \leq 0, 1, \ldots, 9, \quad y_2 = y_3 - 2d_3, \qquad d_3 = 0, 1, \ldots, 5$$

Continuing in this manner, we define

$$y_2 = \leq 0, 1, \ldots, 9, \quad y_1 = y_2 - d_2, \qquad d_2 = 0, 1, \ldots, 9$$

---

† ≤ 0 stands for all nonpositive integers.

and

$$y_1 = \ \leq \ 0, 1, \ldots, 9, \qquad d_1 \geq \frac{y_1}{2}, \qquad\qquad d_1 = 0, 1, \ldots, 10$$

The definitions and feasible values for the state variable $x = (x_1, x_2, x_3, x_4)$ associated with the original constraint are the same as before. That is,

$$x_4 = 10$$

$$x_3 = x_4 - 4d_4, \quad x_3 = \ \leq \ 0, 2, 6, 10$$

$$x_2 = x_3 - 3d_3, \quad x_2 = \ \leq \ 0, 1, 2, 3, 4, 6, 7, 10$$

and $\quad x_1 = x_2 - 2d_2, \quad x_1 = \ \leq \ 0, 1, 2, 3, 4, 5, 6, 7, 8, 10$

The difference between this example and the previous one without the second constraint is in number of calculations only. Many more optimal returns and decisions are calculated. As the optimizations are still one dimensional, Fibonacci search can be used. But instead of 23 optimizations (one for each value of x_n) there are 222 of them (one for each value of (x_n, y_n)).

The first-stage recursion equation is

$$f_1(x_1, y_1) = \min_{d_1 \geq \max(x_1, y_1/2, 0)} [5d_1 + 2d_1^2]$$

Its solution is obviously $d_1 = \max (x_1, [y_1/2], 0)$ where $[y_1/2]$ is the smallest integer equal to or greater than $y_1/2$. The optimal one-stage returns and decisions are given in Table 7. The first entry in Table 7, for each combination of (x_1, y_1), is $f_1(x_1, y_1)$, and the second $d_1(x_1, y_1)$.

Proceeding with the recursive analysis

$$f_2(x_2, y_2) = \min_{d_2 = 0, 1, \ldots, 9} [4d_2 + 3d_2^2 + f_1(x_2 - 2d_2, y_2 - d_2)]$$

$$f_3(x_3, y_3) = \min_{d_3 = 0, 1, \ldots, 5} [3d_3 + 4d_3^2 + f_2(x_3 - 3d_3, y_3 - 2d_3)]$$

and

$$f_4(x_4, y_4) = \min_{d_4 = 0, 1, \ldots, 9} [2d_4 + 5d_4^2 + f_3(x_4 - 4d_4, y_4 - d_4)]$$

The optimal two-, three-, and four-stage returns and decisions are given in Tables 8, 9, and 10 respectively.

We see from Table 10 that with $y_4 = 8$ the minimum return is 39 and $d_4^* = 1$. Similarly with $y_4 = 9$ the minimum return is 47 and the optimal fourth decision is 0 or 1. To establish the remaining optimal decisions, we trace the solutions through Table 7. The results are summarized in Table 11. One star (*) denotes the solution with $y_4 = 8$, and two, three, and four stars denote the three alternate optimal solutions with $y_4 = 9$.

Table 7   ONE-STAGE OPTIMAL RETURNS AND DECISIONS, $f_1(x_1, y_1)$, $d_1(x_1, y_1)$

	x_1							
y_1	≤ 0		1		2		3	
≤ 0	0	0	7	1	18	2	33	3
1	7	1	7	1	18	2	33	3
2	7	1	7	1	18	2	33	3
3	18	2	18	2	18	2	33	3
4	18	2****	18	2*	18	2**	33	3
5	33	3	33	3	33	3	33	3
6	33	3	33	3	33	3	33	3***
7	52	4	52	4	52	4	52	4
8	52	4	52	4	52	4	52	4
9	75	5	75	5	75	5	75	5

	x_1					
y_1	4		5		6	
≤ 0	52	4	75	5	102	6
1	52	4	75	5	102	6
2	52	4	75	5	102	6
3	52	4	75	5	102	6
4	52	4	75	5	102	6
5	52	4	75	5	102	6
6	52	4	75	5	102	6
7	52	4	75	5	102	6
8	52	4	75	5	102	6
9	75	5	75	5	102	6

	x_1					
y_1	7		8		10	
≤ 0	133	7	168	8	250	10
1	133	7	168	8	250	10
2	133	7	168	8	250	10
3	133	7	168	8	250	10
4	133	7	168	8	250	10
5	133	7	168	8	250	10
6	133	7	168	8	250	10
7	133	7	168	8	250	10
8	133	7	168	8	250	10
9	133	7	168	8	250	10

Table 8 TWO-STAGE OPTIMAL RETURNS AND DECISIONS, $f_2(x_2, y_2)$, $d_2(x_2, y_2)$

y_2	$x_2 \leq 0$		$x_2=1$		$x_2=2$		$x_2=3$		$x_2=4$		$x_2=6$		$x_2=7$		$x_2=10$	
0	0	0	7	0,1	7	1	14	1	20	2	38	2	46	3	82	4
1	7	0,1	7	0,1	7	0,1	14	1	20	2	38	2	46	3	82	4
2	7	0	7	0	14	1	14	1	20	2	38	2	46	3	82	4
3	14	1	14	1	14	1	14	1	25	1	38	2	46	3	82	4
4	18	0*****	18	0	18	0	25	1	25	1	38	2	46	3	82	4
5	25	1	25	1	25	1	25	1*	25	1**	38	2	46	3	82	4
6	33	0	33	0	33	0	33	0***	38	2	38	2	46	3	82	4
7	40	1	40	1	40	1	40	1	40	1	53	2	57	3	82	4
8	52	0	52	0	52	0	52	0	52	0	53	2	57	3	82	4
9	59	1	59	1	59	1	59	1	59	1	72	2,3	72	2,3	91	3

Table 9   THREE-STAGE OPTIMAL RETURNS AND DECISIONS,
$$f_3(x_3, y_3), \ d_3(x_3, y_3)$$

	x_3							
y_3	≤ 0		2		6		10	
≤ 0	0	0	7	0,1	21	1	42	2
1	7	0,1	7	0,1	21	1	42	2
2	7	0,1	7	1	21	1	42	2
3	14	1	14	0,1	21	1	42	2
4	14	1	14	1	21	1	42	2
5	21	1	21	1	21	1	42	2
6	25	1	25	1	29	2	42	2
7	32	1	32	1	32	1*	47	2
8	40	1	40	1	40	1***, 2****	47	2
9	47	1,2	47	1	47	1,2	47	2**

Table 10   FOUR-STAGE OPTIMAL RETURNS AND DECISIONS,
$$f_4(x_4, y_4), \ d_4(x_4, y_4)$$

	x_4	
y_4	10	
8	39	1*
9	47	0**, 1***, 1****

Table 11   OPTIMAL SOLUTIONS

	y_4	f_4	d_1	d_2	d_3	d_4
*	8	39	2	1	1	1
**	9	47	2	1	2	0
***	9	47	3	0	1	1
****	9	47	2	0	2	1

Despite the length of computation, the two state variable formulation contains certain important guarantees. It finds all optimal solutions for all desired values of the state variables, and these optima are global. The high cost of solution assures a completely reliable product. Unfortunately, this cost may be prohibitive, so we turn to quicker but sometimes less reliable methods.

8. Generalized Lagrange Multiplier Method

Everett [28] has given a method for using Lagrange multipliers to solve constrained optimization problems with nondifferentiable objective functions and arbitrary constraints. This procedure can be used for state variable reduction in dynamic programming.

We begin with Everett's main result. For the optimization problem

$$\max R(D), \quad D = (d_1, \ldots, d_N) \in S$$

$$\text{subject to } g_i(D) \leq b_i, \quad i = 1, \ldots, M$$

a $D^* \in S$ that globally maximizes the Lagrange function

$$V(D, \Lambda) = R(D) + \sum_{i=1}^{M} \lambda_i g_i(D)$$

for a set of real nonpositive Lagrange multipliers $(\lambda_1, \ldots, \lambda_M) = \Lambda$ is a global maximum to the original constrained problem over all $D \in S$, such that $g_i(D) \leq g_i(D^*)$. The proof of this theorem is very simple. Assume

$$R(D^*) + \sum_{i=1}^{M} \lambda_i g_i(D^*) \geq R(D) + \sum_{i=1}^{M} \lambda_i g_i(D)$$

for all $D \in S$ subject to $\lambda_i \leq 0, \quad i = 1, \ldots, M$

Thus

$$R(D^*) \geq R(D) + \sum_{i=1}^{M} \lambda_i [g_i(D) - g_i(D^*)]$$

Since all λ_i are nonpositive, if

$$g_i(D) \leq g_i(D^*)$$

then $$R(D^*) \geq R(D)$$

Hence, if D^* maximizes $V(D, \Lambda)$ for a set of real nonpositive Lagrange multipliers, then D^* maximizes $R(D)$ subject to $D \in S$ and

$$g_i(D) \leq g_i(D^*)$$

If $g_i(D^*) = b_i, i = 1, \ldots, M$, we have solved our original problem. But generally, with an arbitrary choice of $\lambda_1, \ldots, \lambda_M, g_i(D^*) \neq b_i$. Then we must choose another set of nonpositive Lagrange multipliers, and globally optimize the new Lagrange function.

Everett has shown that with λ_j fixed, $j = 1, \ldots, M$, $j \neq i$, $g_i(D^*)$ is a monotonically nondecreasing function of λ_i. Thus interpolation and extrapolation can be used to guide λ_i to yield the value or values of b_i desired, if such values of λ_i exist. We must state the existence qualification because there may be some values of b_i not generated by any λ_i. An example with this property is given in Section 9. This limitation means that the Lagrange approach does not guarantee that a maximum can be found for all values of b_i, even though a maximum actually exists.

Consider the $M + 1$ dimensional space of $R(D)$ versus $b_1, \ldots, b_M$. A solution $D \in S$ yields a value of $R(D)$ and coresponding values of $b_1, \ldots, b_M$. Consequently, every solution can be represented by a point in the $M + 1$ dimensional space of $R(D)$ versus $b_1, \ldots, b_M$. A subset of these points correspond to the optimal solutions. Everett has shown that when the points corresponding to the optimal solutions yield $R(D)$ as a concave function of $b_1, \ldots, b_M$, all optimal solutions will be generated by the generalized Lagrange multiplier method. However, in regions of nonconcavity the Lagrange multiplier method will not produce solutions. Problems with integer constraints are very apt to have nonconcave regions. This will be illustrated in Section 9. Everett gives some modifications of his basic procedure for determining optimal or near-optimal solutions in nonconcave regions.

The importance of the Lagrange multiplier approach is that a constrained optimization problem can be solved by methods otherwise only applicable to unconstrained problems. It is quite general since $R(D)$, $g_i(D)$, and the set S are completely arbitrary. Certainly the class of problems to which this method is applicable is considerably larger than the class of problems that can be formulated as dynamic programs. But the real value of the multiplier method depends upon how practical it is to optimize the Lagrange function. It must be emphasized that if we want to ensure a *global* maximum to the constrained problem, the maximum obtained for the Lagrange function also must be global.

The Lagrange multiplier and dynamic programming approaches have one great similarity. In both, the original constrained problem with N variables and M constraints is embedded into a space with $M + N$ variables. In the Lagrange method there is a Lagrange multiplier for each constraint; in dynamic programming there is a maximum of M state variables, one for each constraint that requires a state variable.† When it is possible to achieve a dynamic programming formulation, there is the advantage that the $(M + N)$-dimensional problem can be broken into N subproblems, each having one decision variable and a maximum of M state variables. Altogether there is a maximum of $M + 1$ dimensions per subproblem. On the other hand, the optimization of the Lagrange function usually must

---

† See Chapter III, Section 10.

be performed in N-dimensional space. That is, the M Lagrange multipliers are fixed, and a series of N-dimensional subproblems are solved, each with different values of the multipliers, until the desired values of the right-hand sides of the constraints are reached, if they are attainable. Everett has shown that it is sometimes possible to decompose each N-dimensional optimization into a series of one-dimensional optimizations. Although this decomposition is different from the dynamic programming decomposition, it is very much in the spirit of dynamic programming. Comparing the dimensionality of the spaces over which the optimizations must be performed—$M + 1$ for dynamic programming, and generally N with Lagrange multipliers—we see that the dynamic programming approach works best when N is large. However, when the number of state variables is large, the dynamic programming approach may not be computationally feasible. To alleviate the difficulty caused by high state variable dimensionality, and to preserve the advantage of dynamic programming, the Lagrange and dynamic programming approaches can be synthesized by treating some of the constraints with Lagrange multipliers and the remainder with state variables.†

9. State Variable Reduction Using Lagrange Multipliers

Following the methodology of Section 8, we see that a two-constraint problem can be transformed into an equivalent problem with one constraint and a Lagrange multiplier. Thus treating the second constraint of the problem of Section 7 with a Lagrange multiplier, we have

$$\min \sum_{n=1}^{4} (a_n d_n + b_n d_n^2) + \lambda \sum_{n=1}^{4} c_n' d_n$$

$$= \min \sum_{n=1}^{4} [(a_n + \lambda c_n') d_n + b_n d_n^2]$$

or with $a_n' = a_n + \lambda c_n'$

$$= \min \sum_{n=1}^{4} [a_n' d_n + b_n d_n^2]$$

over the variables (d_1, d_2, d_3, d_4) defined on the nonnegative integers,

$$\text{subject to } \sum_{n=1}^{4} c_n d_n \geq 10$$

In this form the problem is identical to the problem of Chapter III, Section 17, except for the new linear coefficients in the objective function. The recursion equations are:

---

† It appears that this idea was originally reported by Dreyfus [25].

$$f_1(x_1) = \min_{d_1 = 0, 1, \ldots, 10} [a_1' d_1 + 2d_1^2], \quad d_1 \geq x_1,$$
$$x_1 = \leq 0, 1, \ldots, 8, 10$$

$$f_2(x_2) = \min_{d_2 = 0, 1, \ldots, 5} [a_2' d_2 + 3d_2^2 + f_1(x_2 - 2d_2)]$$
$$x_2 = \leq 0, 1, 2, 3, 4, 6, 7, 10$$

$$f_3(x_3) = \min_{d_3 = 0, 1, \ldots, 4} [a_3' d_3 + 4d_3^2 + f_2(x_3 - 3d_3)],$$
$$x_3 = \leq 0, 2, 6, 10$$

$$f_4(x_4 = 10) = \min_{d_4 = 0, 1, 2, 3} [a_4' d_4 + 5d_4^2 + f_3(x_4 - 4d_4)]$$

Fixing λ determines a_n' through the relation $a_n' = a_n + \lambda c_n'$. Then solving the recursion equation yields an optimal solution $d_n^*(\lambda)$, and hence a value for $\sum c_n' d_n^*(\lambda) = c'(\lambda)$. We repeat this process for successive values of λ until $c'(\lambda)$ reaches its desired values, in this case 8 and 9. Because $c'(\lambda)$ is a nonincreasing function, interpolation and extrapolation may be used to guide λ to values yielding the appropriate values of $c'(\lambda)$. But since $c'(\lambda)$ may have jump discontinuities, some values of $c'(\lambda)$ may not be generated by any values of λ.

We begin with $\lambda = 0$, since it yields $a_n' = a_n$, the problem of Chapter III, Section 17. The solution $d_n^*(0) = (1, 1, 1, 1)$ yields $c'(0) = 6$. Since $c'(\lambda)$ is a nonincreasing function of λ, we must try smaller values of λ. Our first guess of $\lambda = -2$ is too conservative, since there is no change in the solution, that is, $d_n^*(-2) = (1, 1, 1, 1)$, and $c'(-2) = 6$. Also, there is no luck with the next guess $\lambda = -5$; once again we obtain $d_n^*(-5) = (1, 1, 1, 1)$. This seems to suggest that $c'(\lambda)$ changes very slowly with λ, and so a bigger jump is taken to $\lambda = -10$. Here we have overshot our mark, since $d_n^*(-10) = (4, 1, 2, 1)$, and $c'(-10) = 16$. Thus the appropriate values of λ must lie between -5 and -10. The next guess at $\lambda = -7$ proves to be successful, since $d_n^*(-7) = (2, 1, 1, 1)$, and $c'(-7) = 8$. Thus a solution for $c' = 8$ is $d_n^* = (2, 1, 1, 1)$. Having obtained a solution for $c' = 8$, we decrease λ further to -7.5 and obtain four alternative optimal solutions with $c'(-7.5) = 8, 10$, and 12. The domain of λ has skipped over $c'(\lambda) = 9$. The optimal solutions at $\lambda = -5.5 + \epsilon, -5.5, -5.5 - \epsilon, -7.5 + \epsilon$, and $7.5 - \epsilon$ completely reveal the behavior of $c'(\lambda)$ within the region $-5.5 + \epsilon \geq \lambda \geq -7.5 - \epsilon$. Table 12 gives the optimal solutions as a function of the values of λ calculated. From it we observe the discontinuous behavior of $c'(\lambda)$ in the region $-5.5 + \epsilon \geq \lambda \geq -7.5 - \epsilon$, as shown in Figure 10.

By treating one of the constraints with a Lagrange multiplier and thus eliminating one of the state variables, the computations and storage of optimal data have been reduced considerably. This was quite satisfactory for the case $\sum c_n' d_n \geq 8$, where the optimal solution was obtained after five one-state variable problems had been solved. Each of these problems

Table 12   THE OPTIMAL SOLUTIONS AS A FUNCTION OF λ

Solution	λ	$a_n' = a_n + \lambda c_n'$	$d_n^*(\lambda)$	$c'(\lambda) =$ $\Sigma c_n' d_n^*(\lambda)$	Optimal Return
1	0	5, 4, 3, 2	1, 1, 1, 1	6	28
2	−2	1, 2, −1, 0	1, 1, 1, 1	6	28
3	−5	−5, −1, −7, −3	1, 1, 1, 1	6	28
4	−10	−15, −6, −17, −8	4, 1, 2, 1	16	88
5	−7	−9, −3, −11, −5	2, 1, 1, 1	8	39
6(a)	−7.5	−10, −3.5, −12, −5.5	2, 1, 1, 1	8	39
6(b)	−7.5	−10, −3.5, −12, −5.5	2, 1, 2, 1	10	54
6(c)	−7.5	−10, −3.5, −12, −5.5	3, 1, 1, 1	10	54
6(d)	−7.5	−10, −3.5, −12, −5.5	3, 1, 2, 1	12	69
7	−7.5 + ε	−10 + 2ε, −3.5 + ε, −12 + 2ε, −5.5 + ε	2, 1, 1, 1	8	39
8	−7.5 − ε	−10 − 2ε, −3.5 − ε, −12 − 2ε, −5.5 − ε	3, 1, 2, 1	12	69
9(a)	−5.5	−6, −1.5, −8, −3.5	1, 1, 1, 1	6	28
9(b)	−5.5	−6, −1.5, −8, −3.5	2, 1, 1, 1	8	39
10	−5.5 + ε	−6 + 2ε, −1.5 + ε, −8 + 2ε, −3.5 + ε	1, 1, 1, 1	6	28
11	−5.5 − ε	−6 − 2ε, −1.5 − ε, −8 − 2ε, −3.5 − ε	2, 1, 1, 1	8	39

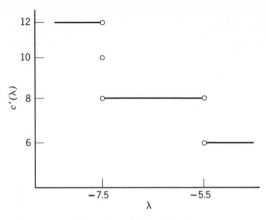

Fig. 10 $c'(\lambda)$ versus λ

had the same number of calculations and storage requirements as the problem in Chapter III, Section 17. They differ only with respect to the coefficients a_n'. However, subsequent solutions at $\lambda = -7.5$, $-7.5 - \epsilon$, and $-7.5 + \epsilon$ showed that the Lagrange method does not produce a solution for $\sum c_n' d_n \geq 9$, even though there are three alternative optimal solutions (see Table 11). Also, neither are solutions obtained for $\sum c_n' d_n = 7$ or 11. Nevertheless, solutions produced by maximizing the Lagrange function are global optima.

Points corresponding to optimal solutions are shown in the space of the optimal return versus c' in Figure 11. Points indicated by circles cor-

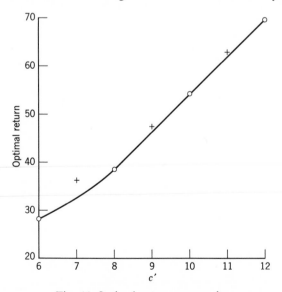

Fig. 11 Optimal return versus c'

respond to solutions produced by the Lagrange method. The $+$'s indicate solutions that cannot be obtained using the multiplier approach. In Section 8 we described the reason for this difficulty. Whenever there are regions of nonconcavity in this space (convexity in the case of a minimization problem) the Lagrange method will not produce solutions. In the example, the integer constraints caused the difficulty. Had they been eliminated, the Lagrange method would have produced all the optimal solutions. Constraint sets consisting of discrete points are very apt to cause trouble. Everett has developed procedures that may be appended to the Lagrange method to improve the likelihood of obtaining all solutions. However, the additional complexities involved may overshadow the savings achieved by eliminating state variables. It is difficult to say whether multipliers should be used in these circumstances.

In this example we have used one Lagrange multiplier to eliminate one state variable from a problem which, in its original form, had two constraints and two state variables. The choice of which constraint to treat with a Lagrange multiplier was completely arbitrary. Generally, for a problem with M constraints, $M - k$ of them can be treated with Lagrange multipliers and added to the objective function, leaving a k state variable dynamic programming formulation. The mix between Lagrange multipliers and state variables must be determined from practical considerations. It is hardly possible to speak of an optimal mix. It is more likely that certain operating constraints will determine a feasible mixture. For example, given a problem with four state variables to be solved on a computer with internal storage for a two state variable formulation, a two state variable, two multiplier formulation would probably be most practical.

10. Two State Variables and Two Decision Variables

Problems with more than one constraint in which some constraints involve different variables lend themselves to other possibilities for state variable reduction. In this section we shall formulate and solve a problem with two constraints as a two state variable dynamic program. Each constraint contains different variables.

We consider the minimization of

$$\frac{5d_1 + 2d_1^2}{e_1 + 1} + \frac{4d_2 + 3d_2^2}{e_2 + 1} + \frac{3d_3 + 4d_3^2}{e_3 + 1} + \frac{2d_4 + 5d_4^2}{e_4 + 1}$$

over the variables (d_1, d_2, d_3, d_4) and (e_1, e_2, e_3, e_4), defined on the nonnegative integers, and subject to the constraints

$$d_1 + 2d_2 + 3d_3 + 4d_4 \geq 10$$

and

$$e_1 + e_2 + e_3 + e_4 \leq 6$$

To initiate a dynamic programming formulation, we introduce a state variable for each constraint, $x = (x_1, x_2, x_3, x_4)$ for the first, and $y = (y_1, y_2, y_3, y_4)$ for the second. Since the decision variables d_n and e_n interact only in the objective function, each constraint can be considered separately in determining the stage transformations. The transformations $x_{n-1} = t_n(x_n, d_n)$ are identical to those of the problem in Chapter III, Section 17. Namely,

$$x_4 = 10, \qquad\qquad x_3 = x_4 - 4d_4, \qquad d_4 = 0, 1, 2, 3$$

$$x_3 = \ \le\ 0, 2, 6, 10, \qquad\qquad x_2 = x_3 - 3d_3, \qquad d_3 = 0, 1, \ldots, 4$$

$$x_2 = \ \le\ 0, 1, 2, 3, 4, 6, 7, 10, \qquad x_1 = x_2 - 2d_2, \qquad d_2 = 0, 1, \ldots, 5$$

$$x_1 = \ \le\ 0, 1, \ldots, 8, 10, \qquad\qquad d_1 \ge x_1, \qquad d_1 = 0, \ldots, 10$$

For the second constraint, $\sum e_n \le 6$, the transformations are of the form $y_{n-1} = t_n'(y_n, e_n)$, and specifically are

$$y_4 = 6, \qquad\qquad y_3 = y_4 - e_4, \qquad e_4 = 0, 1, \ldots, 6$$

$$y_3 = 0, 1, \ldots, 6, \qquad\qquad y_2 = y_3 - e_3, \qquad e_3 = 0, 1, \ldots, 6$$

$$y_2 = 0, 1, \ldots, 6, \qquad\qquad y_1 = y_2 - e_2, \qquad e_2 = 0, 1, \ldots, 6$$

$$y_1 = 0, 1, \ldots, 6, \qquad\qquad e_1 \le y_1, \qquad e_1 = 0, 1, \ldots, 6$$

Using these transformations and the return functions just given, we obtain the recursive equations

$$f_1(x_1, y_1) = \min_{\substack{d_1 \ge x_1 \\ e_1 \le y_1}} \left[\frac{5d_1 + 2d_1^2}{e_1 + 1} \right]$$

$$f_2(x_2, y_2) = \min_{\substack{d_2 \\ e_2 \le y_2}} \left[\frac{4d_2 + 3d_2^2}{e_2 + 1} + f_1(x_2 - 2d_2, y_2 - e_2) \right]$$

$$f_3(x_3, y_3) = \min_{\substack{d_3 \\ e_3 \le y_3}} \left[\frac{3d_3 + 4d_3^2}{e_3 + 1} + f_2(x_3 - 3d_3, y_3 - e_3) \right]$$

and

$$f_4(x_4 = 10, y_4 = 6) = \min_{\substack{d_4 \\ e_4 \le y_4}} \left[\frac{2d_4 + 5d_4^2}{e_4 + 1} + f_3(x_4 - 4d_4, y_4 - e_4) \right]$$

To solve this eight-variable problem by dynamic programming hardly involves more effort than the four-variable problem with two constraints (Section 7). The deleterious effect of an additional four variables is minimized by incorporating each of the additional variables into a separate stage. No doubt there is some increase in difficulty because each of the optimizations is two-dimensional, and the storage requirement for optimal

Table 13 OPTIMAL ONE-STAGE RETURNS AND DECISIONS, $f_1(x_1, y_1)$, $d_1(x_1, y_1)$, $e_1(x_1, y_1)$

x_1

y_1	≤ 0			1			2			3			4		
	f_1	d_1	e_1	f_1	d_1	e_1	f_1	d_1	e_1	f_1	d_1	e_1	f_1	d_1	e_1
0	0.0*	0*	0*	7.0	1	0	18.0	2	0	33.0	3	0	52.0	4	0
1	0.0	0	0,1	3.5	1	1	9.0	2	1	16.5	3	1	26.0	4	1
2	0.0	0	0,1,2	2.33	1	2	6.0	2	2	11.0	3	2	17.33	4	2
3	0.0	0	0,...,3	1.75	1	3	4.5	2	3	8.25	3	3	13.0	4	3
4	0.0	0	0,...,4	1.4	1	4	3.6	2	4	6.60	3	4	10.4	4	4
5	0.0	0	0,...,5	1.17	1	5	3.0	2	5	5.5	3	5	8.67	4	5
6	0.0	0	0,...,6	1.0	1	6	2.57	2	6	4.71	3	6	7.43	4	6

x_1

y_1	5			6			7			8			10		
	f_1	d_1	e_1	f_1	d_1	e_1	f_1	d_1	e_1	f_1	d_1	e_1	f_1	d_1	e_1
0	75.0	5	0	102.0	6	0	133.0	7	0	168.0	8	0	250.0	10	0
1	37.5	5	1	51.0	6	1	66.5	7	1	84.0	8	1	125.0	10	1
2	25.0	5	2	34.0	6	2	44.33	7	2	56.0	8	2	83.33	10	2
3	18.75	5	3	25.5	6	3	33.25	7	3	42.0	8	3	62.5	10	3
4	15.0	5	4	20.4	6	4	26.6	7	4	33.6	8	4	50.0	10	4
5	12.5	5	5	17.0	6	5	22.17	7	5	28.0	8	5	41.67	10	5
6	10.71	5	6	14.57	6	6	19.0	7	6	24.0	8	6	35.71	10	6

decision functions is doubled. Nevertheless, even when exhaustive search is necessary, two-dimensional optimizations are not unmanageable.

Because $r_1(d_1, e_1)$ is increasing with d_1 and decreasing with e_1, the optimal one-stage decision functions are $d_1(x_1, y_1) = x_1$, $e_1(x_1, y_1) = y_1$, and thus

$$f_1(x_1, y_1) = \frac{5x_1 + 2x_1^2}{y_1 + 1}$$

These optimal returns and decisions are listed in Table 13. The three entries, from left to right, for each value of x_1 and y_1, are $f_1(x_1, y_1)$, $d_1(x_1, y_1)$, and $e_1(x_1, y_1)$ respectively.

Because of the irregularities of the multistage return functions $Q_n(x_n, y_n, d_n, e_n)$, generally two-dimensional exhaustive searches must be carried out to determine $f_n(x_n, y_n)$, $d_n(x_n, y_n)$, and $e_n(x_n, y_n)$ for $n = 2, 3,$ and 4. So that we may contrast a two-dimensional optimization with the several one-dimensional optimizations given previously, the function $Q_2(x_2 = 4, y_2 = 3, d_2, e_2)$ is given in Table 14. All of the values in Table 14 are examined to determine the minimum, which is $f_2(x_2 = 4, y_2 = 3) = 5$, and thus $d_2(x_2 = 4, y_2 = 3) = 2$, and $e_2(x_2 = 4, y_2 = 3) = 3$. Had the computations been done on a computer, the whole of the function $Q_2(x_2 = 4, y_2 = 3, d_2, e_2)$ would not have been needed at once. So that we can obtain compact storage, after each successive calculation of Q only the minimum is saved to compare with the next value calculated.

Table 14 $Q_2(x_2 = 4, y_2 = 3, d_2, e_2) = \dfrac{4d_2 + 3d_2^2}{e_2 + 1}$
$$+ f_1(4 - 2d_2,\ 3 - e_2)$$

e_2	d_2 0	1	2
0	0.0 + 13.0	7.0 + 4.5	20.0 + 0.0
1	0.0 + 17.33	3.5 + 6.0	10.0 + 0.0
2	0.0 + 26.0	2.33 + 9.0	6.67 + 0.0
3	0.0 + 52.0	1.75 + 18.0	5.0 + 0.0

e_2	d_2 3	4	5
0	39.0 + 0.0	64.0 + 0.0	95.0 + 0.0
1	19.5 + 0.0	32.0 + 0.0	47.5 + 0.0
2	13.0 + 0.0	21.33 + 0.0	31.67 + 0.0
3	9.75 + 0.0	16.0 + 0.0	23.75 + 0.0

Tables 15 and 16 give the two- and three-stage optimal returns and decisions. Finally, $f_4(x_4 = 10, y_4 = 6)$ is calculated to be 6.73, yielding the optimal decisions $d_4^* = 1$ and $e_4^* = 2$. Returning to Tables 16, 15, and 13, we establish the remainder of the optimal policy $d_3^* = 2$, $e_3^* = 4$, $d_2^* = 0$, $e_2^* = 0$, $d_1^* = 0$, and $e_1^* = 0$.

This two state variable problem could have been converted into a series of one state variable problems by treating one of the constraints with a Lagrange multiplier. A different transformation into a series of one state variable problems is given in Section 11.

11. The One-at-a-Time Method

This state variable reduction method is based on an elementary search procedure called the *one-at-a-time method*. The one-at-a-time method has great theoretical simplicity but is subject to certain pitfalls. It will be helpful to describe its use in ordinary search before extending it to state variable reduction. The method may be applied to optimize functions of any number of variables, but for the purpose of exposition, it is sufficient to consider two variables.

The basic idea is to vary only one variable at a time in the search for the optimum. For a function of two variables, say $r(d_1, d_2)$, we could hold d_2 constant and maximize over d_1, and then fix d_1 at the value yielding the maximum and optimize over d_2. Repeating this procedure (that is, by varying d_1 again with d_2 fixed at the value that yielded a maximum, etc.) until there was no change in the objective function would eventually terminate at a point (d_1^0, d_2^0) with the property that

$$r(d_1, d_2^0) \leq r(d_1^0, d_2^0) \geq r(d_1^0, d_2)$$

It is possible that (d_1^0, d_2^0) may be a global maximum, but it may also be a local maximum, or even worse, neither.

Figure 12 illustrates these possibilities. The surfaces in (a), (b), and (c) represent unimodal functions for which rather different results are obtained. In (a) the global maximum is reached very rapidly; in (b) the global maximum is attained, within a specified degree of accuracy, but more slowly; in (c) the global maximum is not attained at all; and in (d) the one-at-a-time method leads to a local maximum of a bimodal surface. Success may depend on the starting point. In Figure 13 the surfaces for (c) and (d) are reproduced. It is shown that if we start at points different from those in Figure 12, the global maxima are attained.

The reason the one-at-a-time method fails to reach the global optimum is obvious when there is more than one peak, but further explanation must be given for unimodal functions like (c). The termination point in

Table 15 OPTIMAL TWO-STAGE RETURNS AND DECISIONS, $f_2(x_2, y_2)$, $d_2(x_2, y_2)$, $e_2(x_2, y_2)$

y_2	$x_2 = 0$		$\leq$	$x_2 = 1$			$x_2 = 2$			$x_2 = 3$		
0	0.0*	0*	0*	7.0	0	0	7.0	1	0	14.0	1	0
1	0.0	0	0, 1	3.5	1	0	3.5	1	1	10.0	2	1
2	0.0	0	0, 1, 2	2.33	1	1	2.33	1	2	6.67	2	2
3	0.0	0	0, . . . , 3	1.75	1	0	1.75	1	3	5.0	2	3
4	0.0	0	0, . . . , 4	1.4	1	1	1.4	1	4	4.0	2	4
5	0.0	0	0, . . . , 5	1.17	1	0	1.17	1	5	3.33	2	5
6	0.0	0	0, . . . , 6	1.0	0	1	1.0	1	6	2.86	2	6

TABLE 15 (Continued)

y_2	x_2 = 4			6			7			10		
0	20.0	2	0	38.0	2	0	46.0	3	0	82.0	4	0
1	10.0	2	1	19.5	3	1	26.5	3	1	47.5	5	1
2	6.67	2	2	13.0	3	2	20.0	3	2	31.67	5	2
3	5.0	2	3	9.75	3	3	16.0	4	3	23.75	5	3
4	4.0	2	4	7.8	3	4	12.8	4	4	19.0	5	4
5	3.33	2	5	6.5	3	5	10.67	4	5	15.83	5	5
6	2.86	2	6	5.57	3	6	9.14	4	6	13.57	5	6

Table 16   OPTIMAL THREE-STAGE RETURNS AND DECISIONS, $f_3(x_3, y_3)$, $d_3(x_3, y_3)$, $e_3(x_3, y_3)$

y_3	$x_3 \le 0$			$x_3 = 2$			$x_3 = 6$			$x_3 = 10$		
	f_3	d_3	e_3	f_3	d_3	e_3	f_3	d_3	e_3	f_3	d_3	e_3
0	0.0	0	0	7.0	0	0	21.0	1	0	42.0	2	0
1	0.0	0, 1	0	3.5	1	0	11.0	2	1	29.5	3	1
2	0.0	0, 1, 2	0	2.33	1	1	7.33	2	2	21.0	2	1
3	0.0	0, …, 3	0	1.75	1	2	5.5	2	3	17.33	2	2
4	0.0	0, …, 4	0	1.4	1	3	4.4*	2*	4*	14.0	2	2
5	0.0	0, …, 5	0	1.1	1	4	3.67	2	5	12.17	2	3
6	0.0	0, …, 6	0	1.0	1	5	3.14	2	6	10.5	2	3

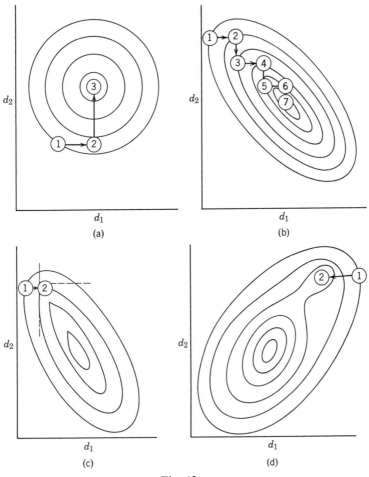

Fig. 12

(c) of Figure 12 by definition satisfies the property

$$r(d_1, d_2^0) \leq r(d_1^0, d_2^0) \geq r(d_1^0, d_2)$$

so only by varying d_1 and d_2 simultaneously can we reach the optimum from (d_1^0, d_2^0). In fact, by examining all points adjacent to (d_1^0, d_2^0) on a "fine enough grid," we can always find a point with greater return than $r(d_1^0, d_2^0)$. Otherwise (d_1^0, d_2^0) would be a local optimum. The necessity of a fine grid was discussed in Section 5. This phenomenon can also occur with discrete variables as illustrated by the function in Table 14 in which a minimum is sought. It is unimodal; nevertheless $Q_2(d_2 = 1, e_2 = 1)$ satisfies

$$Q_2(d_2, e_2 = 1) > Q_2(d_2 = 1, e_2 = 1) < Q_2(d_2 = 1, e_2)$$

but is not the minimum. However, by jumping to the adjacent point ($d_2 =$ 2, $e_2 = 2$) and by proceeding with the one-at-a-time method, we can reach the minimum. Wilde [66] calls this a "resolution ridge." He delves deeply into the properties of ridges and even gives ways of capitalizing on them. For our purpose ridges can be troublesome. But they can be avoided by evaluating the function at all points adjacent to the point in question.

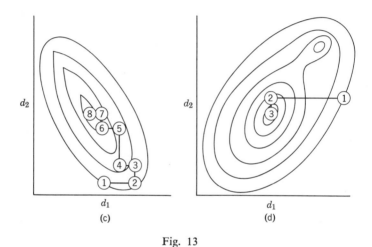

Fig. 13

In problems with several variables the one-at-a-time method can be extended to varying sets of variables at a time. In fact, if we partition the variables into appropriate mutually exclusive and exhaustive sets, and then vary the variables in one set at a time, it is often possible to reduce the number of state variables in a dynamic program like the one in Section 10, with two constraints and $2N$ variables of the form

$$\max_{d_n, e_n} \sum_{n=1}^{N} r_n(d_n, e_n)$$

$$\text{subject to} \sum_{n=1}^{N} g_n(d_n) \geq 0$$

$$\sum_{n=1}^{N} h_n(e_n) \geq 0$$

An important limitation is that the variables d_n appear only in the first constraint and the variables e_n only in the second. Since this is the case, we can partition the variables into two sets, one containing $(d_1, \ldots, d_N)$ and the other $(e_1, \ldots, e_N)$. Then, by applying the one-set-at-a-time method, we can solve the problem as a series of one state variable dynamic programs, because maximization with one set of variables constant means that only one constraint is involved at a time. Bellman calls this the method of *successive approximations*. We must remember that the solution of the resulting series of one state variable, one decision variable, N-stage dynamic programs terminates at a point $(d_n{}^0, e_n{}^0)$ satisfying the property

$$\sum_{n=1}^{N} r_n(d_n, e_n{}^0) \leq \sum_{n=1}^{N} r_n(d_n{}^0, e_n{}^0) \geq \sum_{n=1}^{N} r_n(d_n{}^0, e_n)$$

This solution could be a local maximum or a point along a resolution ridge.

Provided that we accept these risks, a set of variables appearing in only one constraint can be isolated, and then the one-at-a-time or successive approximations method used to eliminate a state variable. Naturally, if there are M constraints, each involving different variables, an M state variable problem can be reduced to a series of one state variable problems. Or, more generally, k sets of variables can be varied at a time, with the remaining $M - k$ sets held constant, yielding a series of k state variable problems. Naturally, as k increases, the number of problems in the series decreases. Clearly, the tactics for applying the one-at-a-time method are by no means fixed. Furthermore, this method may be synthesized with other methods. Even though the Lagrange and one-at-a-time methods are alternatives for state variable reduction, there is no reason why they cannot be used together, each operating on different constraints. The Lagrange method is more flexible in that it can be applied to a single constraint, no matter what variables are involved in the constraint. Furthermore, the Lagrange method is not troubled by local optima. On the other hand, the one-at-a-time method may converge faster and guarantees an answer. Very little is known about the relative merits of the different strategies, and even less about the tactics of employing them in combination.

To illustrate applying the one-at-a-time method we return to the problem of Section 10:

$$\min \sum_{n=1}^{4} \frac{a_n d_n + b_n d_n{}^2}{e_n + 1}$$

over the variables d_n and e_n, defined on the nonnegative integers, and

subject to the constraints $d_1 + 2d_2 + 3d_3 + 4d_4 \geq 10$

$$e_1 + e_2 + e_3 + e_4 \leq 6$$

By alternatively holding d_n and e_n constant, we solve successive four-stage one state variable and one decision variable dynamic programs. When the e_n's are fixed, the problems will be referred to as Form I:

$$\min \sum_{n=1}^{4} a_n' d_n + b_n' d_n^2$$

over the integro-valued variables d_n,

$$\text{subject to } d_1 + 2d_2 + 3d_3 + 4d_4 \geq 10$$

The particular values chosen for e_n determine a_n' and b_n' from the relations

$$a_n' = \frac{a_n}{e_n + 1}, \quad b_n' = \frac{b_n}{e_n + 1}$$

When the d_n's are fixed, the problems will be of Form II:

$$\min \sum_{n=1}^{4} \frac{p_n}{e_n + 1}$$

over the integro-valued variables e_n,

$$\text{subject to } e_1 + e_2 + e_3 + e_4 \leq 6, \quad p_n = a_n d_n + b_n d_n^2$$

As a first approximation to the optimum, we set $e_n = (0, 0, 0, 0)$. Admittedly this is not a very intelligent guess. But it is feasible, and yields the constants $a_n' = (5, 4, 3, 2)$, and $b_n' = (2, 3, 4, 5)$ in Form I, precisely the problem of Chapter III, Section 17. We know that the solution is $d_n = (1, 1, 1, 1)$.

Using these values for d_n to determine p_n, we have $p_n = (7, 7, 7, 7)$, so our first Form II problem is to

$$\min \sum_{n=1}^{4} \frac{7}{e_n + 1}$$

By inspection or, for those who mistrust intuition, from a four-stage one state variable dynamic program, we determine the solutions to be $e_n = (2, 2, 1, 1)$, $(2, 1, 2, 1)$, $(2, 1, 1, 2)$, $(1, 2, 2, 1)$, $(1, 2, 1, 2)$, and $(1, 1, 2, 2)$.

Thus the next solution of Form I can be with a_n' and b_n', determined from any one of the above values of e_n. One hopes that it would make no difference which value of e_n is chosen. Unfortunately, this is not the case. With $e_n = (1, 2, 2, 1)$, and thus $a_n' = (\frac{5}{2}, \frac{4}{3}, 1, 1)$, and $b_n' = (1, 1, \frac{4}{3}, \frac{5}{2})$, a dynamic programming solution of Form I yields $d_n = (0, 0, 2, 1)$. Then Form II is solved with $p_n = (0, 0, 22, 7)$ to obtain $e_n = (0, 0, 4, 2)$. The next solution of Form I with $a_n' = (5, 4, \frac{3}{5}, \frac{2}{3})$ and $b_n' = (2, 3, \frac{4}{5}, \frac{5}{3})$ again yields $d_n = (0, 0, 2, 1)$, so $d_n^0 = (0, 0, 2, 1)$ and $e_n^0 = (0, 0, 4, 2)$. In fact, this solution is the global minimum, as we already know from the two state variable solution of Section 10.

Table 17 SUCCESSFUL ATTEMPT

Form Solved	Fixed Variables	Constants	Solution
I	$e_n = (0, 0, 0, 0)$	$a_n' = (5, 4, 3, 2)$ $b_n' = (2, 3, 4, 5)$	$d_n = (1, 1, 1, 1)$
II	$d_n = (1, 1, 1, 1)$	$p_n = (7, 7, 7, 7)$	$e_n = (2, 2, 1, 1)$ $(2, 1, 2, 1)$ $(2, 1, 1, 2)$ $(1, 2, 2, 1)$ $(1, 2, 1, 2)$ $(1, 1, 2, 2)$
I	$e_n = (1, 2, 2, 1)$	$a_n' = (\tfrac{5}{2}, \tfrac{4}{3}, 1, 1)$ $b_n' = (1, 1, \tfrac{4}{3}, \tfrac{5}{2})$	$d_n = (0, 0, 2, 1)$
II	$d_n = (0, 0, 2, 1)$	$p_n = (0, 0, 22, 7)$	$e_n = (0, 0, 4, 2)$
I	$e_n = (0, 0, 4, 2)$	$a_n' = (5, 4, \tfrac{3}{5}, \tfrac{2}{3})$ $b_n' = (2, 3, \tfrac{4}{5}, \tfrac{5}{3})$	$d_n = (0, 0, 2, 1)$

Table 18　UNSUCCESSFUL ATTEMPT

Form Solved	Fixed Variables	Constants	Solution
I	$e_n = (0, 0, 0, 0)$	$a_n' = (5, 4, 3, 2)$ $b_n' = (2, 3, 4, 5)$	$d_n = (1, 1, 1, 1)$
II	$d_n = (1, 1, 1, 1)$	$p_n = (7, 7, 7, 7)$	$e_n = (2, 2, 1, 1)$ $(2, 1, 2, 1)$ $(2, 1, 1, 2)$ $(1, 2, 2, 1)$ $(1, 2, 1, 2)$ $(1, 1, 2, 2)$
I	$e_n = (2, 2, 1, 1)$	$a_n' = (5/3, 4/3, 3/2, 1)$ $b_n' = (2/3, 1, 2, 5/2)$	$d_n = (1, 1, 1, 1)$

Alternatively, by choosing $e_n = (2, 2, 1, 1)$, we obtain the constants $a_n' = (\frac{5}{3}, \frac{4}{3}, \frac{3}{2}, 1)$ and $b_n' = (\frac{2}{3}, 1, 2, \frac{5}{2})$. This problem has solution $d_n = (1, 1, 1, 1)$, and so we are trapped at the solution $d_n^0 = (1, 1, 1, 1)$, $e_n^0 = (2, 2, 1, 1)$, which is not the global optimum. The results of both the successful and unsuccessful attempts at reaching the global minimum by varying one set of variables at a time are summarized in Tables 17 and 18. The curious reader can investigate the results when any of the other four alternative optima are chosen to initiate a solution of Form I.

The cause of failure in the unsuccessful attempt was due to the resolution ridge effect rather than a local minimum. Discrete variable optimization problems are always more prone to this effect than their continuous counterparts because of the limit on the fineness of grid that can be chosen. At any rate, by examining the objective function at all points adjacent to the termination point, we can always distinguish a point on a resolution ridge from a local minimum. If the point is on a ridge, we can move to an adjacent point and begin the one-at-a-time method again. However, once a local minima is reached, there is no certain way of moving from it. Therefore, we must try to avoid them initially. A refinement of the one-at-a-time method, which avoids local minima, is presented in Section 12.

12. A Refinement of the One-at-a-Time Method

The one-at-a-time method is based on finding successive feasible solutions, each with an improved value of the objective function, and then stopping when there is no improvement from one solution to the next. Therefore it is not surprising that the termination point may be a local instead of a global optimum. To have a better than random chance of reaching a global optimum, we must start off in a direction pointing toward a global optimum and then carefully navigate a course to it. By straying from that course, we face the danger of a collision with a local peak.

The refinement of the one-at-a-time method is based on finding a proper starting point and then steering a course to the global optimum by taking very small steps. Hence convergence may not be very rapid.

To develop the method, we consider a problem with $2N$ variables and two constraints of the form

$$\max_{d_n, e_n} \sum_{n=1}^{N} r_n(d_n, e_n)$$

$$\text{subject to} \sum_{n=1}^{N} g_n(d_n) \leq k_1$$

and

$$\sum_{n=1}^{N} h_n(e_n) \leq k_2$$

In order to apply the refined one-at-a-time method the following two conditions must be satisfied: †

1. For some value of k_2 we must know the global optimum; and
2. The optimum policy, $d_n{}^*(k_2)$ and $e_n{}^*(k_2)$, must be a continuous function of k_2.

Satisfying condition one gives a starting point from which a course can be navigated to the global optimum. It is not an unreasonable condition to satisfy, even if, for the desired value of k_2, there are several optimum. For example, suppose the second constraint with $k_2 = 0$ ($k_2 = 0$ is not the desired value) is satisfied only by $e_n = (0, 0, \ldots, 0)$. Then the problem

$$\max_{d_n,\, e_n} \sum_{n=1}^{N} r_n(d_n, e_n)$$

$$\text{subject to } \sum_{n=1}^{N} g_n(d_n) \leq k_1$$

$$\sum_{n=1}^{N} h_n(e_n) \leq 0$$

can be solved as a one state variable dynamic program to obtain the global optimum, $d_n{}^*(0)$. Since $e_n{}^*(0) = (0, \ldots, 0)$, the recursion equations are

$$f_n(x_n) = \max_{d_n} \ [r_n(d_n, 0) + f_{n-1}(x_n - g_n(d_n))], \qquad n = 1, \ldots, N$$

with $x_N = k_1$

The second condition provides the necessary ingredients to insure the steering of a course to the global optimum for the desired value of k_2. However, it precludes the solution of discrete variable optimization problems, and certainly does not apply to all problems with decision variables defined on a continuous domain. Having determined $d_n{}^*(0)$ and $e_n{}^*(0)$, we can get a first approximation to the global optimum of

$$\max_{d_n,\, e_n} \sum_{n=1}^{N} r_n(d_n, e_n)$$

$$\text{subject to } \sum_{n=1}^{N} g_n(d_n) \leq k_1$$

$$\sum_{n=1}^{N} h_n(e_n) \leq \Delta$$

where Δ is a very small quantity. We solve the one state variable dynamic program

$$f_n(y_n) = \max_{e_n} \ [r_n(d_n{}^*(0), e_n) + f_{n-1}(y_n - h_n(e_n))], \qquad n = 1, \ldots, N$$

---

† k_1 can take the role of k_2 in these two conditions.

with $y_N = \Delta$

Using the solution $e_n{}^*(\Delta)$, we obtain a second and better approximation of the form $d_n{}^*(\Delta)$, $e_n{}^*(\Delta)$ by solving another one state variable dynamic program

$$f_n(x_n) = \max_{d_n} \; [r_n(d_n, e_n{}^*(\Delta)) + f_{n-1}(x_n - g_n(d_n))], \qquad n = 1, \ldots, N$$

with $x_N = k_1$

Two one state variable dynamic programs must be solved to move from the solution at $k_2 = 0$ to the solution at $k_2 = \Delta$. But given that the solution at $k_2 = 0$ is a global optimum, not on a ridge, and the optimal policy is a continuous function of k_2, the solution at $k_2 = \Delta$ is also a global optimum. This is explained further in Figure 14 which represents the $2N$-

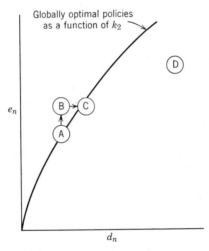

Fig. 14 A = global optimum, $d_n{}^*(O), e_n{}^*(O)$; B = $d_n{}^*(O), e_n{}^*(\;)$; C = global optimum $d_n{}^*(\;), e_n{}^*(\;)$; D = local optimum, $d_n(\Delta), e_n(\;)$.

dimensional solution space (d_n, e_n). Point A is $d_n{}^*(0)$, $e_n{}^*(0)$, by hypothesis the global optimum with $k_2 = 0$. Point B is $d_n{}^*(0)$, $e_n{}^*(\Delta)$. Points C and D are the optima to the problem with $k_2 = \Delta$. We want to show that point C, which represents $d_n{}^*(\Delta)$, $e_n{}^*(\Delta)$, is the global optimum for $k_2 = \Delta$. Assume the solution at D, $d_n(\Delta), e_n(\Delta)$, is the global optimum. But since

$$\lim_{\Delta \to 0} \; (d_n(\Delta), e_n(\Delta)) \neq (d_n{}^*(0), e_n{}^*(0))$$

there is a contradiction to the continuity hypothesis. Hence point C, by definition satisfying

$$\lim_{\Delta \to 0} \; (d_n{}^*(\Delta), e_n{}^*(\Delta)) = (d_n{}^*(0), e_n{}^*(0))$$

is the global optimum for $k_2 = \Delta$. Even if point D were quite close to point A, by choosing Δ small enough we would always reach C, the global optimum, since Δ can always be chosen so that

$$\left| d_n{}^{*}(\Delta) - d_n{}^{*}(0) \right| < \epsilon_1$$

$$\left| e_n{}^{*}(\Delta) - e_n{}^{*}(0) \right| < \epsilon_2$$

for any positive ϵ_1 and ϵ_2, because of the continuity property. Having determined the global optimum for $k_2 = \Delta$, we can repeat the procedure for as long as the continuity property holds, for $k_2 = (2\Delta, 3\Delta, \ldots,)$. It may be slow, but it is safe.

We have discussed two approaches for reducing storage requirements, each based on solving a series of dynamic programs with smaller memory needs than the original problem. The coarse grid approach diminishes storage demands by reducing the feasible values for each state variable. Alternatively, we can eliminate state variables by using Lagrange multipliers and/or the one-at-a-time method. The coarse grid approach and state variable reduction methods can be synthesized.

We have applied classical optimization techniques for a new purpose. Rather than using Lagrange multipliers and the one-at-a-time method directly to find optima, we used them as dressings to prepare a problem for optimization. They precede the dynamic programming transformation, which, in turn, precedes the actual optimization. The potential of this kind of synthesis has just begun to be exploited. Further research will surely yield methods for bringing yet larger problems into the realm of computational feasibility.

13. Concluding Remarks on Computations

In Chapter II we claimed that dynamic programming was an approach to optimization rather than a technique for actually optimizing the objective function. Specifically, we said that dynamic programming yields a transformation of a problem into a different form frequently more suitable for optimization. Once the transformation has been made, the task of optimization is another matter. However a considerable number of pages have been devoted to computational aspects of dynamic programming. At first glance this may seem to be a contradiction. After all, why distinguish computational aspects of dynamic programming from optimization methods in general? Hopefully this chapter has provided the answers.

Although we have the freedom to use any method of optimization to solve the recursive equations, dynamic programming formulations introduce new questions concerning how optimizations should be carried out. If we reduce the dimension of the decision space drastically, optimization techniques capable of handling very few variables (for example, Fibonacci search) take on a new importance in solving complex problems. Even exhaustive search becomes a viable technique for problems with millions of feasible solutions. An important role is established for mathematical induction in optimization, when one uses analytical procedures to solve recursion equations.

However, we do not get these benefits without cost. We pay for having fewer decision variables in each optimization by having to find optimal decision functions. The decisions are determined as functions of state variables and, the state variables introduce new difficulties. The concept of classifying a problem by the number of variables must be altered to one of classification by the *kinds* of variables, state and decision. And new methods must be developed for problems created by state variable dimensionality, quite different from the approaches to decision variable dimensionality. Because of storage and retrieval of large quantities of data, we must reestablish appropriate criteria for evaluating an optimization method. The solution of recursive equations does not necessarily warrant new methods of optimization. But it does require new perspectives on these methods.

Studying computational aspects of dynamic programming may not be as stimulating as studying basic concepts. The question of eliminating one state variable may seem trivial compared to that of finding the general class of problems that can be formulated as dynamic programs. But in order to present a practical solution for the latter question we must address ourselves to the former. For example, without a major breakthrough in theory, a dynamic programming algorithm has been developed which solves large "traveling salesmen" problems in a reasonable amount of time. This was achieved, in part, with devices for overcoming some of the formidable computational difficulties of multi-state-variable analysis. Admittedly, these ploys are not a substitute for theoretical advances. But together with the rapid advances in computer technology, purely computational improvements in optimization methods are extremely important. We could not think of solving many such problems without the computer and the computational devices of recursive optimization.

There are several assumptions implicit in the recursion equation

$$f_n(X_n) = \max_{D_n} \, [r_n(X_n, D_n) 0 \, f_{n-1}(t_n(X_n, D_n))]$$

which need relaxing before our dynamic programming model will be of sufficiently general use for the most universal systems that it can represent. We turn to these now, beginning by removing the assumption that stage returns and transformations are deterministic. However, this chapter on computational aspects is self-contained, since even our most general model with stochastic elements and a nonserial structure will eventually reduce to solving recursive equations of the form just given.

EXERCISES

1. Develop the Fibonacci search procedure for finding the minimum of a unimodal function $g(y)$, $a \leq y \leq b$, where y is a continuous variable.

2. Use the results of Problem 1 to solve

$$\min_{0 \leq y \leq 100} \quad y^2 - 20y + 100$$

Obtain the solution with an accuracy of $\pm$ 0.5 of the true optimal value of y.

3. A manufacturer can increase production in any month at a cost of $4.00 per unit increase in the production rate. Reductions in the production rate cost $3.00 per unit decrease. It is known that demands in the next 3 periods are 2, 4, and 1 units respectively. Production costs per unit are $6.00, $10.00, and $8.00 in periods 1, 2, and 3 respectively. Inventory carrying charges are applied to end of month inventory and amount to $2.00 per unit. Assume that demands are to be met each month, that initial and final inventories are zero, and that production in month zero is zero. Determine optimal production levels.

4. Prove that in the generalized Lagrange multiplier method, $g_i(D^*)$ is a monotonically nondecreasing function of λ_i, with λ_j fixed ($j \neq i$).

5. Solve the problem of Section 7, treating the first constraint with a Lagrange multiplier.

6. Solve the problem of Section 10, treating the first constraint with a Lagrange multiplier.

7. Solve the problem of Section 10, treating the second constraint with a Lagrange multiplier.

8. Assume the integer constraints were removed in the problem of Section 10. Solve it as a two state variable dynamic program, using the coarse grid approach.

9. Solve Problem 8, using one state variable and the refined one-at-a-time procedure.

10. In Problem 17 (Chapter III) assume the total time of vibration is given by

$$T = \alpha_1 + 2\alpha_2 + 3\alpha_3$$

Find the optimal solution with $T \leq 1$ using
    (a) two state variables
    (b) one state variable and a Lagrange multiplier.

11. Suppose in Problem 29 (Chapter III) that in addition to the weight restriction there was a volume restriction that is, each item has a volume v_n per unit, and the total volume of the knapsack is V. Formulate and solve the maximation of value problem, subject to the weight and volume restrictions, as a two state variable dynamic program. In particular, consider $V = 30$ and $(v_1, v_2, v_3, v_4) = (8, 6, 5, 10)$.

12. Solve Problem 11 using one state variable and a Lagrange multiplier.

13. The fixed charge transportation problem may be stated as

$$\min \sum_{i=1}^{m} \sum_{j=1}^{n} r_{ij}(d_{ij}) \qquad r_{ij}(d_{ij}) = c_{ij}d_{ij} + k_{ij}, \qquad d_{ij} > 0$$
$$= 0, \qquad\qquad d_{ij} = 0$$

$$\text{subject to } \sum_{i} d_{ij} = b_j$$

$$\sum_{j} d_{ij} = a_i, \quad d_{ij} \geq 0$$

Formulate the fixed charge problem as a dynamic program. Show that the number of state variables required is the minimum of $(m, n) - 1$. In particular, consider the following data and find the optimal integer solution by
   (a) using two state variables
   (b) using one state variable and a Lagrange multiplier
   (c) using one state variable and successive approximations

b_j		4	7	3	5
			j		
a_i	i	1	2	3	4
5	1	6,1	5,1	3,3	7,0
6	2	3,3	2,2	1,1	4,2
8	3	5,2	4,1	4,2	6,1
			c_{ij}, k_{ij}		

14. In the "shortest-route problem" there is a network with nodes numbered $0, 1, \ldots, N$ and an arc $\bar{ij}$ connecting pairs of nodes i and j. Associated with each arc is a nonnegative distance c_{ij}. If there is no arc between nodes i and j, c_{ij} is assumed to be infinite. The objective is to find a shortest path between nodes O and N. A path between two nodes is a set of arcs connecting the two nodes and containing no loops. Let $f_i = $ the distance of the shortest route between nodes i and N. Show that

$$f_i = \min_{j} [c_{ij} + f_j], \qquad i = 0, \ldots, N-1, \qquad c_{ii} = 0$$

with $f_N = 0$

Show that the following successive approximation scheme converges monotonically to the optimal solution in a finite number of steps

$$g_i^{(0)} = c_{iN}, \qquad i = 0, \ldots, N-1$$
$$g_N^{(0)} = 0$$
$$g_i^{(k)} = \min_{j} (c_{ij} + g_j^{(k-1)})$$
$$g_N^{(k)} = 0$$

In other words, establish that $g_i^{(k)} \leq g_i^{(k-1)}$, and if equality holds $g_i^{(k)} = f_i$.†

---

† This approach to the shortest route problem is given in Bellman and Dreyfus [13]. For a summary of various approaches see Pollack and Wiebenson [56].

15. Use the method developed in Problem 14 to find the shortest route through the network given in Figure 15.

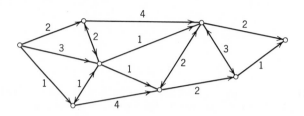

Fig. 15

16. Extend the method developed in Problem 14 to the problem of finding the kth shortest route through a network. In particular, find the second shortest route for the network in Figure 15.

V

Risk, Uncertainty, and Competition

1. Terminology and Classification

The models of Chapters II-IV all had the property that the return, optimal or not, was unambiguously specified by fixing values for the decision variables. In the language of decision theorists this is *deterministic* decision making or decision making under *certainty*. Although there are difficult problems of optimization in deterministic decision making, at least the objective is clear. Undeniably, it is the maximization of return, assuming that return is an adequate measure of preference. That is, if the return from policy A is greater than the return from policy B, then policy A is preferred to policy B.

Indeterminateness exists when the return is not unambiguously specified, by fixing values of the decision variables. In other words, for each decision policy there is a set of possible returns.

There are various degrees of indeterminateness. At the lowest level there is a *known* probability of occurrence associated with each return, resulting from a decision policy. The technical terms for decision making under these circumstances are "decision making under *risk*," "*probabilistic* decision making," or "*stochastic* decision making." For convenience, returns that cannot occur as the result of a particular decision policy are often included in the set of possibilities and then assigned zero probability. Thus decision making under certainty is a special case of decision making under risk in which, for a particular decision policy, one return is assigned a probability of unity and the remainder, zero.

At the other extreme of indeterminateness there is complete ignorance about the probabilities. This is referred to as "decision making under *uncertainty*." One intermediate case, for which recursive methods have direct application, is "*adaptive* decision making." In this latter situation, information gleaned from an ongoing process generates estimates of probabilities transforming the indeterminateness from uncertainty to risk.

In the spectrum from certainty to uncertainty, the assumption remains that functionally there is a single decision maker. In other words, the return depends only on stated parameters and constants, the decision variables, and perhaps random elements. This kind of model does not represent situations with conflict of interest, resulting in various degrees of competition and cooperation among functionally distinct decision makers. Situations with more than one functionally distinct decision maker are referred to as "*group* decision making." The quantitative analysis of group decision making under competition is generally known as "*game theory.*"

The construction of models of decision making under risk, uncertainty, and competition involves many subtleties. In particular, the objective of optimization is neither obvious nor, in some circumstances, agreed upon. The clear objective in the deterministic case is destroyed when the return is no longer completely within control, but instead depends on stochastic elements or actions of other decision makers. We shall pass lightly over these difficulties and direct attention to recursive equations. There are, however, ample references on game theory and modern statistical decision theory. Some of the outstanding ones are Von Neumann and Morgenstern [64], Luce and Raiffa [45], McKinsey [49], and Chernoff and Moses [22].

2. Decision Making Under Risk

We begin with a single-stage stochastic return function $r(D, k)$ where, as usual, D denotes the decision variables. The stochastic element enters through the discrete random variable k. The probability distribution of k is given by $p(k)$. For a fixed set of decisions D, we would expect, on the average, to receive a return of

$$\bar{r}(D) = \sum_k p(k)\, r(D, k)$$

We have determined $\bar{r}(D)$ by weighting each return by its frequency of occurrence. Similarly, for a stochastic return function $r(D, z)$ with continuous random variable z and probability density $p(z)$

$$\bar{r}(D) = \int p(z)\, r(D, z)\, dz$$

$\bar{r}(D)$ is called the *expected value* of return or simply the expected return. An important property of expected return is that statistically it represents an estimate of average return from any one trial, even though it may not actually be possible to receive the amount $\bar{r}(D)$. For example, if returns of 0 and 1 each occur with probability $\frac{1}{2}$, $\bar{r}(D) = \frac{1}{2}$, but the actual return from one trial must be 0 or 1.

A decision policy D^* is globally optimal (maximal) under risk if and only if

$$\bar{r}(D^*) \geq \bar{r}(D)$$

for all feasible D. There have been some objections to maximizing expected value under risk, but these can be accounted for by defining return properly. The following example illustrates the objections, and demonstrates why they are superfluous. Let there be two alternative decision policies (D_1, D_2), with returns and probabilities as shown in Table 1.

Table 1

	D_1		D_2	
p	$\frac{2}{3}$	$\frac{1}{3}$	$\frac{1}{2}$	$\frac{1}{2}$
r	0	10	2	4

The expected returns are

$$\bar{r}(D_1) = \tfrac{2}{3}(0) + \tfrac{1}{3}(10) = 3\tfrac{1}{3}$$

and
$$\bar{r}(D_2) = \tfrac{1}{2}(2) + \tfrac{1}{2}(4) = 3$$

So under the criterion of maximizing expected return, D_1 is chosen as the optimal policy.

The main, and superficially valid, objection is that the expected value criterion does not take into account the variations in return. Would it not be better to accept a slightly lower return (that is, from D_2) and forsake the large risk of receiving no return from D_1? This argument seems to be reinforced when the decision is only going to be used once. Furthermore, even if our intention is to repeat the optimal decisions over and over again, a run of bad luck could literally bankrupt us and ruin these good intentions.

If, for example, the returns were measured in dollars, but the number of dollars themselves were not equivalent to the utility of dollars, the above points would have indeed been valid. But if circumstances are such that D_2 is preferred to D_1 in the example, this simply indicates that we have not assigned proper returns (utilities) to the various outcomes. It is wrong to measure returns entirely in dollars, when our utility function actually contains several other factors. Thus to justify choosing D_2 over D_1, we could argue that an outcome that produces zero dollars would endanger survival and consequently must be assigned a negative return; or a yield of 10 dollars is not worth five times a yield of 2 dollars and thus must be reevaluated downwards, since any yield over 7 dollars is just surplus wealth. In general, objections to the expected return criterion are only superficially against expected return. The real objection is to the measurement of return. If the measure is correct, expected return is the valid criterion for comparing alternative decision policies under risk. Our justification of this has been intuitive. For an axiomatic development of utility theory and consequently a rigorous justification of the expected return criterion, see Chernoff and Moses [22] or Luce and Raiffa [45].

Having accepted the expected return criterion, we see that, theoretically, optimization under risk is no more difficult than optimization under certainty. However, we would expect correspondingly more computations under risk, since for each decision policy several returns must be computed, weighted by the appropriate probabilities and then summed. These increases in computations can become severe, particularly when there are several random variables each contributing a stochastic element to the return. Fortunately, these difficulties can often be kept to a minimum by using a dynamic programming approach.

3. Multistage Optimization Under Risk

An N-stage stochastic system (Figure 1) is similar to an N-stage deterministic system except that at each stage there is a random variable that

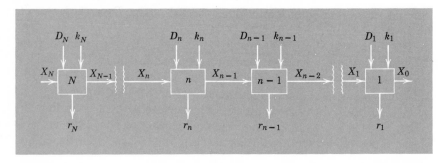

Fig. 1

affects the stage return and transformation. At stage n, $n = 1, \ldots, N$, there is an input state X_n, decision D_n, and random variable k_n, which together determine the return

$$r_n = r_n(X_n, D_n, k_n)$$

and the transformation

$$X_{n-1} = t_n(X_n, D_n, k_n), \qquad n = 1, \ldots, N$$

The random variables $k_1, \ldots, k_N$ are assumed to be independently distributed with probability distributions $p_1(k_1), \ldots, p_N(k_N)$ respectively.

The total return from N stages is assumed to be the sum of the stage returns, that is,

$$R_N(X_N, \ldots, X_1, D_N, \ldots, D_1, k_N, \ldots, k_1) = \sum_{n=1}^{N} r_n(X_n, D_n, k_n)$$

$$\text{subject to } X_{n-1} = t_n(X_n, D_n, k_n)$$

It is important to realize that the nth stage return depends on the random variables $k_N, \ldots, k_{n+1}$ as well as k_n, since X_n depends on $k_N, \ldots, k_{n+1}$. In the deterministic case, it was sufficient to specify values of X_N and $D_N, \ldots, D_1$ to describe completely the operation of the system. However, for the stochastic system, the input states depend on previously observed random variables as well as decision variables. Thus, even if a decision policy is given, the input to stage n is unknown until particular values of the random variables $k_N, \ldots, k_{n+1}$ have been realized.

To determine the expected value of R_N we must know how to calculate the expected values of functions of more than one random variable. In general, given a function $r(D, k_1, \ldots, k_N)$ where $k_1, \ldots, k_N$ are independently distributed random variables with density functions $p_1(k_1), \ldots, p_N(k_N)$, its expected value is

$$\bar{r}(D) = \sum_{k_1} \cdots \sum_{k_N} \left(\prod_{n=1}^{N} p_n(k_n) \, r(D, k_1, \ldots, k_N) \right)$$

Thus the expected value of the N-stage return $R_N(X_N, D_N, \ldots, D_1, k_N, \ldots, k_1)$ is

$$\bar{R}_N(X_N, D_N, \ldots, D_1) = \sum_{k_1} \cdots \sum_{k_N} \left[\prod_{n=1}^{N} p_n(k_n) \sum_{n=1}^{N} r_n(X_n, D_n, k_n) \right]$$

$$= \sum_{k_1} \cdots \sum_{k_N} \left[\prod_{n=1}^{N} p_n(k_n) \, r_N(X_N, D_N, k_N) \right] + \ldots$$

$$+ \sum_{k_1} \cdots \sum_{k_N} \left[\prod_{n=1}^{N} p_n(k_n) r_1(X_1, D_1, k_1) \right]$$

$$\text{subject to } X_{n-1} = t_n(X_n, D_n, k_n), \qquad n = 1, \ldots, N$$

Because the Nth stage return does not depend on $k_{N-1}, \ldots, k_1$, we have

$$\bar{R}_N(X_N, D_N, \ldots, D_1) =$$

$$\sum_{k_N} \left[p_N(k_N) \, r_N(X_N, D_N, k_N) \sum_{k_{N-1}} \left[p_{N-1}(k_{N-1}) \ldots \sum_{k_1} p_1(k_1) \ldots \right] \right] + \ldots$$

$$+ \sum_{k_N} \left[p_N(k_N) \ldots \sum_{k_2} \left[p_2(k_2) \sum_{k_1} \left[p_1(k_1) \, r_1(X_1, D_1, k_1) \right] \right] \ldots \right]$$

$$\text{Since } \sum_{k_n} p_n(k_n) = 1, \qquad n = 1, \ldots, N$$

$$\bar{R}_N(X_N, D_N, \ldots, D_1) = \sum_{k_N} p_N(k_N) \, r_N(X_N, D_N, k_N) + \ldots$$

$$+ \sum_{k_N} \left[p_N(k_N) \ldots \sum_{k_2} \left[p_2(k_2) \sum_{k_1} [p_1(k_1)r_1(X_1, D_1, k_1)] \right] \ldots \right]$$

$$\text{subject to } X_{n-1} = t_n(X_n, D_n, k_n), \qquad n = 1, \ldots, N$$

Our objective is to maximize the expected N-stage return over $D_N, \ldots, D_1$. The effect of the random variables, particularly the compounding of them as exemplified by the stage one return, makes multistage optimization enormously more difficult when methods dealing with all of the variables simultaneously are used. Thus there is an even greater need, in decision making under risk, to turn to the powerful recursive procedures of dynamic programming. Let $\bar{f}_N(X_N)$ be the maximum expected return as a function of X_N, that is,

$$\bar{f}_N(X_N) = \max_{D_N, D_{N-1}, \ldots, D_1} \bar{R}_N(X_N, D_N, \ldots, D_1)$$

$$= \max_{D_N, D_{N-1}, \ldots, D_1} \left[\sum_{k_N} p_N(k_N) \, r_N(X_N, D_N, k_N) \right.$$

$$+ \sum_{k_N} \left[p_N(k_N) \sum_{k_{N-1}} [p_{N-1}(k_{N-1}) \, r_{N-1}(X_{N-1}, D_{N-1}, k_{N-1})] \right]$$

$$\left. + \ldots + \sum_{k_N} \left[p_N(k_N) \ldots \sum_{k_2} \left[p_2(k_2) \sum_{k_1} [p_1(k_1) \, r_1(X_1, D_1, k_1)] \right] \ldots \right]$$

Factoring out $\sum_{k_N} p_N(k_N)$ which is common to every term, we obtain

$$\bar{f}_N(X_N) = \max_{D_N, D_{N-1}, \ldots, D_1} \left[\sum_{k_N} p_N(k_N) \left[r_N(X_N, D_N, k_N) \right.\right.$$

$$+ \sum_{k_{N-1}} [p_{N-1}(k_{N-1}) \, r_{N-1}(X_{N-1}, D_{N-1}, k_{N-1})] + \ldots$$

$$\left.\left. + \sum_{k_{N-1}} \left[p_{N-1}(k_{N-1}) \ldots \sum_{k_2} \left[p_2(k_2) \sum_{k_1} [p_1(k_1) \, r_1(X_1, D_1, k_1)] \right] \ldots \right]\right]\right]$$

$$\text{subject to } X_{n-1} = t_n(X_n, D_n, k_n), \qquad n = 1, \ldots, N$$

Following the procedure used in the derivation of the deterministic recursive equations (Chapter II), we replace

$$\max_{D_N, D_{N-1}, \ldots, D_1} \bar{R}_N(X_N, D_N, \ldots, D_1)$$

by

$$\max_{D_N} \max_{D_{N-1}, \ldots, D_1} \bar{R}_N(X_N, D_N, \ldots, D_1)$$

and then remove the Nth stage return from the inner maximization since it is not a function of $D_{N-1}, \ldots, D_1$. This yields

$$
\bar{f}_N(X_N) = \max_{D_N} \left[\sum_{k_N} p_N(k_N) \left[r_N(X_N, D_N, k_N) \right. \right.
$$

$$
+ \max_{D_{N-1}, \ldots, D_1} \left[\sum_{k_{N-1}} [p_{N-1}(k_{N-1})\ r_{N-1}(X_{N-1}, D_{N-1}, k_{N-1})] + \ldots \right.
$$

$$
\left. \left. \left. + \sum_{k_{N-1}} \left[p_{N-1}(k_{N-1}) \ldots \sum_{k_2} \left[p_2(k_2) \sum_{k_1} [p_1(k_1)\ r_1(X_1, D_1, k_1)] \right] \ldots \right] \right] \right] \right]
$$

But

$$
\bar{f}_{N-1}(X_{N-1}) = \bar{f}_{N-1}(t_N(X_N, D_N, k_N))
$$

$$
= \max_{D_{N-1}, \ldots, D_1} \left[\sum_{k_{N-1}} [p_{N-1}(k_{N-1})\ r_{N-1}(X_{N-1}, D_{N-1}, k_{N-1})] \right.
$$

$$
\left. + \ldots + \sum_{k_{N-1}} \left[p_{N-1}(k_{N-1}) \ldots \sum_{k_2} \left[p_2(k_2) \sum_{k_1} [p_1(k_1)r_1(X_1, D_1, k_1)] \right] \ldots \right] \right]
$$

Combining the expression for $\bar{f}_{N-1}$ with the equation for $\bar{f}_N$, we have the recursion equation

$$
\bar{f}_N(X_N) = \max_{D_N} \sum_{k_N} p_N(k_N)\ [r_N(X_N, D_N, k_N) + \bar{f}_{N-1}(t_N(X_N, D_N, k_N))]
$$

By induction, for any number of stages $1 \leq n \leq N$, we have the fundamental stochastic recursion equations

$$
\bar{f}_n(X_n) = \max_{D_n} \sum_{k_n} p_n(k_n)\ Q_n(X_n, D_n, k_n), \qquad 1 \leq n \leq N
$$

where

$$
Q_n(X_n, D_n, k_n) = r_n(X_n, D_n, k_n) + \bar{f}_{n-1}(t_n(X_n, D_n, k_n)), \qquad 2 \leq n \leq N
$$

and

$$
Q_1(X_1, D_1, k_1) = r_1(X_1, D_1, k_1)
$$

The recursion equations eliminate the usual complexities caused by interactions among N random variables. Compare the simplicity of the stochastic recursion equations with the cumbersome defining equation for the optimal N-stage stochastic return. The introduction of risk causes no increase in state variables. The solution of successive recursion equations simply involves maximizing the expected value of $Q_n(X_n, D_n, k_n)$. Since Q_n is a function of only one random variable, some of the formidable difficulties of optimizing functions with several random variables have been overcome.

The optimal decision policy resulting from multistage optimization under risk is itself stochastic, except for the first optimal decision $D_N{}^*(X_N)$. The remaining optimal decisions, obtained from the recursive analysis in the form $D_{N-1}(X_{N-1}), \ldots, D_1(X_1)$ cannot be expressed deterministically in terms of X_N until the stochastic elements that precede them are revealed. Thus substituting

$$D_N{}^*(X_N) \text{ into } X_{N-1} = t_N(X_N, D_N, k_N)$$

yields

$$X_{N-1}^* = t_N(X_N, D_N{}^*(X_N), k_N) = t_N(X_N, k_N)$$

so the optimal value of X_{N-1}^* is known only probabilistically. Then the same must hold true for the optimal value of D_{N-1} since

$$D_{N-1}(X_{N-1}^*) = D_{N-1}(t_N(X_N, k_N)) = D_{N-1}(X_N, k_N)$$

In a sense then, an N-stage stochastic optimization yields incomplete results, since only the first optimal decision is obtained. The remaining optimal decisions are determined one by one as the stochastic process reveals itself. Of course, this is not a deficiency of the dynamic programming analysis, but a property of the stochastic multistage system.

In the very special case of quadratic stage returns and linear transformations it has been shown by Tou [63] that the independent random variables k_n, $n = 1, \ldots, N$, can be replaced by their expected values $(\bar{k}_n)$, where

$$\bar{k}_n = \sum_{k_n} k_n \, p_n(k_n), \qquad n = 1, \ldots, N$$

Then $D_N{}^*(X_N)$ can be found by solving the deterministic problem

$$\bar{f}_n(X_n) = \max_{D_n} Q_n(X_n, D_n, \bar{k}_n), \qquad 1 \leq n \leq N$$

where

$$Q_n(X_n, D_n, \bar{k}_n) = r_n(X_n, D_n, \bar{k}_n) + \bar{f}_{n-1}(t_n(X_n, D_n, \bar{k}_n)), \qquad 2 \leq n \leq N$$

and

$$Q_1(X_1, D_1, \bar{k}_1) = r_1(X_1, D_1, \bar{k}_1)$$

This yields a great computational saving. However, in a general stochastic optimization problem, replacing the random variables by their expectations will lead to erroneous results.

We used the composition operator "o" to combine stage returns in deriving the basic recursion equation for deterministic multistage optimization. However, this generality is not possible for stochastic optimization. The recursion equations still apply to maximizing the product of stage returns, but are not valid for maximizing the minimum individual stage return.

In the case of multiplication of stage returns, we have

$$R_N(X_N, \ldots, X_1, D_N, \ldots, D_1, k_N, \ldots, k_1) = \prod_{n=1}^{N} r_n(X_n, D_n, k_n)$$

subject to $X_{n-1} = t_n(X_n, D_n, k_n), \quad n = 1, \ldots, N$

Taking the expected value of the N-stage return yields

$$\bar{R}_N(X_N, \ldots, X_1, D_N, \ldots, D_1) = \sum_{k_N} \left[p_N(k_N) \; r_N(X_N, D_N, k_N) \sum_{k_{N-1}} \right.$$

$$\left[p_{N-1}(k_{N-1}) \; r_{N-1}(X_{N-1}, D_{N-1}, k_{N-1}) \cdots \sum_{k_1} [p_1(k_1) \; r_1(X_1, D_1, k_1)] \cdots \right] \right]$$

subject to $X_{n-1} = t_n(X_n, D_n, k_n), \quad n = 1, \ldots, N$

Following a derivation along the lines of the derivation just given for composition by addition, we obtain the recursion equations:

$$\bar{f}_n(X_n) = \max_{D_n} \sum_{k_n} p_n(k_n) \; Q_n(X_n, D_n, k_n), \quad 1 \leq n \leq N$$

where

$$Q_n(X_n, D_n, k_n) = r_n(X_n, D_n, k_n) \; \bar{f}_{n-1}(t_n(X_n, D_n, k_n)), \quad 2 \leq n \leq N$$

$$Q_1(X_1, D_1, k_1) = r_1(X_1, D_1, k_1)$$

Recall from Chapter II that in the case of composition by multiplication we need

$$r_n(X_n, D_n, k_n) \geq 0, \text{ for all } X_n, D_n, \text{ and } k_n, \quad n = 1, \ldots, N$$

for the recursive equations to yield a maximum.

When we maximize the minimum stage return, the expected return from two stages is

$$\bar{R}_2(X_2, X_1, D_2, D_1) =$$

$$\sum_{k_2} \sum_{k_1} p_2(k_2) \, p_1(k_1) \cdot \min \, (r_2(X_2, D_2, k_2), \, r_1(X_1, D_1, k_1))$$

subject to $X_1 = t_2(X_2, D_2, k_2)$

However, as

$$\bar{R}_2 \neq \sum_{k_2} p_2(k_2) \left[\min \left[r_2(X_2, D_2, k_2), \, \sum_{k_1} p_1(k_1) \, r_1(X_1, D_1, k_1) \right] \right]$$

decomposition is not possible.

The assumption of independent random variables can be removed. State variables are needed to account for the dependence. For a first degree dependence, assume the distribution of k_n is dependent on k_{n+1}, that is, the probability function of k_n is given by $p_n(k_n, k_{n+1})$ $n = 1, \ldots, N - 1$. The optimal return from n stages is a function of k_{n+1} as well as X_n. Mathematically

$$f_N(X_N) = \max_{D_N} \sum_{k_N} p_N(k_N) \; Q_N(X_N, D_N, k_N)$$

and

$$f_n(X_n, k_{n+1}) = \max_{D_n} \sum_{k_n} p_n(k_n, k_{n+1}) \; Q_n(X_n, D_n, k_n), \qquad 1 \leq n \leq N - 1$$

Each degree of dependence adds another state variable and makes the recursion equations more unwieldly. In the most general and worst case, k_n is dependent on $k_N, \ldots, k_{n+1}$. So the nth stage recursion equation has $N - n + 1$ state variables. Specifically,

$$f_n(X_n, k_N, \ldots, k_{n+1}) = \max_{D_n} \sum_{k_n} p_n(k_n, k_{n+1}, \ldots, k_N) Q_n(X_n, D_n, k_n)$$

This formulation with dependence among random variables anticipates the approach for adaptive optimization (Section 6). It is a repeating stochastic process in which information from the preceding stages generates the probability distribution for the next stochastic stage.

4. Markovian Decision Processes

Markovian decision processes constitute an important class of stochastic optimization problems. A first-order, time-invariant *Markov process* is a stochastic process in which the state of the system at any stage depends only on the state of the system at the previous stage and on known probabilities. We assume there are a finite number of states at each stage and a finite number of stages. The states at stage n are denoted by $i, i = 1, \ldots, M$, and $n = 1, \ldots, N$. The probability of transition from state i at stage n to state j at stage $n - 1$ is denoted by p_{ij}, independent of n. Thus p_{ij} is the probability of being in state j at stage $n - 1$, given that the state is i at stage n. This set of transition probabilities is conveniently represented by the transition matrix P,

$$
P = \begin{pmatrix}
p_{11} & \cdots & p_{1j} & \cdots & p_{1M} \\
\vdots & & \vdots & & \vdots \\
p_{i1} & \cdots & p_{ij} & \cdots & p_{iM} \\
\vdots & & \vdots & & \vdots \\
p_{M1} & \cdots & p_{Mj} & \cdots & p_{MM}
\end{pmatrix}
$$

The M rows and columns correspond to the M feasible states of the system. The elements in row i are the probabilities of transition to state j. Thus

$$0 \leq p_{ij} \leq 1 \quad \text{and} \quad \sum_j p_{ij} = 1$$

The probability of being in state j at stage $n - 1$ denoted by $\pi_{n-1}(j)$ is determined from multiplying the probability of being in state i at stage n ($\pi_n(i)$) by the transition probability p_{ij} and then summing over all states at stage n. Thus

$$\pi_{n-1}(j) = \sum_{i=1}^{M} p_{ij}\, \pi_n(i), \qquad j = 1, \ldots, M$$
$$n = 1, \ldots, N$$

The solution of this difference equation yields such results as the state probabilities after n transitions, as a function of the initial state, and the limiting state probabilities (if they exist) as n approaches infinity. The mathematical analysis of Markovian systems and their applications to the physical and social sciences is a subject in itself about which several books have been written. See, for example, Bharucha–Reid [15] and Kemeny and Snell [40].

In the analysis that follows no background in Markov processes, except the notion of transition probabilities, is required. In fact, in the way we use the transition probabilities it is not necessary to assume that they remain constant from stage to stage. We make this assumption for simplicity of notation and because it will be necessary to invoke it later, when we consider a Markov decision system with an infinite number of stages.

Howard [38] has introduced the notion of returns or rewards, as he prefers to call them, into a Markov process. Corresponding to the transition matrix P there is a return matrix R

$$R = \begin{pmatrix} r_{11} & \cdots & r_{1j} & \cdots & r_{1M} \\ \vdots & & \vdots & & \vdots \\ r_{i1} & \cdots & r_{ij} & \cdots & r_{iM} \\ \vdots & & \vdots & & \vdots \\ r_{M1} & \cdots & r_{Mj} & \cdots & r_{MM} \end{pmatrix}$$

which gives the return r_{ij} from a transition from state i to state j. The total expected return from an n-stage Markov process starting in state i, expressed recursively, is the expected value of the return from stage n plus the expected $(n - 1)$-stage return from the resulting state, summed over all states. Thus, for a one-stage process, we have

$$\bar{R}_1(i) = \sum_{j=1}^{M} p_{ij}\, r_{ij}$$

and for an n-stage process

$$\bar{R}_n(i) = \sum_{j=1}^{M} p_{ij}[r_{ij} + \bar{R}_{n-1}(j)] \qquad n = 2, \ldots, N$$

Decision making is introduced into the multistage Markovian model by permitting a choice among several transition and return matrices. A decision variable $d_n = k$, $k = 1, \ldots, K$ designates the choice of the kth transition matrix and kth return matrix at the nth stage. Or more specifically, if the system is in state i, $d_n = k$ means that the relevant transition probabilities and returns at stage n are the ith row of the kth transition matrix and the ith row of the kth return matrix. Generally, there is no need to assume that the same matrices are available for selection at each stage or that the transition and return matrices are chosen in pairs rather than separately. These assumptions are made only for simplicity. The probability of transition is denoted by $p_{ij}(d_n)$ and the return by $r_{ij}(d_n)$. The expected return from n stages, starting in state i, is then

$$\bar{R}_1(i, d_1) = \sum_{j=1}^{M} p_{ij}(d_1) \, r_{ij}(d_1)$$

and

$$\bar{R}_n(i, d_n, \ldots, d_1) = \sum_{j=1}^{M} p_{ij}(d_n)[r_{ij}(d_n) + \bar{R}_{n-1}(j, d_{n-1}, \ldots, d_1)]$$

$$n = 2, \ldots, N$$

This is just a variation of the multistage stochastic optimization models given in the previous section, in which the distribution of the random variable depends on the decision variable. We modified the notation because of the special characteristics of the Markovian decision model. Using the terminology of the previous section, we have:

1. the Markovian return matrix $r_{ij}(d_n) = r_n(X_n, D_n, k_n)$, and
2. the Markovian transition matrix $p_{ij}(d_n) = t_n(X_n, D_n, k_n)$, where in the Markovian model

   (a) the state variable X_n is represented by i, the state of the Markovian system at the nth stage;

   (b) the decision variable D_n is represented by $d_n = k$, $k = 1, \ldots, K$, and specifies the choice of particular transition and return matrices;

   (c) the random variable k_n is completely hidden in the new notation. It is a chance device which determines the output state j, given the input state and decision. The distribution of the random variable for the ith input state is given by the ith row of the transition matrix.

To maximize expected return from N stages as a function of the initial state, let

$$f_N(i) = \max_{d_N,\ldots,d_1} \sum_{j=1}^{M} p_{ij}(d_N) \, [r_{ij}(d_N) + \bar{R}_{N-1}(j, d_{N-1}, \ldots, d_1)]$$

Applying recursive optimization, we have

$$\bar{f}_1(i) = \max_{d_1=1,\ldots,K} \sum_{j=1}^{M} p_{ij}(d_1) \, r_{ij}(d_1)$$

and

$$\bar{f}_n(i) = \max_{d_n=1,\ldots,K} \sum_{j=1}^{M} p_{ij}(d_n) \, [r_{ij}(d_n) + \bar{f}_{n-1}(j)], \qquad n = 2, \ldots, N$$

The term $\sum_{j=1}^{M} p_{ij}(d_n) r_{ij}(d_n)$ is just the expected return from stage n, $n = 1$, $\ldots, N$, and is denoted by $q_i(d_n)$. With this change in notation, the recursive equations simplify to

$$\bar{f}_1(i) = \max_{d_1=1,\ldots,K} q_i(d_1), \quad i = 1, \ldots, M$$

and

$$\bar{f}_n(i) = \max_{d_n=1,\ldots,K} \left[q_i(d_n) + \sum_{j=1}^{M} p_{ij}(d_n) \, \bar{f}_{n-1}(j) \right], \quad i = 1, \ldots, M,$$

$$n = 2, \ldots, N$$

Howard [38] calls the solution of these recursive equations *value iteration*. From our present point of view, they are just an important special case of stochastic multistage optimization to be solved by using the usual computational methods of dynamic programming.

To illustrate the solution of Markovian decision processes by dynamic programming, consider the following simple example. There are two possible decisions at each stage. With $d_n = 1$,

$$P_1 = \begin{pmatrix} \frac{1}{2} & \frac{1}{2} \\ \frac{3}{4} & \frac{1}{4} \end{pmatrix} \quad \text{and} \quad R_1 = \begin{pmatrix} 0 & 6 \\ -3 & 8 \end{pmatrix}$$

and with $d_n = 2$,

$$P_2 = \begin{pmatrix} 1 & 0 \\ \frac{1}{2} & \frac{1}{2} \end{pmatrix} \quad \text{and} \quad R_2 = \begin{pmatrix} 2 & 4 \\ 1 & -1 \end{pmatrix}$$

The computations and solution are given in Tables 2, 3, 4, and 5 for four stages. Note after the first stage, the optimal decision from state one is $d_n = 2$, and the optimal decision from state two is $d_n = 1$, despite the fact that the immediate return from state one is higher with $d_n = 1$ and from state two is higher with $d_n = 2$. Had we extended the analysis to five stages or more, the same result would have been produced. This is not really very surprising. We might expect that with a small number of stages remaining, the optimal decisions would depend on both the state and stage number. But when there are a great number of stages remaining, the optimal decisions would be independent of the specific stage number. We also note a somewhat less intuitive result. With more than one stage remaining, the optimal expected return per stage is constant at two, regardless of the state. The example produced these phenomena, called *steady state* or *asymptotic behavior,* very rapidly, in fact in two stages.

Table 2   STAGE ONE

i	d_1	$q_i(d_1)$	$\bar{f}_1(i)$	$d_1(i)$
1	1	$\frac{1}{2}(0)\ \ +\frac{1}{2}(6)\ \ = 3$	3	1
	2	$1(2)\ \ +0(4)\ \ = 2$		
2	1	$\frac{3}{4}(-3)+\frac{1}{4}(8)\ \ = -\frac{1}{4}$		
	2	$\frac{1}{2}(1)\ \ +\frac{1}{2}(-1) = 0$	0	2

Table 3   STAGE TWO

i	d_2	$q_i(d_2) + \sum_{j=1}^{2} p_{ij}(d_2)\bar{f}_1(j)$	$\bar{f}_2(i)$	$d_2(i)$
1	1	$3 + \frac{1}{2}(3) + \frac{1}{2}(0) = 4.5$		
	2	$2 + 1(3) + 0(0) = 5$	5	2
2	1	$-\frac{1}{4} + \frac{3}{4}(3) + \frac{1}{4}(0) = 2$	2	1
	2	$0 + \frac{1}{2}(3) + \frac{1}{2}(0) = 1.5$		

Table 4   STAGE THREE

i	d_3	$q_i(d_3) + \sum_{j=1}^{2} p_{ij}(d_3)\bar{f}_2(j)$	$\bar{f}_3(i)$	$d_3(i)$
1	1	$3 + \frac{1}{2}(5) + \frac{1}{2}(2) = 6.5$		
	2	$2 + 1(5) + 0(2) = 7$	7	2
2	1	$-\frac{1}{4} + \frac{3}{4}(5) + \frac{1}{4}(2) = 4$	4	1
	2	$0 + \frac{1}{2}(5) + \frac{1}{2}(2) = 3.5$		

Table 5   STAGE FOUR

i	d_4	$q_i(d_4) + \sum_{j=1}^{2} p_{ij}(d_4)\bar{f}_3(j)$	$\bar{f}_4(i)$	$d_4(i)$
1.	1	$3 + \frac{1}{2}(7) + \frac{1}{2}(4) = 8.5$		
	2	$2 + 1(7) + 0(4) = 9$	9	2
2	1	$-\frac{1}{4} + \frac{3}{4}(7) + \frac{1}{4}(4) = 6$	6	1
	2	$0 + \frac{1}{2}(7) + \frac{1}{2}(4) = 5.5$		

We shall investigate the intricacies of steady state behavior in multistage systems in Chapter VII.

5. A Variable Stage Stochastic Problem

The gambler is always faced with the dilemma—given the amount of his winnings (losses) at a certain stage of a game, should he press his luck further or be content with his present lot, and quit? The following is typical of this kind of problem. A number x is drawn from a density function $p(x)$. The player may choose to keep a monetary (utility) reward of x or draw again to attempt to get a higher return. After each turn, the player can decide to stop or draw again, but if he stops, he receives a return equal to the number obtained on the last draw. *A priori*, the maximum number of draws permitted is fixed at N. Thus at each stage of the game, the player always knows the maximum number of draws remaining n, $1 \leq n \leq N$. The number drawn when there are $n + 1$ draws remaining is x_n. Thus x_{N-1} is the first number drawn, and x_n the $(N - n)$th number drawn, if we choose to draw that many times. There are simply two alternatives at each stage—stop or draw. Clearly the choice between these two depends on n, x_n, and $p(x)$.

With $n = 1$ if we stop, the return is x_1, and if we draw, the expected return is the mean of the distribution, that is,

$$\int_{-\infty}^{\infty} xp(x)dx = a_1$$

Hence, if $a_1 \geq x_1$, the optimal decision is to draw, and if $a_1 \leq x_1$, the optimal decision is to stop. The optimal one-stage, expected return is

$$\bar{f}_1(x_1) = \max\ (x_1, a_1)$$

If there are two stages remaining, the decision to stop leads to a return of x_2. Assuming that we choose to draw a number x_1, and then follow an optimal policy after the draw, the expected return is

$$\int_{-\infty}^{\infty} \bar{f}_1(x_1)p(x)\, dx = \int_{a_1}^{\infty} xp(x)\, dx + a_1 \int_{-\infty}^{a_1} p(x)\, dx = a_2$$

Thus

$$\bar{f}_2(x_2) = \max\,(x_2, a_2)$$

In general with n stages remaining,

$$\bar{f}_n(x_n) = \max\,(x_n, a_n), \qquad a_n = \int_{a_{n-1}}^{\infty} xp(x)\, dx + a_{n-1} \int_{-\infty}^{a_{n-1}} p(x)\, dx$$

If $a_n \geq x_n$, the optimal decision is to draw, and if $a_n \leq x_n$, we should stop.

Assume that $p(x)$ is such that the probabilities of drawing any real numbers between α and β are equal. This is known as the uniform distribution

$$p(x) = \frac{1}{\beta - \alpha}, \quad \alpha \leq x \leq \beta$$

For the sake of simplicity, let $\alpha = 0$, and $\beta = 1$, so $p(x) = 1$, $0 \leq x \leq 1$.

To restate the problem, given a number x_N between zero and one, should we accept a return of x_N or draw at least once, but no more than N times, from a uniform distribution to try to get a higher return? Following an optimal policy, if $a_N \geq x_N$, we should draw, and if $a_N \leq x_N$, we should stop. The sequence $(a_1, \ldots, a_N)$ is computed as

$$a_1 = \int_0^1 x\, dx = \tfrac{1}{2}$$

and for $n \geq 2$,

$$a_n = \int_{a_{n-1}}^1 x_{n-1}\, dx + a_{n-1} \int_0^{a_{n-1}} dx = \frac{1 - a_{n-1}^2}{2} + a_{n-1}^2 = \frac{1 + a_{n-1}^2}{2}$$

As is expected from intuition, the limiting value of the sequence is one. That is

$$\lim_{n \to \infty} a_n = a = \lim_{n \to \infty} \frac{1 + a_{n-1}^2}{2} = \frac{1 + a^2}{2}$$

or $a^2 - 2a + 1 = 0$, which is satisfied only by $a = 1$. The asymptotic ascent to one is rather slow, as can be seen from the first 10 values of the sequence given in Table 6.

Having had all the information about the probability distribution, we were able to determine an optimal policy. Suppose, however, in the example given, that the endpoints of the uniform distribution were unknown. What would constitute an optimal policy in this case? This is an intriguing problem. The theory needed to solve it is given in Section 6.

Table 6

n	1	2	3	4	5
a_n	.500	.625	.695	.742	.755

n	6	7	8	9	10
a_n	.800	.820	.836	.849	.860

6. Uncertainty and Adaptive Optimization

Under uncertainty there is complete ignorance of the probabilities attached to each outcome. This precludes the possibility of computing an expected value or, in fact, combining the returns from each outcome in any universally acceptable way. Several criteria have been proposed, such as choosing the alternative maximizing the minimum possible return (Wald maxmin). This is conservative. As an alternative, we could consider both the minimum and maximum return from each alternative and then weight these two by a coefficient of optimism (Hurwicz criterion). Adopting an entirely different point of view, Savage proposed the minimization of maximum regret. Regret is the loss of utility resulting from not choosing the alternative maximizing return, had the uncertainty been removed. Historically, the first criterion suggested is based on the "principle of insufficient reason." This asserts that, under complete ignorance, we assign each outcome equal probability. For a critical analysis of these various proposals, see Luce and Raiffa [45]. They show that different criteria can lead to different decisions. In fact, there can even be a complete reversal of order of preference among decisions. To judge the merits and liabilities rationally, they give a set of requirements that should be met by a universally satisfactory criterion. Unfortunately, not one of the criteria proposed meets all of the requirements.

It has been said that decision making under uncertainty does not exist. The reason is based on the assumption that it is impossible to delineate the problem meticulously enough to know all decision policies and returns and yet be completely ignorant of the probabilities. Whether this is generally true is not of great concern to us. However, any information about the probabilities, no matter how sparse, destroys the assumption of complete ignorance.

The result of tossing a coin four times and obtaining two heads is not very strong evidence for judging the coin "fair." Nevertheless, it is evidence from which some assertions can be made. We know the coin is not two-headed or two-tailed. Furthermore, with some degree of confidence, we can assert that the probability of heads on one toss is between 0.1 and 0.9. Further experimentation would, of course, narrow the confidence interval or increase the confidence of a given interval. Having made four tosses, we can no longer assume complete ignorance about the probabilities. By doing so, we would ignore relevant evidence.

Adaptive optimization is based on this idea—specifically adapting a problem of decision making under uncertainty into one of risk, by estimating the probabilities from evidence obtained from prior results. This can only be done for a sequential decision process. Therefore it is not surprising that dynamic programming is an appropriate approach to adaptive optimization.

We shall briefly develop the role of dynamic programming in adaptive optimization. Except for one example, the related problem of statistical estimation will not be discussed. A more complete discussion of dynamic programming in adaptive optimization is contained in Bellman's *Adaptive Control Processes* [12].

Consider a multistage optimization problem under uncertainty which can be represented by the recursion equations

$$\bar{f}_n(X_n) = \max_{D_n} \sum_{k_n} p_n(k_n) Q_n(X_n, D_n, k_n), \quad 1 \leq n \leq N$$

where

$$Q_n(X_n, D_n, k_n) = r_n(X_n, D_n, k_n) + \bar{f}_{n-1}(t_n(X_n, D_n, k_n)), \quad 2 \leq n \leq N$$

and

$$Q_1(X_1, D_1, k_1) = r_1(X_1, D_1, k_1)$$

The uncertainty exists because the $p_n(k_n)$ are unknown for some or all of the random variables k_n, $n = 1, \ldots, N$. Now suppose, just as in the coin-tossing problem, that as the sequential process unfolds from stage N onward, the values for the random variables already known can be used to estimate probabilities for the random variables at subsequent stages. In the most uncertain circumstances the distribution functions are entirely unknown. However, uncertainty exists even if the form of the distribution function is known, but some or all of the values of the parameters are unknown. For example, k_n may be normally distributed with unknown mean and variance. In the following discussion we assume that k_n, $n = 1$, $\ldots, N$ are identically and independently distributed random variables.

When only the parameters of the distribution function are unknown, past observations of the random variables can be used to generate statistical estimates for the parameters. Let the density function of k_n be given by

$$p_n(k_n) = p(k_n, \theta_1, \ldots, \theta_m), \qquad n = 1, \ldots, N$$

where $\theta_1, \ldots, \theta_m$ are unknown parameters. Returning to recursive equations, we define the optimal adaptive n-stage return as

$$\bar{f}_n(X_n, \theta_1, \ldots, \theta_m) = \max_{D_n} \sum_{k_n} p_n(k_n) \, Q_n(X_n, D_n, k_n, \theta_1, \ldots, \theta_m),$$

$$1 \leq n \leq N$$

where

$$Q_n(X_n, D_n, k_n, \theta_1, \ldots, \theta_m) = r_n(X_n, D_n, k_n, \theta_1, \ldots, \theta_m)$$

$$+ \, \bar{f}_{n-1}(t_n(X_n, D_n, k_n), \theta_1, \ldots, \theta_m), \qquad 2 \leq n \leq N$$

and $\quad Q_1(X_1, D_1, k_1, \theta_1, \ldots, \theta_m) = r_1(X_1, D_1, k_1, \theta_1, \ldots, \theta_m)$

The sequence of optimal return and decision functions $\bar{f}_n(X_n, \theta_1, \ldots, \theta_m)$ and $D_n(X_n, \theta_1, \ldots, \theta_m)$ is calculated for all feasible values of X_n and $\theta_1, \ldots, \theta_m$.

The adaptive scheme works as follows: suppose we are at stage n in the sequential process, so that $k_N, \ldots, k_{n+1}$ have been observed. Then estimates

$$\theta_{in} = \theta_i(k_N, \ldots, k_{n+1}), \qquad i = 1, \ldots, m$$

are made for the unknown parameters. Substituting the estimates (θ_{in}, $\ldots, \theta_{mn}$) into $D_n(X_n, \theta_1, \ldots, \theta_m)$ yields the optimal adaptive nth stage decision. Subsequently, k_n is observed, and our parameter estimates are revised to

$$\theta_{i,n-1} = \theta_i(k_N, \ldots, k_{n+1}, k_n) = \theta_i(\theta_{in}, k_n)$$

so that $D_{n-1}(X_{n-1}, \theta_1, \ldots, \theta_m)$ is determined using the most up-to-date information available. As the sequential process unfolds, new evidence is continually keeping the estimates current. Because the whole sequence $D_n(X_n, \theta_1, \ldots, \theta_m)$ is calculated *a priori* for all feasible values of the argument, the optimal decisions are available as soon as the estimates are revised. However, we do not achieve this without cost. There is an m-fold increase in state variable dimensionality, an additional state variable for each of the m unknown parameters of the distribution. Fortunately, many common and useful statistical distributions, such as the normal, Poisson, and uniform distributions, contain only one, two, or at most three parameters.

The basic idea of adaptive optimization is the same when the distribution function is entirely unknown, but the procedure of estimation generally causes a much greater increase in state variable dimensionality.

Assume that k_n is a discrete random variable with values $1, \ldots, j, \ldots, J$. Let the frequency of occurrence of outcome j, after $k_N, \ldots, k_{n+1}$ have been observed, be m_{jn}. Note that m_{jn} is an integer between 0 and $N - n$ inclusive and $\sum_{j=1}^{J} m_{jn} = N - n$. Then estimates based on relative frequencies for $p_n(k_n = j)$ are given by

$$\bar{p}_n(k_n = j) = \frac{m_{jn}}{N - n}, \qquad j = 1, \ldots, J$$

These estimates are the relative frequencies of occurrence. After k_n is observed, the estimates are revised to

$$m_{j,n-1} = m_{jn}, \text{ if } k_n \neq j$$

$$m_{j,n-1} = m_{jn} + 1, \text{ if } k_n = j$$

and

$$\bar{p}_{n-1}(k_{n-1} = j) = \frac{m_{j,n-1}}{N - n + 1}, \qquad j = 1, \ldots, J$$

Since $\sum_{j=1}^{J} m_{jn} = N - n$, $n = 1, \ldots, N$, $J - 1$ of the estimates m_{jn} are sufficient to characterize the distribution. The recursion equations are

$$f_n(X_n, m_{1n}, \ldots, m_{J-1,n})$$
$$= \max_{D_n} \sum_{k_n} \bar{p}_n(k_n = j) \, Q_n(X_n, D_n, k_n, m_{1n}, \ldots, m_{J-1,n}),$$
$$1 \leq n \leq N$$

where

$$Q_n(X_n, D_n, k_n, m_{1n}, \ldots, m_{J-1,n}) =$$
$$= r_n(X_n, D_n, k_n) + f_{n-1}(t_n(X_n, D_n, k_n, m_{1n}, \ldots, m_{J-1,n})$$

and

$$Q_1(X_1, D_1, k_1, m_{11}, \ldots, m_{J-1,1}) = r_1(X_1, D_1, k_1, m_{11}, \ldots, m_{J-1,1})$$

The sequence of optimal return and decision functions

$$f_n(X_n, m_{1n}, \ldots, m_{J-1,n}) \quad \text{and} \quad D_n(X_n, m_{1n}, \ldots, m_{J-1,n})$$

is calculated for all feasible values of X_n and $m_{1n}, \ldots, m_{J-1,n}$. Then as the process unfolds, given $k_N, \ldots, k_{n+1}$, we can calculate $m_{1n}, \ldots, m_{J-1,n}$, and thus determine f_n and D_n.

We might expect that, generally, the $J - 1$ values of k_n would be much larger than m, the number of unknown parameters. Thus there is usually a much larger increase in dimensionality when the form of the distribution is unknown.

7. Gambling with Unknown Probabilities—An Example of Adaptive Optimization

We return to the problem of drawing numbers from a uniform distribution

$$p(x) = \frac{1}{\beta - \alpha}, \qquad \alpha \leq x \leq \beta$$

with the previous rules except that, in this case, α and β are unknown. In this problem a sequence of numbers is drawn from the distribution. After each draw the participant has the option of terminating play and receiving a return equal to the number obtained on the last draw (x_n), or continuing play with the possibility of drawing up to n more times.

When α and β are known, the optimal solution is to stop when $x_n \geq a_n$, and to draw when $x_n \leq a_n$, where the sequence a_n is given by

$$a_1 = \frac{\alpha + \beta}{2}$$

and
$$a_n = \frac{1}{\beta - \alpha} \left[\int_{a_{n-1}}^{\beta} x_{n-1}\, dx + a_{n-1} \int_{\alpha}^{a_{n-1}} dx \right],$$

$$= \frac{\beta^2 + a_{n-1}^2 - 2\alpha a_{n-1}}{2(\beta - \alpha)} \qquad n \geq 2$$

The optimal expected return is given by

$$f_n(x_n) = \max\ (x_n, a_n)$$

To treat adaptively the case when α and β are unknown, we estimate values of α and β from the numbers obtained on previous draws. There are several methods of estimation. In the example, the method of moments is used.[†] The mean of the uniform distribution (μ) is

$$\mu = \frac{1}{\beta - \alpha} \int_{\alpha}^{\beta} x\, dx = \frac{\alpha + \beta}{2}$$

and the variance (σ^2) is

$$\sigma^2 = \frac{1}{\beta - \alpha} \int_{\alpha}^{\beta} x^2\, dx - \mu^2 = \frac{(\beta - \alpha)^2}{12}$$

Solving for α and β in terms of μ and σ^2, we obtain

$$\alpha = \mu - \sqrt{3\sigma^2}$$

and
$$\beta = \mu + \sqrt{3\sigma^2}$$

[†] We make no claim that this estimation procedure is optimal, or even preferable to, say, maximum likelihood estimators. It is used simply for illustrative purposes.

Estimates for α and β ($\bar{\alpha}$ and $\bar{\beta}$) are obtained by substituting statistical estimates for μ and σ^2 ($\bar{x}$ and s^2) into the expression just given. Generally, appropriate estimates for the mean and variance of a distribution $p(x)$ from which m observations $(x_1, \ldots, x_m)$ have been made are

$$\bar{x} = \frac{1}{m} \sum_{i=1}^{m} x_i$$

and

$$s^2 = \frac{1}{m-1} \left[\sum_{i=1}^{m} x_i^2 - m\bar{x}^2 \right]$$

Thus after having drawn $N - n$ times from the uniform distribution, that is, with n draws remaining,

$$\bar{x}_n = \frac{1}{N-n} \sum_{i=n}^{N-1} x_i$$

and

$$s_n^2 = \frac{1}{N-n-1} \left[\sum_{i=n}^{N-1} x_i^2 - (N-n)\bar{x}_n^2 \right]$$

Substituting these estimators into the equations for α and β, we obtain

$$\bar{\alpha}_n = \frac{u_n}{N-n} - \left[\frac{3}{N-n-1} \left(v_n - \frac{u_n^2}{N-n} \right) \right]^{1/2}$$

and

$$\bar{\beta}_n = \frac{u_n}{N-n} + \left[\frac{3}{N-n-1} \left(v_n - \frac{u_n^2}{N-n} \right) \right]^{1/2}$$

where

$$u_n = \sum_{i=n}^{N-1} x_i \quad \text{and} \quad v_n = \sum_{i=n}^{N-1} x_i^2$$

The sequential updating of the estimates $\bar{\alpha}_n$ and $\bar{\beta}_n$ to $\bar{\alpha}_{n-1}$ and $\bar{\beta}_{n-1}$ is achieved by replacing n by $n - 1$ in the estimates just given, where

$$u_{n-1} = u_n + x_{n-1} \quad \text{and} \quad v_{n-1} = v_n + x_{n-1}^2$$

Having found the appropriate estimators, we adapt the optimal policy under uncertainty to an optimal policy under risk. The optimal decision policy is: if $x_n \geq \bar{a}_n$, stop, and if $x_n \leq \bar{a}_n$, draw. The sequence $\{\bar{a}_n\}$ is given by

$$\bar{a}_1 = \frac{\bar{\alpha}_1 + \bar{\beta}_1}{2} = \frac{\displaystyle\sum_{n=1}^{N-1} x_n}{N-1}$$

and

$$\bar{a}_n = \frac{\bar{\beta}_n^2 + \bar{a}_{n-1}^2 - 2\bar{\alpha}_n \bar{a}_{n-1}}{2(\bar{\beta}_n - \bar{\alpha}_n)}$$

So with one draw remaining, we have the intuitively reasonable decision rule—if the average of all past draws is greater than the most recent draw, draw again; and if the most recent draw exceeds the average of all past draws, stop. The remaining members of the sequence are not readily computable in closed form so they must be tabulated for all feasible values of $\bar{\alpha}_n$ and $\bar{\beta}_n$, $n = 2, \ldots, N$. When we are computing $\bar{a}_n$ from the difference equation just given, the values of $\bar{\alpha}_n$ and $\bar{\beta}_n$ are used to determine $\bar{a}_1, \ldots, \bar{a}_{n-1}$.

To illustrate just one of these calculations, suppose $N = 10$, $u_3 = 4.10$, $v_3 = 2.67$, and $x_2 = 0.70$. There is a maximum of two draws remaining. To determine whether we should draw again, we first calculate u_2 and v_2;

$$u_2 = 4.10 + 0.70 = 4.80$$

$$v_2 = 2.67 + (0.70)^2 = 3.16$$

These values are used to calculate $\bar{\alpha}_2$ and $\bar{\beta}_2$, that is,

$$\bar{\alpha}_2 = \frac{4.80}{8} - \left[\frac{3}{7} \left(3.16 - \frac{4.80^2}{8} \right) \right]^{\frac{1}{2}} = 0.25$$

and $$\bar{\beta}_2 = \frac{4.80}{8} + \left[\frac{3}{7} \left(3.16 - \frac{4.80^2}{8} \right) \right]^{\frac{1}{2}} = 0.95$$

Hence $$\bar{a}_1 = \frac{0.95 + 0.25}{2} = 0.60$$

which leads to

$$\bar{a}_2 = \frac{(0.95)^2 + (0.60)^2 - 2(0.25)\,0.60}{2(0.95 - 0.25)} = 0.6875$$

Since the expected return from drawing is less than 0.70, the optimal solution is to stop. We calculated $\bar{a}_2$ for one value of the state variables $(x_2, \bar{\alpha}_2, \bar{\beta}_2)$. Generally $\bar{a}_2$ would have to be calculated for all feasible combinations of these three state variables, if a complete policy were to be available *a priori*.

8. Two-Person, Zero-Sum Games

We consider competitive problems where there are two decision makers whose objectives are diametrically opposed. Specifically, the situation in a two-person, zero-sum game is:

1. there are two players (decision makers) designated P_A and P_B.
2. P_A has m alternative decisions, $i = 1, \ldots, m$.
3. P_B has n alternative decisions, $j = 1, \ldots, n$.
4. A play of the game occurs when each player chooses an alternative simultaneously.
5. As a result of the play (i, j), there is a payment of a_{ij} from P_B to P_A

or equivalently, a payment of $(-a_{ij})$ from P_A to P_B. The game is called zero-sum because the total payment to both players is always zero.

The information for a two-person, zero-sum game can be summarized in a payoff matrix as shown in Table 7. The element a_{ij} represents the payoff to P_A (payment by P_B) when P_A chooses his ith alternative and P_B chooses his jth alternative.

Each player's objective is to maximize his payoff. Obviously, P_A's and P_B's objectives are in direct conflict. To express the objective mathematically, let $X = (x_1, x_2, \ldots, x_m)$ correspond to the probabilities that P_A will

Table 7   GENERAL PAYOFF MATRIX FOR A TWO-PERSON, ZERO-SUM GAME

		P_B			
		1	2	j	n
	1	a_{11}	a_{12} $\cdot$ $\cdot$	$\cdot$ a_{1j} $\cdot$	$\cdot$ $\cdot$ a_{1n}
	2	a_{21}	a_{22} $\cdot$ $\cdot$	$\cdot$ a_{2j} $\cdot$	$\cdot$ $\cdot$ a_{2n}
	.	.	.	.	.
	.	.	.	.	.
P_A	.	.	.	.	.
	i	a_{i1}	a_{i2}	a_{ij}	a_{in}
	.	.	.	.	.
	.	.	.	.	.
	.	.	.	.	.
	m	a_{m1}	a_{m2}	a_{mj}	a_{mn}

use alternatives $(1, 2, \ldots, m)$ respectively, and $Y = (y_1, y_2, \ldots, y_n)$ correspond to the probabilities that P_B will use alternatives $(1, 2, \ldots, n)$ respectively. The vectors X and Y, which satisfy the properties

$$x_i \geq 0, \qquad \sum_{i=1}^{m} x_i = 1$$

$$y_j \geq 0, \qquad \sum_{j=1}^{n} y_j = 1$$

are called strategies for P_A and P_B since they provide prescriptions for how to play. In the situation $x_k = 1$, $x_i = 0$ for $i \neq k$, P_A is certain to choose alternative k, and his strategy is called a pure strategy. Generally, however, it will be to a player's advantage to use a mixed strategy, one in which alternatives $(1, \ldots, m)$ are chosen by a chance device with corresponding probabilities $(x_1, \ldots, x_m)$.

Given the strategies X and Y, the expected value from a play of the game is

$$E(X, Y) = \sum_i \sum_j a_{ij} x_i y_j$$

P_A's objective is to maximize $E(X, Y)$ while simultaneously P_B attempts to choose a strategy that will minimize $E(X, Y)$. Combining these two opposite positions we see that optimal strategies, X^* and Y^*, are defined by the relations

$$E(X, Y^*) \leq E(X^*, Y^*) \leq E(X^*, Y)$$

where $E(X^*, Y^*) = V$ is called the value of the game.

The interpretation of these inequalities is that an optimal strategy for P_A will produce an expected payoff to P_A at least equal to the value of the game. If P_B does not use an optimal strategy, the payoff to P_A may be greater. Similarly if P_B uses an optimal strategy, his expected payment is certain to be no more than V. Thus if both players use optimal strategies, the expected payoff to P_A will be V.

The fundamental theorem of two-person, zero-sum games states the existence of an optimal solution (X^*, Y^*) (of which there may be more than one) and a unique value V, given by

$$\max_X \min_Y E(X, Y) = \min_Y \max_X E(X, Y) = E(X^*, Y^*) = V$$

Necessary and sufficient conditions for V to be the value of the game and for (X^*, Y^*) to be optimal strategies are

$$E(X_P, Y^*) \leq V \leq E(X^*, Y_P)$$

where X_P, Y_P denote all pure strategies for P_A and P_B respectively. In some cases, there are pure strategies (X^*, Y^*) which satisfy the necessary and sufficient conditions. A game with this property is known as a *saddle-point* game. A saddle point is an element of the payoff matrix which is both minimum in its row and maximum in its column, or if a_{pq} is a saddle point

$$V = a_{pq} = \max_i \min_j a_{ij} = \min_j \max_i a_{ij}$$

The pure strategies $(x_p = 1, y_q = 1)$ are optimal if and only if a_{pq} is a saddle point. Thus if a game has no saddle point, the optimal strategies will be mixed.

In the payoff matrix of Table 8, $a_{12} = 2$ is a saddle point, so $V = 2$, $X^* = (1, 0, 0)$ and $Y^* = (0, 1, 0)$. On the other hand, the game of Table 9 has no saddle point, so we must apply the necessary and sufficient conditions directly to find an optimal solution.

Table 8   A SADDLE-POINT GAME

		P_B		
		1	2	3
	1	3	2	3
P_A	2	6	1	2
	3	−1	0	4

Table 9   A GAME WITHOUT A SADDLE POINT

		P_B	
		1	2
	1	−2	3
P_A	2	1	−2

Applying the conditions we obtain

$$-2x_1 + x_2 \geq V \qquad\qquad -2y_1 + 3y_2 \leq V$$

$$3x_1 - 2x_2 \geq V \qquad\qquad y_1 - 2y_2 \leq V$$

$$x_1 + x_2 = 1 \qquad\qquad y_1 + y_2 = 1$$

$$x_1, x_2 \geq 0 \qquad\qquad y_1, y_2 \geq 0$$

The unique solution is $V = -\frac{1}{8}$, $X^* = (\frac{3}{8}, \frac{5}{8})$ and $Y^* = (\frac{5}{8}, \frac{3}{8})$.

In the general case, where P_A has m alternatives and P_B has n alternatives, the necessary and sufficient conditions yield $m + n$ inequality constraints, $m + n$ nonnegativity constraints, and two equality constraints in $m + n + 1$ variables. For large m and n, finding an optimal solution is a cumbersome computational problem. Transforming the game into a linear program is perhaps the easiest method of solution.

There is an extensive literature on two-person, zero-sum games. Three outstanding books are Luce and Raiffa [45], McKinsey [49], and Von Neumann and Morgenstern [64].

9. Games in Extensive Form

Our particular interest is in games in which each player has more than one move before a payoff occurs. These are called games in *extensive form*. A graphical representation or "tree" of a particular game in extensive form is shown in Figure 2. Once again the game is two-person, zero-sum, but in this game each player has two moves before a payoff occurs. The tree specifies the rules of the game.

Starting at the bottom of the tree, P_A moves first and chooses the number 1 or 2. At the next move P_B chooses the number 1 or 2. We must indicate whether P_B, upon making his first move, is aware of player A's first move. This is done by enclosing points on the tree which are indistinguishable because of ignorance of past moves. Thus, in Figure 2, P_B makes his first move, in ignorance of P_A's first move. Naturally, this corresponds to the two players making their first moves simultaneously. At move 3, P_A makes his second move by choosing the number 1 or 2, after having been informed of P_B's first move and remembering his own first move. The final move is made by P_B choosing the number 1 or 2, knowing his own and P_A's first move but not P_A's second move. The numbers at the top of the tree are the payoffs to P_A. For example, the sequence of moves $(1, 2, 2, 2)$ yields a payoff of 10 to P_A.

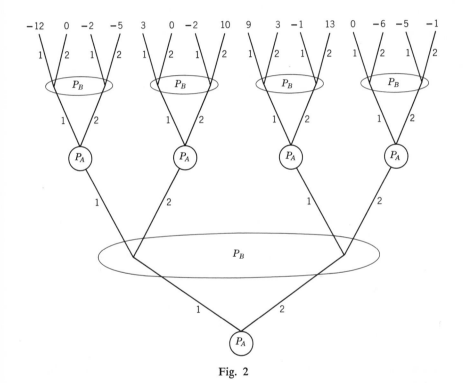

Fig. 2

By defining a pure strategy as a complete set of rules specifying the alternatives to be chosen under all circumstances, we are able to *normalize* a game in extensive form, that is, put it into the two-person, zero-sum form in which each player essentially makes only one move. Unfortunately, normalization generally leads to a large number of pure strategies. For example, in the game just given, a pure strategy for P_A is given by the ordered triplet $u = (u_1, u_2, u_3)$, where $u_1 = 1, 2$ denotes his choice on the first move; $u_2 = 1, 2$ denotes his choice on his second move, given that P_B's first move is 1; and $u_3 = 1, 2$ denotes his second move given P_B's first move is 2. In all there are $2^3 = 8$ pure strategies for P_A. The particular strategy $u = (1, 2, 1)$ indicates that P_A's first move is 1 and his second move is 2 if P_B's first move is 1, and 1 if P_B's first move is 2. Pure strategies are defined similarly for P_B, and are denoted by $v = (v_1, v_2, v_3)$. P_B's first move is given by v_1 and his second move by v_2 or v_3, where v_2 stands for his second move when P_A's first move is 1, and v_3 for his second move when P_A's first move is 2. Having enumerated all of the strategies, we are able to construct a payoff matrix in normal form, as shown in Table 10.

Table 10   PAYOFF MATRIX FOR EXAMPLE OF FIGURE 2

u_1, u_2, u_3	v_1, v_2, v_3							
	111	112	121	122	211	212	221	222
111	-12	-12	0	0	3	3	0	0
112	-12	-12	0	0	-2	-2	10	10
121	-2	-2	-5	-5	3	3	0	0
122	-2	-2	-5	-5	-2	-2	10	10
211	9	3	9	3	0	-6	0	-6
212	9	3	9	3	-5	-1	-5	-1
221	-1	13	-1	13	0	-6	0	-6
222	-1	13	-1	13	-5	-1	-5	-1

The game can now be solved using the necessary and sufficient conditions for two-person, zero-sum games. This would be formidable using manual computations. Even if a computer were available, games with several moves would become unmanageable. In a game where each player has N moves and two choices for each move, there are $2^{2^N - 1}$ pure strategies for each player. Consequently, there is an astronomical increase in the number of pure strategies with N, for example, with $N = 5$, each player has more than 10^9 pure strategies. Fortunately recursive procedures make it possible for us to overcome these computational difficulties.

The game of Figure 2 can be looked upon as two interdependent sequential games. In the first game, in which each player makes one move simultaneously, there is no direct payoff but an advancement to a higher point on the tree from which a second game is initiated. The first two moves (one by each player) are designated to take place at stage two, and the last two at stage one. The results from stage two specify which game is to be played at stage one. The results at stage one yield the payoffs. The four possible games that can be played at stage one correspond to the four combinations of moves at stage two, as shown in Table 11.

Table 11   STAGE ONE GAMES

Stage Two: (1, 1)				Stage Two: (1, 2)		
	P_B				P_B	
P_A	1	2		P_A	1	2
1	−12	0		1	3	0
2	−2	−5		2	−2	10

Stage Two: (2, 1)				Stage Two: (2, 2)		
	P_B				P_B	
P_A	1	2		P_A	1	2
1	9	3		1	0	−6
2	−1	13		2	−5	−1

Let the (i, j)th game at stage one be the game played at stage one if P_A and P_B use alternatives i and j at stage two, and let its corresponding value be $V_1(i, j)$ with optimal strategies $X_1^*(i, j)$ and $Y_1^*(i, j)$. It is clear that if i and j were the moves at stage two, $X_1^*(i, j)$ and $Y_1^*(i, j)$ are the optimal strategies at stage one, and the expected value of the entire game to player A is $V_1(i, j)$. Hence the optimal value for the entire game may be found by solving the second-stage game with payoffs $a_{ij} = V_1(i, j)$. The optimal second-stage strategies X_2^*, Y_2^* are the strategies found by solving this game.

Returning to the illustration, we find the optimal payoffs and decisions at stage one to be those shown in Table 12.

Table 12

	j	
i	1	2
1	$V_1 = -4$ $X_1^* = (\frac{1}{5}, \frac{4}{5})$ $Y_1^* = (\frac{1}{3}, \frac{2}{3})$	$V_1 = 2$ $X_1^* = (\frac{4}{5}, \frac{1}{5})$ $Y_1^* = (\frac{2}{3}, \frac{1}{3})$
2	$V_1 = 6$ $X_1^* = (\frac{7}{10}, \frac{3}{10})$ $Y_1^* = (\frac{1}{2}, \frac{1}{2})$	$V_1 = -3$ $X_1^* = (\frac{2}{5}, \frac{3}{5})$ $Y_1^* = (\frac{1}{2}, \frac{1}{2})$

Using the values from the stage-one games, we obtain the payoff matrix for the stage-two game, given in Table 13.

Table 13

		P_B	
P_A	1		2
1	−4		2
2	6		−3

The solution $V_2 = 0$, $X_2^* = (\frac{3}{5}, \frac{2}{5})$, $Y_2^* = (\frac{1}{3}, \frac{2}{3})$ says that the value for the entire game is zero; at stage two, which is the first play, P_A should choose alternative 1 with probability $\frac{3}{5}$ while P_B chooses alternative 1 with probability $\frac{1}{3}$. After making the first moves, the resulting position is established, and Table 12 is used to establish the optimal one-stage strategies.

Although we restricted ourselves to a two-stage problem, the principle of solving a sequence of games applies to any number of stages. The greater the number of stages, the greater the computational advantage of recursive analysis.

The type of strategies we determined are called *behavioral* strategies by game theorists. Behavioral strategies specify a way of playing from each point of the game tree. Strategies determined from the normalized form of the game specify a complete strategy for the entire game. Generally, far fewer variables have to be determined to establish an optimal behavioral strategy. Kuhn [43] has shown that it is sufficient to consider behavorial strategies so long as a player remembers all of his prior moves when making his present move. This is not to infer that optimal behavioral strategies are always easier to determine or that recursive analysis can always be used to find them. A great deal depends upon the rules of the game, particularly with respect to the knowledge a player has of past moves when making his present move. We have considered only the case of two moves made simultaneously, after which both players are informed of the other players' move. By modifying the game of Figure 2, such that each player did not know the other player's first move when making his own second move, we find that it would have been more difficult to determine optimal behavioral strategies by recursive analysis. Moreover, it would have been easier to solve the game in normalized form.

There are other applications of recursive analysis in game theory. One interesting problem concerns a single-stage game (that is, a payoff is made after each play) being played repetitively, in which each player begins with only a finite sum of money. Surprisingly enough, the simple theory ignores this basic assumption, and in attempting to maximize expected value, neglects the possibility that a player may go broke at some stage of the game. To incorporate the element of survival into the game, we must determine optimal strategies as a function of the amount of capital the player has. Bellman [12] studies this type of game from a dynamic programming point of view.

EXERCISES

1. Derive the recursion equations for

$$\max \prod_{n=1}^{N} r_n(X_n, D_n, k_n), \qquad r_n(X_n, D_n, k_n) \geq 0$$

$$\text{subject to } X_{n-1} = t_n(X_n, D_n, k_n), \qquad n = 1, \dots, N$$

where k_n is a random variable with known density function.

2. In Problem 24 of Chapter III, assume that the estimated grades are given more accurately as follows. With probability $\frac{1}{2}$ the grade will be one lower (except for an F, which remains an F with probability 1). Determine a studying policy to maximize expected total points.

3. Solve Problem 26 of Chapter III with probabilities of sales as given below

Demand	February	March	April
0	$\frac{1}{4}$	0	$\frac{2}{3}$
1	$\frac{1}{2}$	$\frac{1}{4}$	$\frac{1}{3}$
2	$\frac{1}{4}$	$\frac{1}{2}$	0
3	0	$\frac{1}{4}$	0

In addition, assume that if demand is not met in any month, there is a shortage cost of $10,000 per unit (shortages in any month are not carried over to the next month). The following costs are associated with inventories at the end of April.

Inventory	0	1	2	3
Cost ($1000)	10	0	5	10

4. At stage n, $n = 1, \dots, 4$ a system can be in any one of two states (A, B). From each of these two states two decisions can be made (I, II). The following table gives transition probabilities and rewards under the two decision policies. Determine an optimal policy to maximize expected reward from a four-stage process, given that the system is initially in state A.

Transition Probabilities

	Decision I				Decision II	
	A	B			A	B
A	0.5	0.5		A	0.8	0.2
B	0.4	0.6		B	0.7	0.3

Rewards

	Decision I				Decision II	
	A	B			A	B
A	9	3		A	4	4
B	3	-7		B	1	-19

5. A firm decides each week whether to advertise a particular product. Sales during the week depend on whether there is an advertisement that week and on sales level of the previous week. There are three basic policies, major advertisement (I), minor advertisement (II), and no advertisement (III). Based on empirical data, the following probabilities of transition from high (H), medium (M), and low (L) sales levels have been obtained.

Policy	I			II			III		
	H	M	L	H	M	L	H	M	L
H	0.7	0.3	0.0	0.5	0.4	0.1	0.3	0.4	0.3
M	0.3	0.6	0.1	0.2	0.6	0.2	0.1	0.6	0.3
L	0.1	0.7	0.2	0.1	0.5	0.4	0.0	0.3	0.7

Profits from sales are $H = 10$, $M = 6$, $L = 0$, from which must be deducted the costs of advertising which are I = 5, II = 2, and III = 0. In addition, there is a labor cost associated with changing weekly sales, namely a change to or from M costs 1 unit and a change from L to H or H to L costs 3 units. Given that the system starts in state M, determine a policy to maximize profit over the next three weeks.

6. Consider a game in which a maximum of 5 draws are made from the following distribution. After any draw a player may keep an amount of dollars equivalent to the number obtained on *that draw* or draw again (except after the fifth draw). Determine a policy to maximize expected return.

x	-2	-1	0	1	2
$p(x)$	$\frac{1}{12}$	$\frac{1}{4}$	$\frac{1}{3}$	$\frac{1}{4}$	$\frac{1}{12}$

7. Solve Problem 6 when the probability distribution is normal with mean 0 and variance 1.

8. "Whiz-Quiz" is (now) an illegal game which used to be popular on Martian television. The game consists of 3 stages. At each stage the contestant decides whether to try to answer an "easy" question, to answer a "hard" question, or not to answer any question. If he answers the easy question correctly, his money is doubled; if he answers the hard question correctly his money is quadrupled; if he is wrong (in either case), he loses all his money— except for a $100 "consolation prize"—and is out of the game. If he decides not to answer either question, he goes on to the next stage with no gain or loss.

The contestant starts with $100, and the probabilities of being able to answer the various questions are as given in the following table:

	First Question	Second Question	Third Question
Easy Question	0.80	0.60	0.40
Hard Question	0.30	0.25	0.20

What should the contestant do at each stage to maximize his expected winnings? Winnings are defined in the usual sense as the amount of money with which the contestant leaves the game.

9. Consider a stochastic shortest-route problem in which, when a particular arc is chosen from a given node, there is a finite probability that another adjacent arc will actually be traversed instead. Assume there are no loops in the network, that is, once a particular node has been reached it is impossible to return to it. Develop recursive equations for solving this problem, and apply them to find the shortest route through the network of Figure 3. Assume that, if an arc is chosen, the probability of traversing the chosen arc is 0.6 and is 0.2 for each of the other two arcs; whereas, if there is only one adjacent arc, the probability of traversing the chosen arc is 0.7; and, of course, if there are no adjacent arcs, there is a probability of 1 of traversing the chosen arc.

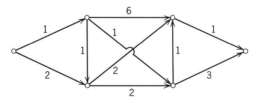

Fig. 3

10. Consider a water-supply system using a reservoir with a capacity of 5×10^5 gallons of water and an "alternate source" with capacity 2×10^5 gallons of water per quarter. Water drawn from the reservoir is free, and water drawn from the alternate source costs c_1 \$/gallon; if no water is available from either source, a shortage cost of c_2 \$/gallon occurs. The amount of water that enters the reservoir each quarter (x) is given by the probability distribution $p(x)$, and it is assumed that $p(x)$ for each quarter is identically and independently distributed. It is also assumed that all of the water enters the reservoir at the beginning of the quarter and that any water for which there is no immediate space in the reservoir is lost. Also, any water entering during one quarter of the year must be purified and is, therefore, not available for use until the next quarter.

Given the following data, find how much water should be drawn from the reservoir and how much from the alternate source each quarter to minimize expected cost over the year as a function of the initial volume of water in the reservoir.

$$c_1 = 1, \quad c_2 = 10, \quad p(x) = \tfrac{1}{3}, \quad x = (0, 1, 2) \times 10^5$$

The amounts drawn from each source are assumed discrete, and are considered only in intervals of 10^5 (that is, 0, 10^5, $2 \times 10^5, \ldots$).
Demands for water in quarters 1, 2, 3, 4 are respectively $1, 3, 2, 4 \times 10^5$ gallons of water.

11. An item is subject to a series of tests. The tests may be performed in any sequence whatsoever. The cost of conducting the ith test is c_i, and the probability of the item passing the ith test is p_i (with $1 - p_i =$ probability of failing the ith test). If the test sequence $s = (A, B, \ldots, N)$ is chosen, then the item is first subjected to test A; if it fails test A, then no further tests are performed. If it passes A, then B is performed $\ldots$; if it fails test i, then no further tests are performed; if it passes test i, then test $i + 1$ is performed. The probability of passing any one test is independent of the probability of passing any other test. Determine the testing sequence that minimizes expected cost.†

12. In the "gold-mining" problem discussed extensively by Bellman [10], we have two gold mines, Anaconda and Bonanza. Anaconda contains x tons of gold and Bonanza, y tons of gold. We have a gold-mining machine which can be used at either mine. If it is used at Aanaconda, there is a probability p_A that it will mine a fraction r_A of the gold there and remain in working order, and a probability $1 - p_A$ that it will mine no gold and be damaged beyond repair. Likewise associated with Bonanza, there is a probability p_B and a fraction r_B. If the machine, after being used once, is still in good order, it is used again at either of the two mines. However, after three minings the machine is always useless. Determine how the machine should be used to maximize the expected amount of gold mined. Let $p_A = 0.8$, $p_B = 0.6$, $r_A = 0.2$, $r_B = 0.5$, and $x = y = 100$.

13. John and Dick each put out one or two fingers simultaneously three times. At each play the result is called "even" or "odd," depending on the total number of fingers put out. The payoff at the end of the three plays depends only on the number of odds and evens. John's payoff (the negative of Dick's) is shown in the table following. Determine optimal strategies and the value of the game.

---

† Bellman [10] has solved this problem by dynamic programming. For an alternative approach see Mitten [50].

Number of Evens	Payoff to John
3	6
2	0
1	−1
0	−3

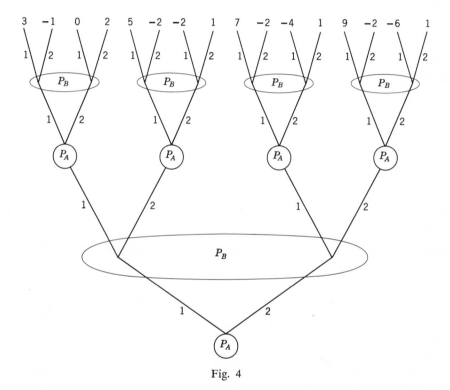

Fig. 4

14. For the game in extensive form with the tree shown in Figure 4, determine optimal strategies and the value of the game.

15. Develop an optimal policy for Problem 7 of this chapter when the mean of the normal distribution is unknown.

16. A gambler who starts off with two cents can play one of two slot machines; each takes a penny. Machine A pays an additional penny (two cents) with probability 0.5 and pays nothing with probability 0.5, while machine B pays an additional two cents with probability 0.4 and nothing with probability 0.6. Assume the gambler's value for money is equal to the actual amount of money and that he quits playing if his total resources are equal to or greater than five cents. Determine an optimal strategy for playing the machines.

17. Suppose, in Problem 16, that the gambler does not know whether machine B pays off with probability 0.3 or 0.4. How should he play?

VI

Nonserial Systems

1. A Review of Serial Systems

In Chapter II we introduced serial multistage decision systems and subsequently developed methods for optimizing these systems. We traversed the spectrum from discrete to continuous variables, from one to many variables per stage, and from deterministic to stochastic to adaptive to competitive models. But we never violated the serial structure of Figure 1.

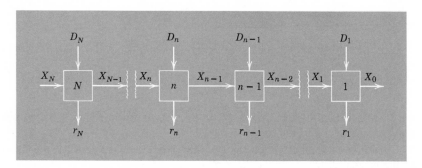

Fig. 1. A Serial System

The interstage relations in a serial system are: stage outputs are functions of inputs and decisions, that is,

$$X_{n-1} = t_n(X_n, D_n), \qquad n = 1, \ldots, N$$

and the stage returns are functions of the input state and decisions, that is,

$$r_n = r_n(X_n, D_n), \qquad n = 1, \ldots, N$$

The stage returns are combined such that the total return from stages one through n is

$$R_n = r_n(X_n, D_n) \text{ o } r_{n-1}(X_{n-1}, D_{n-1}) \text{ o } \ldots \text{ o } r_1(X_1, D_1)$$

The general meaning of "o" was given in Chapter II. We found that two useful interpretations of "o" are arithmetic addition, and multiplication (under the assumption that $r_n(X_n, D_n) \geq 0$ for all X_n and D_n).

The key characteristic of the serial system is that the return from stages one through n can be expressed as a function of only the input state to stage n and the decisions at stages n through 1, that is,

$$R_n = R_n(X_n, D_n, \ldots, D_1)$$

This enables us to find an optimal n-stage return as a function of the input state X_n,

$$f_n(X_n) = \max_{D_n, \ldots, D_1} R_n(X_n, D_n, \ldots, D_1)$$

It is important to note that this optimal return function is found independent of stages $n + 1$ through N. The basic recursive scheme of dynamic programming is to find the sequence $f_1(X_1), \ldots, f_N(X_N)$, using the equations

$$f_1(X_1) = \max_{D_1} r_1(X_1, D_1)$$

and $\quad f_n(X_n) = \max_{D_n} [r_n(X_n, D_n) \text{ o } f_{n-1}(X_{n-1})], \qquad n = 2, \ldots, N$

$$\text{subject to } X_{n-1} = t_n(X_n, D_n)$$

Consequently, the optimal solution for the N-stage system is established one stage at a time.

The determination of $f_N(X_N)$, the optimal return as a function of the input state X_N, is the initial state optimization problem. In Chapter II, we also introduced the initial-final state problem, the determination of $f_N(X_N, X_0)$. To calculate $f_N(X_N, X_0)$ we first calculate $f_1(X_1, X_0)$ as

$$f_1(X_1, X_0) = \max_{D_1} r_1(X_1, D_1, X_0)$$

$$\text{subject to } X_0 = t_1(X_1, D_1)$$

Or if the transformation can be used to eliminate D_1

$$f_1(X_1, X_0) = r_1(X_1, \hat{t}_1(X_1, X_0), X_0)$$

We then solve $N - 1$ two state variable problems, namely

$$f_n(X_n, X_0) = \max_{D_n} [r_n(X_n, D_n) \text{ o } f_{n-1}(X_{n-1}, X_0)], \qquad n = 2, \ldots, N$$

Note that X_0 appears as a state variable in each of the $N - 1$ optimizations. If the amount of storage space required for tabular computations exceeds the amount of rapid-access storage space available, it is desirable to solve a series of one state variable problems, one for each value of X_0. As soon as one subproblem is solved, the optimal results $f_N(X_N)$ and $D_n^*(X_N)$ would be printed out to make room for the next subproblem. The recursive equations for the kth subproblem, $k = 1, \ldots, K$ are

$$f_1(X_1, X_0 = k) = r_1(X_1, X_0 = k)$$

and

$$f_n(X_n, X_0 = k) = \max_{D_n} [r_n(X_n, D_n) \circ f_{n-1}(X_{n-1}, X_0 = k)], \quad n = 2, \ldots, N$$

The notation $f_n(X_n, X_0 = k)$ may be confusing, since it still appears that we are determining functions of both X_n and X_0, that is, two state variable functions. But $X_0 = k$ means that we are solving only as a function of the kth value of X_0. Since X_0 is a constant, the problem contains only one state variable per stage. It is only because the state variable X_0 does not affect the stage returns or transformations at stages 2 through N that we can make the rather obvious conversion of a two state variable problem into a series of one state variable problems. In a general two state variable problem, this simple conversion is not possible. We would have to use a Lagrange multiplier or one of the other approaches given in Chapter IV for state variable reduction.

To solve the final state problem for $f_N(X_0)$, we can simply solve the initial-final state problem and then maximize over X_N. Thus

$$f_N(X_0) = \max_{X_N} f_N(X_N, X_0)$$

where $f_N(X_N, X_0)$ is the optimal return from the initial-final state problem. But, as discussed in Section 10 of Chapter II, if

$$X_{n-1} = t_n(X_n, D_n), \quad n = 1, \ldots, N$$

can be inverted to yield

$$X_n = \bar{t}_n(X_{n-1}, D_n), \quad n = 1, \ldots, N$$

there is a far more efficient way of solving the final state problem. Substituting for X_n in $r_n(X_n, D_n)$, we obtain

$$r_n(X_n, D_n) = r_n(\bar{t}_n(X_{n-1}, D_n), D_n) = r_n(X_{n-1}, D_n)$$

Then proceeding recursively in a forward direction from stages N through 1, we obtain the dynamic programming equations

$$f_1(X_{N-1}) = \max_{D_N} r_N(X_{N-1}, D_N)$$

and

$$f_n(X_{N-n}) = \max_{D_{N-n+1}} [r_{N-n+1}(X_{N-n}, D_{N-n+1}) \circ f_{n-1}(X_{N-n+1})]$$

$$n = 2, \ldots, N$$

Thus to solve the final state problem by forward recursion we require only one state variable per stage.

In Chapters III and IV we did not emphasize any difference between initial versus final state problems and correspondingly backward versus forward recursion. There was really no need to do so. All of the serial problems were structured as initial state problems and solved by backward recursive analysis. For most of them this structure was arbitrary, and forward recursion would have done as well. However, to generate efficient algorithms for nonserial problems, it is crucial to distinguish between backward and forward recursion. We begin with an illustration of a final state problem solved by forward recursive analysis.

2. An Illustration of Forward Recursive Analysis

Consider the problem with returns and transformations as shown in Table 1. The stages are numbered backwards, as usual. The stage returns are additive, and we want to find the minimum total return as a function of the final output x_0.

We begin by expressing each input state as a function of the output states and decisions at the corresponding stage. Thus

$$x_2 = 2x_3 + d_3$$

is inverted to yield

$$x_3 = \frac{x_2 - d_3}{2}$$

At stage two, there are two output states (x_{11}, x_{12}) and only one input state (x_2) and one decision (d_2). Consequently, we can use the equation

$$x_{11} = x_2 + d_2$$

to solve for x_2 as

$$x_2 = x_{11} - d_2$$

and the remaining transformation

$$x_{12} = x_2 - d_2$$

generates a restriction on d_2, namely

$$x_{12} = x_{11} - 2d_2 \quad \text{or} \quad d_2 = \frac{x_{11} - x_{12}}{2}$$

However, at stage one we can eliminate only one of the input state variables, either x_{11} or x_{12}. Arbitrarily choosing to eliminate x_{11}, we obtain

$$x_{11} = x_0 - x_{12} + 2d_1$$

These inverted transformations are substituted into the stage returns. The results are summarized in Table 2.

Table 1

Stage	Return	Transformation
3	$3x_3 + 3(x_3 - d_3)^2$	$x_2 = 2x_3 + d_3$
2	$(x_2 - d_2)^2$	$x_{11} = x_2 + d_2$
		$x_{12} = x_2 - d_2$
1	$(x_{11} + 2x_{12} - d_1)^2$	$x_0 = x_{11} + x_{12} - 2d_1$

Table 2

Stage	Return	Transformation	Constraints
3	$\dfrac{3(x_2 - d_3)}{2} + \dfrac{3(x_2 - 3d_3)^2}{4}$	$x_3 = \dfrac{(x_2 - d_3)}{2}$	——
2	$(x_{11} - 2d_2)^2$	$x_2 = x_{11} - d_2$	$d_2 = \dfrac{(x_{11} - x_{12})}{2}$
1	$(x_0 + x_{12} + d_1)^2$	$x_{11} = x_0 - x_{12} + 2d_1$	——

Beginning the forward recursion at stage three, we find the optimal stage-three return as a function of its output x_2 is

$$f_1(x_2) = \min_{d_3} \left[\frac{3(x_2 - d_3)}{2} + \frac{3(x_2 - 3d_3)^2}{4} \right]$$

Using differential calculus to determine necessary and sufficient conditions for a minimum and then solving the resulting equations yields

$$d_3(x_2) = \frac{x_2}{3} + \frac{1}{9} \quad \text{and} \quad f_1(x_2) = x_2 - \frac{1}{12}$$

Continuing with the forward recursion by considering a two-stage system with stage two included, we have

$$f_2(x_{11}, x_{12}) = \min_{d_2 = \frac{x_{11} - x_{12}}{2}} \left[(x_{11} - 2d_2)^2 + x_{11} - d_2 - \frac{1}{12} \right]$$

The constraint fixes the value of d_2, so there is no optimization; hence

$$d_2(x_{11}, x_{12}) = \frac{x_{11} - x_{12}}{2} \quad \text{and} \quad f_2(x_{11}, x_{12}) = x_{12}^2 + \frac{x_{11} + x_{12}}{2} - \frac{1}{12}$$

Turning to the three-stage system, we find that since the output from stage one (x_0) is unidimensional, and the input (x_{11}, x_{12}) is two-dimensional, either x_{11} or x_{12} is a decision variable. Taking x_{12} to be the additional decision variable, the three-stage optimal return is

$$f_3(x_0) = \min_{d_1, x_{12}} \left[(x_0 + x_{12} + d_1)^2 + x_{12}^2 + \frac{x_0 + 2d_1}{2} - \frac{1}{12} \right]$$

$$x_{12}^* = x_{12}(x_0) = \frac{1}{2}, \quad d_1^* = d_1(x_0) = -x_0 - 1, \quad f_3(x_0) = \frac{-x_0}{2} - \frac{7}{12}$$

Using these optimal values, we trace back the remainder of the optimal solution. The results are summarized in Table 3.

Table 3

Stage	Optimal Decision	Optimal Input	Optimal Return
3	$d_3^* = \dfrac{-x_0}{6} - \dfrac{2}{9}$	$x_3^* = \dfrac{-x_0}{6} - \dfrac{7}{18}$	$\dfrac{-x_0}{2} - \dfrac{13}{12}$
2	$d_2^* = \dfrac{-x_0 - 3}{2}$	$x_2^* = \dfrac{-x_0}{2} - 1$	$\dfrac{1}{4}$
1	$d_1^* = -x_0 - 1$	$x_{11}^* = -x_0 - \dfrac{5}{2}$	$\dfrac{1}{4}$
		$x_{12}^* = \dfrac{1}{2}$	

The advantage of forward recursion is state variable reduction. Had backward recursion been used, x_0 as well as the input state would have been state variables at each stage. Generally, forward recursion is preferred for the final-value problem, and backward recursion for the initial-value problem. On the other hand, for an initial-final state problem it makes no difference in state variable dimensionality whether forward or backward recursion is used. Also when X_N and X_0 can be chosen, backward and forward recursion are equivalent with regard to state variable dimensionality. Usually, we would choose backward recursion to avoid state inversion.

3. Basic Nonserial Structures

Nonserial structures appear commonly in the technology of the process industries, and are basic to the field of automatic control. There are four elementary nonserial structures:

1. the *diverging branch*—there are two or more output states from a stage, each of these being the input to a different serial system (Figure 2);

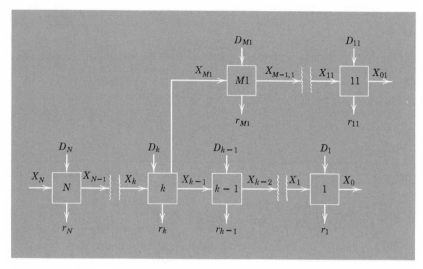

Fig. 2. A Diverging Branch System.

2. the *converging branch*—the outputs from two or more different serial systems constitute the input to a serial system (Figure 3);

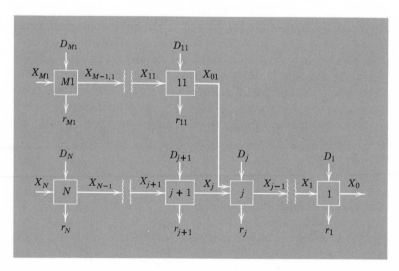

Fig. 3. A Converging Branch System.

3. the *feedforward loop*—there is a diverging branch from some stage of a serial system, which converges at a later stage of the original serial system (Figure 4);

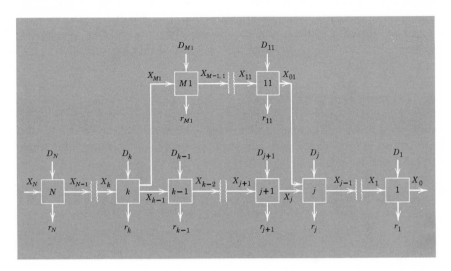

Fig. 4. A Feedforward Loop System.

4. the *feedback loop*—there is a diverging branch from some stage of a serial system, which converges at an earlier stage of the original serial system (Figure 5).

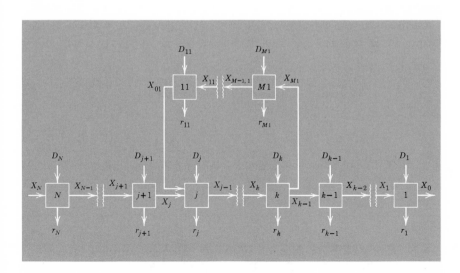

Fig. 5. A Feedback Loop System.

More complex nonserial structures can be constructed by combining, in various ways, the elementary structures. In this chapter we show how the recursive procedures for serial systems can be extended to treat nonserial systems. The development follows the work of Mitten and Nemhauser [52] and Aris, Nemhauser, and Wilde [4]. Recursive schemes are developed for each of the elementary nonserial structures. Then a complex system is studied exhibiting all of the basic nonserial characteristics.

4. Diverging Branch Systems

We begin with diverging branch systems because they are conceptually the easiest of the elementary nonserial structures to analyze. The stage transformations are

$$X_{n-1} = t_n(X_n, D_n), \qquad n = 1, \ldots, N$$

$$X_{m-1,1} = t_{m1}(X_{m1}, D_{m1}), \qquad m = 1, \ldots, M$$

and $\qquad X_{M1} = t_{k1}(X_k, D_k)$

the latter being the additional transformation at stage k which joins the diverging branch to the main serial system. The key property of serial systems—that the return from any stage can be expressed as a function only of the input and decisions at that stage and of the decisions at the following stages—holds for diverging branch systems as well. As a consequence of this, diverging branch systems can be optimized with no more effort than would be required for a serial system with an equivalent number of stages.

Certainly for stages 11 through $M1$ and 1 through $k - 1$, which are merely serial systems, the property holds, that is,

$$R_{M1} = r_{M1}(X_{M1}, D_{M1}) \circ r_{M-1,1}(X_{M-1,1}, D_{M-1,1}) \circ \ldots \circ r_{11}(X_{11}, D_{11})$$

$$= R_{M1}(X_{M1}, D_{M1}, D_{M-1,1}, \ldots, D_{11})$$

and

$$R_{k-1} = r_{k-1}(X_{k-1}, D_{k-1}) \circ r_{k-2}(X_{k-2}, D_{k-2}) \circ \ldots \circ r_1(X_1, D_1)$$

$$= R_{k-1}(X_{k-1}, D_{k-1}, D_{k-2}, \ldots, D_1)$$

Now it remains to be shown that the total return from stages 11 through $M1$ and 1 through k (R_{k+M1})

where $\qquad R_{k+M1} = r_k \circ R_{k-1} \circ R_{M1}$

can be expressed as a function of X_k, D_k and the following decisions $(D_{k-1}, \ldots, D_1, D_{M1}, \ldots, D_{11})$. By substituting the equations for the stage-k transformations into the equations for R_{k-1} and R_{M1}, we obtain

$$R_{k+M1} = r_k(X_k, D_k) \circ R_{k-1}(t_k(X_k, D_k), D_{k-1}, \ldots, D_1) \circ R_{M1}(t_{k1}(X_k, D_k),$$
$$D_{M1}, \ldots, D_{11})$$

$$= r_k(X_k, D_k) \circ R_{k-1}(X_k, D_k, D_{k-1}, \ldots, D_1) \circ R_{M1}(X_k, D_k, D_{M1},$$
$$\ldots, D_{11})$$

$$= R_{k+M1}(X_k, D_k, D_{k-1}, \ldots, D_1, D_{M1}, \ldots, D_{11})$$

This establishes the intuitively obvious fact that stages 11 through $M1$ and 1 through $k - 1$ can be optimized, using usual recursive procedures, as two disjoint serial systems. Then the optimal returns, as functions of the inputs to each of these systems, can be combined with the stage-k return and the remainder of the optimization, from stage k through N, can be carried out recursively.

The recursion equations are:

1. for the diverging branch, stages 11 through $M1$,

$$f_{11}(X_{11}) = \max_{D_{11}} r_{11}(X_{11}, D_{11})$$

$$f_{m1}(X_{m1}) = \max_{D_{m1}} [r_{m1}(X_{m1}, D_{m1}) \circ f_{m-1,1}(t_{m1}(X_{m1}, D_{m1}))],$$
$$m = 2, \ldots, M$$

2. for stages one through $k - 1$,

$$f_1(X_1) = \max_{D_1} r_1(X_1, D_1)$$

$$f_n(X_n) = \max_{D_n} [r_n(X_n, D_n) \circ f_{n-1}(t_n(X_n, D_n))], \qquad n = 2, \ldots, k - 1$$

3. for the diverging stage k,

$$f_{k+M1}(X_k) = \max_{D_k} [r_k(X_k, D_k) \circ f_{k-1}(t_k(X_k, D_k)) \circ f_{M1}(t_{k1}(X_k, D_k))]$$

4. for the remaining stages $k + 1$ through N,

$$f_{n+M1}(X_n) = \max_{D_n} [r_n(X_n, D_n) \circ f_{n-1+M1}(t_n(X_n, D_n))],$$
$$n = k + 1, \ldots, N$$

The extra term f_{M1}, which appears in the equation for f_{k+M1}, can be thought of as representing an absorption of the diverging branch into the main serial system.

The same principles, of course, apply when there is more than one diverging branch. Each branch is optimized recursively so that we can find its optimal return as a function of its input, and then absorbed into the serial system at the divergent stages.

An interesting case occurs when there are, say, p diverging branches from stage k with the transformation

$$t_k(X_k, D_k) = Y_k = X_{k-1} + X_{M1} + X_{M2} + \ldots + X_{Mp}$$

In this situation the state-decision combination X_k, D_k only determines a single output Y_k, which must be split optimally among the branches and the remainder of the main system. We need an additional multivariable optimization to achieve this optimal split. It can be done recursively. Let $f_{M1}(X_{M1}), \ldots, f_{Mp}(X_{Mp})$ be the optimal branch returns. Then the optimal return from the branches, including stages 1 through $k - 1$ of the main system as a function of Y_k is

$$f_{k-1+\Sigma Mi}(Y_k) = \max_{Y_k \, = \, X_{k-1} + X_{M1} + \ldots X_{Mp}} [f_{k-1}(X_{k-1}) + f_{M1}(X_{M1}) + \ldots$$
$$+ f_{Mp}(X_{Mp})]$$

The determination of $f_{k-1+\Sigma Mi}(Y_k)$ is of course a straightforward $(p + 1)$-stage dynamic program. Once $f_{k-1+\Sigma Mi}(Y_k)$ has been determined, it is combined with the stage-k return to yield

$$f_{k+\Sigma Mi}(X_k) = \max_{D_k} [r_k(X_k, D_k) \circ f_{k-1+\Sigma Mi}(t_k(X_k, D_k))]$$

Unfortunately, the analyses of the other elementary nonserial systems are not as direct, since the key property—that the return from any stage can be expressed as a function only of the input state and decisions at that stage and the decisions at the following stages—does not hold. However, for converging branches a similar property holds—namely, that the return from any stage can be expressed as a function only of the output state and decisions at that stage and the decisions at the preceding stages. Thus final state problems and forward recursion are the keys for solving converging branch systems.

5. Converging Branch Systems

A converging branch system is shown in Figure 3. The transformation at stage j, where the convergence occurs, is

$$X_{j-1} = t_j(X_{01}, X_j, D_j)$$

At all other stages we have the usual serial transformations

$$X_{n-1} = t_n(X_n, D_n), \qquad n = 1, \ldots, N, \quad n \neq j$$

$$X_{m-1,1} = t_{m1}(X_{m1}, D_{m1}), \qquad m = 1, \ldots, M$$

The stage returns are

$$r_j = r_j(X_{01}, X_j, D_j)$$

$$r_n = r_n(X_n, D_n), \qquad n = 1, \ldots, N \quad n \neq j$$

and $\qquad r_{m1} = r_{m1}(X_{m1}, D_{m1}), \qquad m = 1, \ldots, M$

Using the composition operator, we find that the return from stages one through j is

$$R_j = r_j(X_{01}, X_j, D_j) \circ r_{j-1}(X_{j-1}, D_{j-1}) \circ \ldots \circ r_1(X_1, D_1)$$

$$= R_j(X_{01}, X_j, D_j, D_{j-1}, \ldots, D_1)$$

and the total return from the converging branch is

$$R_{M1} = r_{M1}(X_{M1}, D_{M1}) \circ \ldots \circ r_{11}(X_{11}, D_{11})$$

$$= R_{M1}(X_{M1}, D_{M1}, \ldots, D_{11})$$

A dilemma seems to exist if we attempt to combine R_{M1} with R_j. The trouble is caused by X_{01}. If we optimize the branch to obtain $f_{M1}(X_{M1})$, this would fix X_{01} through the transformations t_{m1}, $m = 1, \ldots, M$. But R_j depends on X_{01}, and the value of X_{01} obtained from optimizing the branch alone will not generally be an optimal input to stage j. However, providing that the optimal branch return is found as a function of X_{01}, it can be combined with the return from the main serial system. Then the optimal value of X_{01} can be established if we take into account the effect of X_{01} on both the branch and main chain. This is the basic idea for handling combining branches. There are some variations depending upon whether it is necessary to find the optimal system return as a function of X_{M1}, and whether it is possible to use state inversion.

When the branch input can be chosen, the branch optimization is a final state problem—the determination of $f_{M1}(X_{01})$. If state inversion is possible and computationally feasible, it is used to solve the final state problem. The stage returns are expressed as functions of the decisions and outputs, that is,

$$r_{m1} = r_{m1}(X_{m1}, D_{m1}) = r_{m1}(\hat{t}_{m1}(X_{m-1,1}, D_{m1}), D_{m1})$$

$$= r_{m1}(X_{m-1,1}, D_{m1}), \qquad m = 1, \ldots, M$$

The forward recursion equations for the optimization of the branch are

$$f_{11}(X_{M-1,1}) = \max_{D_{M1}} r_{M1}(X_{M-1,1}, D_{M1})$$

and

$$f_{m1}(X_{M-m,1}) = \max_{D_{M-m+1,1}} [r_{M-m+1,1}(X_{M-m,1}, D_{M-m+1,1}) \circ f_{m-1,1}(\hat{t}_{M-m+1,1}$$

$$(X_{M-m,1}, D_{M-m+1,1}))], \qquad m = 2, \ldots, M$$

The M-stage solution yields $f_{M1}(X_{01})$, which can be combined with the main serial system. Had X_{M1} been fixed, the optimization of the branch to determine $f_{M1}(X_{01})$ would have been the same, except that at the first stage there would be no optimization if D_{M1} were determined uniquely from the equation

$$D_{M1} = \hat{t}_{M1}(X_{M1}, X_{M-1,1})$$

The main serial system through stage $j-1$ is optimized in the usual way to obtain $f_{j-1}(X_{j-1})$, that is,

$$f_1(X_1) = \max_{D_1} r_1(X_1, D_1)$$

$$f_n(X_n) = \max_{D_n} [r_n(X_n, D_n) \circ f_{n-1}(t_n(X_n, D_n))], \qquad n = 2, \dots, j-1$$

At stage j the branch return is combined with the serial return from stages one through $j-1$, using the recursion equation

$$f_{j+M1}(X_j) = \max_{X_{01}, D_j} [r_j(X_{01}, X_j, D_j) \circ f_{j-1}(t_j(X_{01}, X_j, D_j)) \circ f_{M1}(X_{01})]$$

Note that at this point we also optimize over X_{01}, since the objective is to determine the total optimal return only as a function of X_N. This differs from the procedure for diverging branches, where there was only one optimization at the point where the branch return was combined with the main serial system. Having combined the branch optimally with the main serial system, we accomplish the analysis of stages $j+1$ through N with standard backward recursion. The equations are

$$f_{n+M1}(X_n) = \max_{D_n} [r_n(X_n, D_n) \circ f_{n-1+M1}(t_n(X_n, D_n))], \qquad n = j+1, \dots, N$$

When state inversion is not possible, $f_{M1}(X_{01})$ must be found by first solving the initial-final state problem for $f_{M1}(X_{M1}, X_{01})$ and then maximizing over X_{M1}. Of course, we must also find $f_{M1}(X_{M1}, X_{01})$ when the problem requires that the optimal system return be given as a function of X_{M1}. Carrying X_{M1} as an additional state variable in the branch optimization is certainly a computational burden, although it is possible to handle the added calculations and storage requirements in a reasonably effective way. In the direct approach we determine the optimal branch return as an initial-final state problem, using backward recursion with the equations

$$f_{11}(X_{11}, X_{01}) = \max_{D_{11}} r_{11}(X_{11}, D_1)$$

$$\text{subject to } X_{01} = t_{11}(X_{11}, D_{11})$$

and

$$f_{m1}(X_{m1}, X_{01}) = \max_{D_{m1}} [r_{m1}(X_{m1}, D_{m1}) \circ f_{m-1,1}(t_{m1}(X_{m1}, D_{m1}), X_{01})],$$

$$m = 2, \dots, M$$

Then the optimal branch return $f_{M1}(X_{M1}, X_{01})$ is combined with the stage-j return and the optimal return from stages one through $j-1$, using the recursion equation

$$f_{j+M1}(X_j, X_{M1}) = \max_{X_{01}, D_j} [r_j(X_{01}, X_j, D_j) \circ f_{j-1}(t_j(X_{01}, X_j, D_j)) \circ$$

$$f_{M1}(X_{M1}, X_{01})]$$

Naturally, at stages $j + 1$ through N, X_{M1} must also be kept as a state variable; thus

$$f_{n+M1}(X_n, X_{M1}) = \max_{D_n} [r_n(X_n, D_n) \circ f_{n-1+M1}(t_n(X_n, D_n), X_{M1})],$$

$$n = j + 1, \ldots, N$$

In determining the optimal two state return $f_{M1}(X_{M1}, X_{01})$, the procedure given previously, whereby the two state variable function is determined as a series of one state variable functions, will be of great advantage in tabular calculations. An even greater computational savings than that in an ordinary two state problem may be achieved. Since X_{01} is eventually optimized, it may not be necessary to calculate $f_{M1}(X_{M1}, X_{01})$ for all values of X_{01}. Suppose we begin by calculating f_{M1} for the kth value of X_{01}, f_{M1} $(X_{M1}, X_{01} = k)$. This optimal branch return for the particular value of X_{01} is combined with the stage-j return, and an optimization over D_j is carried out to yield $f_{j+M1}(X_j, X_{M1}, X_{01} = k)$. The calculations are repeated for successive values of X_{01} using a sequential search procedure, until an optimum value of X_{01} is located. In the favorable case where X_{01} is a scalar variable and f_{j+M1} is a unimodal function of X_{01}, Fibonacci search can be used to guide X_{01} to its optimum value very quickly. But even in the worst case, when the search is exhaustive, there is still a storage saving. Once the optimum value of X_{01} is established, we know the optimal function $f_{j+M1}(X_j, X_{M1})$, and the remainder of the analysis proceeds as before. If the optimal system return is desired as a function of X_{M1}, we continue in the usual manner with stages $j + 1$ through N. An optimization over X_{M1} precedes the inclusion of stages $j + 1$ through N, if X_{M1} were kept as a state variable only because inversion was not possible.

We have shown that in certain cases, by using forward recursion, it is possible to optimize a converging branch system with about the same computational effort required for a diverging branch system. When the optimal return must be found as a function of the input to the combining branch, additional computational effort is required either in the form of increased dimensionality or a sequential search. This procedure for converging branches provides a clue to handling feedforward loops.

6. Feedforward Loop Systems

A feedforward loop system consists of an N-stage serial system with a diverging branch at stage k, which converges with the main system again at stage j, $j < k$. The transformations and returns are (a) the usual serial ones for all stages other than j and k; (b) the diverging stage transformations and returns at stage k; and (c) the converging stage transformations and returns at stage j (see Figure 4). Thus

$$X_{n-1} = t_n(X_n, D_n)$$

$$r_n = r_n(X_n, D_n), \qquad n = 1, \ldots, N, \quad n \neq j$$

$$X_{m-1,1} = t_{m1}(X_{m1}, D_{m1})$$

$$r_{m1} = r_{m1}(X_{m1}, D_{m1}), \qquad m = 1, \ldots, M$$

$$X_{j-1} = t_j(X_{01}, X_j, D_j)$$

$$r_j = r_j(X_{01}, X_j, D_j)$$

$$X_{M1} = t_{k1}(X_k, D_k)$$

When we design a computational scheme for a feedforward loop system, it is important to realize that because the branch is both diverging and converging, its input X_{M1} and its output X_{01} affect the return from the serial system. If the branch is optimized separately as a serial system, its optimal return must be determined as a function of both its input and output. Given this fundamental premise, there are several variations that can be used. The optimal branch return can be absorbed into the main serial system at the converging stage j or at the diverging stage k. It is also possible, and desirable in tabular computations, to treat the two state branch problem as a series of one state variable problems, using sequential search to direct the output state to an optimum value.

If the optimal branch return is absorbed into the main system at stage k, we have the recursion equation

$$f_{k+M1}(X_k) = \max_{X_{01}, D_k} [r_k(X_k, D_k) \circ f_{k-1}(t_k(X_k, D_k), X_{01}) \circ$$
$$f_{M1}(t_{k1}(X_k, D_k), X_{01})]$$

The optimal branch return as a function of its input and output states is $f_{M1}(t_{k1}(X_k, D_k), X_{01}) = f_{M1}(X_{M1}, X_{01})$, and is determined from

$$f_{11}(X_{11}, X_{01}) = \max_{D_{11}} r_{11}(X_{11}, D_{11})$$

$$\text{subject to } X_{01} = t_{11}(X_{11}, D_{11})$$

and

$$f_{m1}(X_{m1}, X_{01}) = \max_{D_{m1}} [r_{m1}(X_{m1}, D_{m1}) \circ f_{m-1,1}(t_{m1}(X_{m1}, D_{m1}), X_{01})],$$
$$m = 2, \ldots, M$$

The optimal return from stages one through $k-1$ is $f_{k-1}(t_k(X_k, D_k), X_{01})$ $= f_{k-1}(X_{k-1}, X_{01})$, and is determined from

$$f_j(X_j, X_{01}) = \max_{D_j} [r_j(X_j, X_{01}, D_j) \circ f_{j-1}(t_j(X_{01}, D_j))]$$

and

$$f_n(X_n, X_{01}) = \max_{D_n} [r_n(X_n, D_n) \circ f_{n-1}(t_n(X_n, D_n), X_{01})],$$

$$n = j+1, \ldots, k-1$$

where $f_{j-1}(t_j(X_{01}, D_j)) = f_{j-1}(X_{j-1})$ is determined from

$$f_1(X_1) = \max_{D_1} r_1(X_1, D_1)$$

and

$$f_n(X_n) = \max_{D_n} [r_n(X_n, D_n) \circ f_{n-1}(t_n(X_n, D_n))], \qquad n = 2, \ldots, j-1$$

By fixing X_{01} we eliminate it as a state variable in the calculation of f_{M1}, f_{k-1}, and f_{k+M1}. After determining f_{k+M1}, for a particular value of X_{01}, we determine a new value of X_{01} from a sequential search procedure until the optimum value of $f_{k+M1}(X_k)$ over X_{01} is established. Finally, after we have computed $f_{k+M1}(X_k)$, the remainder of the serial system, stages $k + 1, \ldots, N$ are optimized in the usual way, that is,

$$f_{n+M1}(X_n) = \max_{D_n} [r_n(X_n, D_n) \circ f_{n-1+M1}(t_n(X_n, D_n))], \qquad n = k+1, \ldots, N$$

About the same number of calculations are required if the two state optimal branch return is absorbed at stage j. At stage j the recursion equation is

$$f_{j+M1}(X_j, X_{M1}) = \max_{D_j, X_{01}} [r_j(X_j, X_{01}, D_j) \circ f_{j-1}(t_j(X_j, D_j)) \circ f_{M1}(X_{M1}, X_{01})]$$

where f_{j-1} and f_{M1} are calculated as just shown. The optimal returns through stage $k - 1$ are computed from

$$f_{n+M1}(X_n, X_{M1}) = \max_{D_n} [r_n(X_n, D_n) \circ f_{n-1+M1}(t_n(X_n, D_n), X_{M1})],$$

$$n = j+1, \ldots, k-1$$

At stage k,

$$f_{k+M1}(X_k) = \max_{D_k} [r_k(X_k, D_k) \circ f_{k-1+M1}(t_k(X_k, D_k), t_{k1}(X_k, D_k))]$$

The remainder of the analysis to determine $f_{N+M1}(X_N)$ uses the recursion equation for stages $k + 1, \ldots, N$ just given.

The only difference between absorption at stages k and j is the place at which X_{01} is optimized. In the former case, the optimization is deferred to stage k, and X_{01} is carried as a state variable in stages $j + 1$ through $k - 1$; in the latter, the optimization over X_{01} is done earlier in the analysis, but X_{M1} is carried as a state variable in stages $j + 1$ through $k - 1$. If a sequential search procedure is used to direct X_{01} to its optimum, there is some advantage to absorbing the branch return at stage k. If it is done at stage j, the optimizations at stages $j + 1$ through $k - 1$ require two state variables as compared with one state variable plus the constant value of X_{01} when the absorption is at stage k. No matter whether the branch return is absorbed at stage k or j, the optimizations at stages 11 through $M1$ and j through $k - 1$ require two state variables. But in the former case, X_{01} is the additional state variable at stages j through $k - 1$, and in the latter, X_{M1} is an extra state variable at stages j through $k-1$. The advantage of X_{01} as the additional state variable is that it is eventually optimized. Thus X_{01} may be directed to an optimal value by sequential search.

Although this section contains one notationally complicated recursive equation after another, the basic procedures are simple.

1. Stages one through $j-1$ are optimized to find $f_{j-1}(X_{j-1})$.

2. The branch consisting of stages 11 through $M1$ is optimized to find $f_{M1}(X_{M1}, X_{01})$.

3a. If the branch is absorbed at stage j, X_{01} is optimized at stage j to yield $f_{j+M1}(X_j, X_{M1})$. Then stages $j+1$ through $k-1$ are optimized to find $f_{k-1+M1}(X_{k-1}, X_{M1})$, and stage k is optimized to find $f_{k+M1}(X_k)$.

3b. If the branch is absorbed at stage k, stages j through $k-1$ are optimized to find $f_{k-1}(X_{k-1}, X_{01})$ and then at stage k, $f_{M1}(X_{M1}, X_{01})$ is included, and there is an optimization over X_{01} to find $f_{k+M1}(X_k)$.

3c. In both 3a and 3b, it is possible to eliminate X_{01} as a state variable and solve a series of one state variable problems, one for each feasible value of X_{01}. Using this procedure it may be possible to direct X_{01} to its optimal value by using a sequential search procedure, and thus exclude calculations for some feasible values of X_{01}.

4. Stages $k+1$ through N are optimized to find $f_{N+M1}(X_N)$.

7. An Example of Feedforward Loop Optimization

To illustrate the optimization of a feedforward loop system, we consider an example with the structure shown in Figure 6 and the data given in

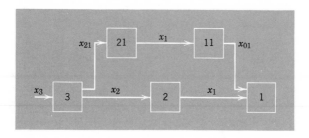

Fig. 6

Table 4. The objective is to minimize the sum of the stage returns as a function of the input x_3.

Table 4

Stage	Decision	Return
1	d_1	$0.1d_1^2$
11	d_{11}	$0.2d_{11}^2$
21	d_{21}	$375 - 10d_{21}$
2	d_2	$600 - 100\sqrt{x_2 + d_2}$
3	d_3	$0.1(50 - d_3)^2$

Stage	Transformation	Constraints
1	———	$d_1 = x_1 + x_{01}$
11	$x_{01} = x_{11} - d_{11}$	———
21	$x_{11} = x_{21} + d_{21}$	———
2	$x_1 = x_2 + d_2$	———
3	$x_2 + x_{21} = x_3 + d_3$	$x_2 \leq \dfrac{x_3 + d_3}{2}$

Since there are no stages after the converging stage, that is, stage one equals stage j in the general case, we begin with the two-stage system consisting of stages 11 and 21, and determine $f_{21}(x_{21}, x_{01})$. At stage 11

$$f_{11}(x_{11}, x_{01}) = r_{11}(x_{11}, x_{01}) = 0.2(x_{11} - x_{01})^2$$

since $d_{11} = x_{11} - x_{01}$.

Turning to the two-stage process consisting of stages 21 and 11, we see that

$$f_{21}(x_{21}, x_{01}) = \min_{d_{21}} [375 - 10d_{21} + 0.2(x_{21} + d_{21} - x_{01})^2]$$

The optimal value of d_{21} is readily found to be

$$d_{21}(x_{21}, x_{01}) = 25 + x_{01} - x_{21}$$

which yields

$$f_{21}(x_{21}, x_{01}) = 250 - 10x_{01} + 10x_{21}$$

Since calculations are being done analytically, the arguments for using a sequential search procedure to direct x_{01} to its optimal value do not apply, and the mathematics are considerably easier if we absorb the optimal branch return into the main system at stage one. Thus

$$f_{1+21}(x_1, x_{21}) = \min_{x_{01}, d_1} [0.1d_1^2 + 250 - 10x_{01} + 10x_{21}]$$

$$\text{subject to } d_1 = x_1 + x_{01}$$

Substituting the constraint into the recursion equation, we obtain

$$f_{1+21}(x_1, x_{21}) = \min_{x_{01}} \; [0.1(x_1 + x_{01})^2 + 250 - 10x_{01} + 10x_{21}]$$

Differentiating the term in brackets with respect to x_{01} and setting the derivative to zero yields

$$x_{01}(x_1, x_{21}) = 50 - x_1, \qquad d_1(x_1, x_{21}) = 50$$

$$\text{and} \quad f_{1+21}(x_1, x_{21}) = 10(x_1 + x_{21})$$

Continuing with the inclusion of stage two, we have

$$f_{2+21}(x_2, x_{21}) = \min_{d_2} \; [600 - 100 \sqrt{x_2 + d_2} + 10(x_2 + d_2 + x_{21})]$$

Carrying out the required minimization, we obtain

$$d_2 = 25 - x_2 \quad \text{and} \quad f_{2+21}(x_2, x_{21}) = 350 + 10x_{21}$$

Since the transformation at stage three

$$x_2 + x_{21} = x_3 + d_3$$

yields only the sum of the outputs, the transformation can be used only to eliminate one of the outputs. The other is optimized. Thus

$$f_3(x_3) = \min_{x_2, d_3} \; [0.1(50 - d_3)^2 + 350 + 10(x_3 + d_3 - x_2)]$$

$$\text{subject to } x_2 \leq \frac{x_3 + d_3}{2}$$

The minimizing value of x_2 is $x_2 = (x_3 + d_3)/2$; hence

$$f_3(x_3) = \min_{d_3} \; [0.1(50 - d_3)^2 + 350 + 5(x_3 + d_3)]$$

It is easily established that $d_3 = 25$ is the solution; consequently $f_3(x_3) = 537.5 + 5.0 \, x_3$.

Retracing our analysis, we find the remainder of the optimal solution, which is summarized in Table 5.

Table 5

Stage	Optimal Decision	Optimal Input	Optimal Return
1	$d_1 = 50$	$x_1 = x_{01} = 25$	250
11	$d_{11} = 25$	$x_{11} = 50$	125
21	$d_{21} = 37.5 - 0.5 \, x_3$	$x_{21} = 12.5 + 0.5 \, x_3$	100
2	$d_2 = 12.5 - 0.5 \, x_3$	$x_2 = 12.5 + 0.5 \, x_3$	$5x_3$
3	$d_3 = 25$	x_3	62.5

8. Feedback Loop Systems

A feedback loop system is identical to a feedforward loop system except that the relative positions of stages j and k are reversed. In the feedback loop, $k < j$, where stage k is the diverging stage and j the converging stage. With the numbering of the stages shown in Figure 5 the transformations and returns for the feedback loop are identical with those of the feedforward loop. However, because of the different positions of stages j and k, there is a slight difference in the recursion equations for the feedforward and feedback loops. Once again, we can either absorb the branch at the converging or diverging stage. Without repeating all the details of the recursion equations, we present the basic procedure.

1. Optimize stages one through $k - 1$, to obtain $f_{k-1}(X_{k-1})$.

2. Optimize the branch consisting of stages 11 through $M1$ to obtain $f_{M1}(X_{01}, X_{M1})$.

3a. Assuming that the optimal branch return is combined with the main system at stage k, the recursion equation is

$$f_{k+M1}(X_k, X_{01}) = \max_{D_k} \left[r_k(X_k, D_k) \circ f_{k-1}(t_k(X_k, D_k)) \circ f_{M1}(X_{01}, t_{k1}(X_k, D_k)) \right]$$

Then stages $k + 1$ through $j - 1$ are optimized to find $f_{j-1+M1}(X_{j-1}, X_{01})$. At stage j, X_{01} is optimized with recursion equation

$$f_{j+M1}(X_j) = \max_{X_{01}, D_j} \left[r_j(X_{01}, X_j, D_j) \circ f_{j-1+M1}(t_j(X_j, D_j), X_{01}) \right]$$

3b. Assuming that the optimal branch return is combined with the main system at stage j, the situation is somewhat more awkward. At stage k we cannot choose D_k since

$$X_{M1} = t_{k1}(X_k, D_k)$$

and X_{M1} cannot be specified as a function of X_k until the branch has been absorbed. Assuming at stage k that we can express D_k as a function of X_k and X_{M1}, then X_{k-1} can be written as a function of X_k and X_{M1}, that is,

$$D_k = \hat{t}_{k1}(X_k, X_{M1})$$

$$X_{k-1} = t_k(X_k, D_k) = t_k(X_k, \hat{t}_{k1}(X_k, X_{M1})) = t_k(X_k, X_{M1})$$

At stage k there is no optimization since

$$f_k(X_k, X_{M1}) = r_k(X_k, \hat{t}_{k1}(X_k, X_{M1})) \circ f_{k-1}(t_k(X_k, X_{M1}))$$

Of course, if $\hat{t}_{k1}$ does not exist, there is a maximization over D_k for all feasible values of X_{M1},

$$\text{subject to } X_{M1} = t_{k1}(X_k, D_k)$$

Stages $k + 1$ through $j - 1$ are optimized in the usual recursive fashion to obtain $f_{j-1}(X_{j-1}, X_{M1})$. At stage j the optimal branch return is absorbed, and there is an optimization over three variables. Specifically

$$f_{j+M1}(X_j) = \max_{X_{01}, X_{M1}, D_j} [r_j(X_{01}, X_j, D_j) \circ f_{j-1}(t_j(X_j, D_j), X_{M1}) \circ f_{M1}(X_{01}, X_{M1})]$$

The same total number of variables are optimized whether we absorb at stage j or k. The advantage of absorbing at stage k is that we distribute the optimizations more evenly over the stages.

3c. In both 3a and 3b, X_{01} can be eliminated as a state variable, and a series of one state variable problems solved instead. However, if 3b is used, it would be better to sequentially search over X_{M1} since it is the additional state variable in the optimization of stages $k + 1$ through $j - 1$, and is optimized at stage j.

4. Optimize the remainder of the main system to obtain $f_{N+M1}(X_N)$.

9. A Complex Nonserial System

Having developed recursive optimization schemes for all of the elementary nonserial systems, we can consider a complex system with several loops and branches. Such a system is shown in Figure 7.

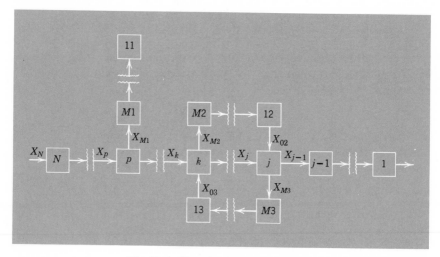

Fig. 7. A Complex Nonserial System.

The basic procedure is to break the complex system into a main serial system, and into branches and loops emanating from it. Then we optimize each of the component parts separately, and combine them into the main system. Each loop optimal return can be combined with the main system at the converging or diverging stage. Furthermore, the definition of what constitutes the main system and the loops is somewhat arbitrary. In general, then, there are several recursive procedures for optimizing a complex system. We shall give one approach to the problem of Figure 7. Choosing the best recursive optimization plan is difficult. However having even a nonoptimal recursive plan may be far better than simultaneously optimizing over all variables.

For the problem of Figure 7, as the stage numbering reveals, stages one through N have been chosen as the main system from which there is a diverging branch (stages $M1$ through 11) at stage p, a feedforward loop (stages $M2$ through 12) which diverges at stage k and converges at stage j, and a feedback loop (stages 13 through $M3$) which diverges at stage j and converges at stage k. The following is our step-by-step procedure for optimizing the complex system.

1. Optimize stages one through $j-1$ recursively to obtain $f_{j-1}(X_{j-1})$.

2. Optimize the branch system of stages $M1$ through 11 recursively to obtain $f_{M1}(X_{M1})$.

3. Optimize the branch of the feedforward loop (stages 12 through $M2$) to obtain $f_{M2}(X_{M2}, X_{02})$.

4. Optimize the branch of the feedback loop (stages $M3$ through 13) to obtain $f_{M3}(X_{M3}, X_{03})$.

5. At stage j combine the stage return r_j with f_{M2}, f_{M3}, and f_{j-1}, and then optimize over X_{02} as well as D_j to obtain $f_{j+M2+M3}(X_j, X_{M2}, X_{03})$, that is,

$$f_{j+M2+M3}((X_j, X_{M2}, X_{03}) =$$

$$\max_{X_{02}, D_j} \; [r_j(X_j, X_{02}, D_j) \circ f_{M2}(X_{M2}, X_{02}) \circ f_{M3}(X_{M3}, X_{03}) \circ f_{j-1}(X_{j-1})]$$

6. Optimize stages $j+1$ through $k-1$ to obtain

$$f_{k-1+M2+M3}(X_{k-1}, X_{M2}, X_{03}).$$

7. At stage k optimize over X_{03} as well as D_k to obtain $f_{k+M2+M3}((X_k)$, that is,

$$f_{k+M2+M3}(X_k) \; \max_{X_{03}, D_k} \; [r_k(X_k, X_{03}, D_k) \circ f_{k-1+M2+M3}(X_{k-1}, X_{M2}, X_{03})]$$

8. Optimize stages $k+1$ through $p-1$ to obtain $f_{p-1+M2+M3}(X_{p-1})$.

9. At stage p composite the diverging branch optimum return with the stage p return and $f_{p-1+M2+M3}$, and then optimize over D_p to obtain $f_{p+M1+M2+M3}(X_p)$, that is,

$$f_{p+M1+M2+M3}(X_p) = \max_{D_p} \; [r_p(X_p, D_p) \circ f_{M1}(X_{M1}) \circ f_{p-1+M2+M3}(X_{p-1})]$$

10. At stages $p + 1$ through N optimize recursively to obtain $f_{N+M1+M2+M3}(X_N)$.

During the analysis, sequential search may be used to direct X_{02} and X_{03} to their optimum values and thus reduce dimensionality.

As we have said, the procedure just given is just one way to optimize the system recursively. All we can suggest is that the basic principle of decomposing the system into elementary structures be adhered to. If this is followed, and if the main serial system and its substructures are chosen in a way yielding serial subsystems consisting of as many stages as possible, the resulting recursive optimization plan should be a good one.

When a loop structure dominates the system (for example, two or three stages forming a feedback loop), recursive optimization may be more difficult than optimizing over all variables simultaneously. As the number of stages connected serially increases, recursive optimization becomes more advantageous. For systems containing loops, additional state variables are required in a dynamic programming analysis. When a loop contains only two or three stages, the advantage of recursive analysis may be offset by state variable dimensionality.

EXERCISES

1. Solve the problem of Section 2 using backward recursion.

2. Solve the problem of Section 7 by absorbing the branch return at stage three. What difficulties occur?

3. Minimize the sum of the stage returns as a function of the inputs x_3 and x_{21}, for the problem with the structure given in Figure 8 and the data given in the table.

Table 6

Stage	Decision	Return	Transformation	Constraint
1	d_1	$0.1d_1^2$	—	$d_1 = x_1 + x_{01}$
11	d_{11}	$0.2d_{11}^2$	$x_{01} = x_{11} - d_{11}$	—
21	d_{21}	$375 - 10d_{21}$	$x_{11} = x_{21} + d_{21}$	—
2	d_2	$600 - 100x_2 + d_2$	$x_1 = x_2 + d_2$	—
3	d_3	$0.1(50 - d_3)^2$	$x_2 = x_3 + d_3$	—

4. Consider the chemical plant shown in Figure 9 [52]. Raw material is fed into a heater at the rate of 10,000 lb/day, where it is heated to a suitable temperature and sent to a reactor. The output from the reactor is product plus unreacted raw material. Part of the product is withdrawn from the

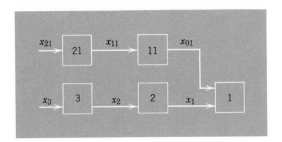

Fig. 8

stream in a separator and prepared for sale as pure product; the remaining
mixture is sent to a purifier unit which converts a portion of the mixture back
to raw materials. The output of the purifier unit is recycled back to the heater,
where it merges with the main stream. The inputs to the heater are 10,000
lb/day of new raw materials and x_{01} lb/day of recovered materials from the
output of stage 11. The output from the heater enters stage two, the reactor,
as a stream of x_2 lb/day of material heated to a temperature of $T°$. The
daily heater costs depend on the amount of material heated and the temperature attained; specifically, $r_3 = -10^{-7} T^2 x_2$, with T the stage-three decision
variable, subject to the restriction $200° \leq T \leq 450°$.

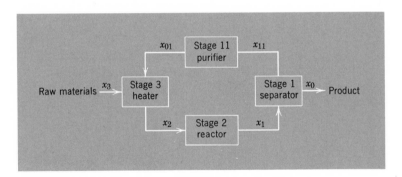

Fig. 9

Two different reactors, A and B, are under consideration for use at stage
two. Daily costs for reactor A are $r_2(x_2, T, A) = 3x_2$, and it achieves a conversion of $p_1(A) = 0.002T$ lb product/lb material processed; for reactor B
the daily costs are $r_2(x_2, T, B) = 2x_2$ with a conversion rate of $p_1(B) =
0.001T$ lb product/lb material processed. The output from the reactor is a
stream of $x_1 (= x_2)$ lb of mixture/day, of which a fraction p_1 is product and
the remainder is unconverted raw material.

Either of two separators, I or II, may be used at stage one, with daily
costs of $r_1(x_1, p_1, I) = 3x_1 + 100/p_1$, and $r_1(x_1, p_1, II) = x_1 + 200/p_1$, respectively. The separator outputs are pure product at the rate of x_0 lb/day
and x_{11} lb/day of a mixture consisting of the remaining product and the un-

Table 7

Stage, n	Input, x_n	Decision, d_n	Output	Return, $r_n(x_n, d_n)$	
1 (Separator)	x_1 lb/day (of mixture), fraction p_1 of product	I II	x_0 lb/day pure product $+ x_{11}$ lb/day mixture	$40x_0 - 3x_1 - 100/p_1$ $40x_0 - x_1 - 200/p_1$	(I) (II)
11 (Purifier)	x_{11} lb/day (mixture)	1	$x_{01} = 0.75x_{11}$	$-4\,x_{01}$	(1)
		2	$x_{01} = 0.50x_{11}$ lb/day raw material	$-3\,x_{01}$	(2)
2 (Reactor)	x_2 lb/day mixture at temperature T	A	$x_1 = x_2$ $p_1 = 0.002T$	$-3\,x_2$	(A)
		B	$x_1 = x_2$ $p_1 = 0.001T$	$-2\,x_2$	(B)
3 (Heater)	10,000 lb/day new raw material $+ x_{01}$ lb/day recovered raw material	Temperature $200° \le T \le 450°$	x_2 lb/day material at temperature T $x_2 = 10{,}000 + x_{01}$	$-10^{-7}T^2x_2$	

reacted raw material which is sent to the purifier. Two purifier designs, 1 and 2, are possible with daily costs of $r_{11}(x_{01}, 1) = 4x_{01}$ and $r_{11}(x_{01}, 2) = 3x_{01}$ respectively, where x_{01} is the lb/day of recovered raw material sent back to the heater. Purifier 1 converts 75% of the input into reusable raw material, while purifier 2 converts 50%. Table 7 summarizes the technical and operating data given. Determine optimal decisions to maximize the total return.

5. Give recursive equations for several alternative ways of absorbing the feed-forward and feedback loops of Figure 7 into the main serial system. Discuss the merits and drawbacks of each alternative.

VII

Infinite-Stage Systems

1. Introduction

Problems containing an infinite number of decisions arise in two fundamentally different ways. There is the natural extension of an N-stage system to an infinite-stage one, accomplished by letting N approach infinity. We can represent such a system by the model

$$\max \sum_{n=1}^{\infty} r_n(X_n, D_n)$$

$$\text{subject to } X_{n-1} = t_n(X_n, D_n), \qquad n = 1, 2 \dots$$

Of course, an infinite-stage model is meaningful only if, for all feasible combinations of the decision variables, the total return is bounded from above. Models of this type are used frequently when the stages correspond to time periods and when there are many periods. For example, consider the problem of determining an optimal monthly allocation of resources over a ten-year period. Although it is fictional to represent this 120-stage system by an infinite-stage model, the mathematical abstraction containing an infinite number of stages (infinite time horizon) can be very useful for understanding the structure of the optimal decision policy.

In general, we have seen that an optimal decision depends on both the stage and state of the system. However, when there are a very large number of stages remaining and there is regularity in the stage returns and transformations, we might expect the optimal decision to be independent of the particular stage number. For example, in the following equations, suppose f_{117} were approximately equal to f_{118}; then it would not be surprising to find the optimal decisions $D_{118}(X_{118})$ and $D_{119}(X_{119})$ given by

$$f_{118}(X_{118}) = \max_{D_{118}} [r(X_{118}, D_{118}) + f_{117}(X_{117})]$$

and

$$f_{119}(X_{119}) = \max_{D_{119}} [r(X_{119}, D_{119}) + f_{118}(X_{118})]$$

to be in close agreement. Note that the subscripts have been omitted from r so that the stage returns have identical functional forms. Carrying this argument one step further, we see that, under certain circumstances, the solution to the infinite-stage problem

$$f(X) = \lim_{n \to \infty} f_n(X_n) = \lim_{n \to \infty} [\max_{D_n} r(X_n, D_n) + f_{n-1}(t(X_n, D_n))]$$

$$= \max_{D} [r(X, D) + f(t(X, D))]$$

might serve as a good approximation to the optimal returns and decisions when there are a large number of stages remaining. A situation of this nature is represented in Figures 1 and 2. We see that $f_n(X_n)$ asymptotically

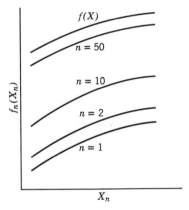

Fig. 1

approaches $f(X)$, and $D_n(X_n)$ approaches $D(X)$ in the limit. Presuming that we can solve the equation just given for $f(X)$ and $D(X)$, we see the advantage of doing so. Rather than solving for the entire sequences $f_1(X_1)$, $f_2(X_2), \ldots, f_{120}(X_{120})$, and $D_1(X_1), D_2(X_2), \ldots, D_{120}(X_{120})$, we can, instead, solve for $f(X)$, $D(X)$ and perhaps only for the first few members of the original sequences. If we want numerical results, $f(X)$ and $D(X)$ can serve as approximations, in addition to providing a guide to the structure of the optimal solution. Borrowing terminology from differential equations, the optimal stage-invariant solution, $f(X)$ and $D(X)$, are called the *steady state* solution. In many practical situations where the transient effects are negligible, only the steady state solution is required.

To introduce the second kind of infinite-stage process, we again assume that stages correspond to time periods, although this is not the only possible interpretation. Here the horizon is finite, but the time periods are very small. Specifically, the time between successive decisions is negligible compared with the horizon. In the limit, as the size of the time periods approaches zero, we assume that decisions are made continuously. Thus for any finite horizon there will be an infinite number of decisions.

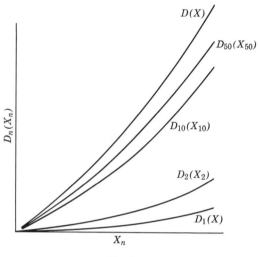

Fig. 2

Automatic control systems are often of this nature. For example, in a chemical process, controlled by an analogue computer, the yield (or output) and the temperature (control or independent variable) are adjusted continually. The objective is to find the temperature function of output and time yielding optimal control.

A different problem of this type is finding the shortest distance between two points in a finite-dimensional Euclidean space, or simply in two dimensions of proving that the shortest distance between two points (A, B) is a straight line. We can couch this problem in the following terms: A moving point (C) starting at point A must travel to point B in such a way that the distance traveled is minimum. We assume that in moving from A or B, point C takes a very large number of very short steps. The problem is to determine the direction of each of the steps of infinitesimal length so that the sum of the distances traveled is minimum. By taking an infinite number of these infinitesimal steps, point C traces out a curve of shortest distance between A and B. We know intuitively that this curve is a straight line.

A model of a continuous multistage process analogous to our model of a discrete multistage process

$$\max_{D_n} \sum_{n=1}^{N} r_n(X_n, D_n)$$

$$\text{subject to } X_{n-1} = t_n(X_n, D_n), \qquad n = 1, \ldots, N$$

$$X_N = k$$

is

$$\max_{U(t)} \int_{t_1}^{t_2} F(t, X, U)\, dt$$

$$\text{subject to } \frac{dX}{dt} = g(t, X, U), \qquad t_1 \le t \le t_2$$

$$X_1 = X(t_1) = k$$

Table 1 shows the correspondence between the common components of the respective models. We changed notation in the model of the continuous multistage process in order to conform with conventional symbolism. As shown in Table 1, the main differences between the two models are that the stage index n is replaced by a continuous stage parameter t which usually represents time or distance; the sum of stage returns is replaced by the integral of stage returns, and the difference equations which represent the stage transformations are replaced by differential equations.

Table 1

	Discrete Model Index $n, n = 1, \ldots, N$ N = initial condition	Continuous Model Parameter $t, t_1 \le t \le t_2$ t_1 = initial condition
Decision variable	D	U
State variable	X	X
Stage return	$r_n(X_n, D_n)$	$F(t, X, U)\, dt$
Total return	$\displaystyle\sum_{n=1}^{N} r_n(X_n, D_n)$	$\displaystyle\int_{t_1}^{t_2} F(t, X, U)\, dt$
Stage transformation	$X_{n-1} = t_n(X_n, D_n)$	$\dfrac{dX}{dt} = g(t, X, U)$

The determination of a function to optimize an integral is a problem in the *calculus of variations*. There is a close connection between dynamic programming and the calculus of variations. The formal relationship is that a dynamic programming approach can be used to derive the usual necessary conditions; in addition, discrete recursive optimization can be used to find approximate numerical solutions to computationally difficult variational problems.

We see there are two ways of creating an infinite-stage decision process from a finite one; by preserving the discreteness of the stages and allowing the stage index to extend to infinity; and by replacing the discrete stage index with a continuous one. We call the former a *discrete infinite-stage decision process* and the latter a *continuous infinite-stage decision process*. The total return in the discrete case is given by an infinite series and by an integral in the continuous case. The corresponding stage transformations are given by difference and differential equations respectively. Thus the two are closely related. Sacrificing elegance for simplicity, we shall treat them separately, beginning with the discrete infinite-stage process.

2. An Elementary Infinite-Stage Discrete Decision Process

We consider a problem containing a quadratic objective function and an infinite number of decisions. In particular,

$$\min_{d_1, d_2, \ldots} \sum_{n=1}^{\infty} [c_1 d_n^2 + c_2(x_n - d_n)^2], \qquad c_1, c_2 > 0$$

subject to $x_{n-1} = b(x_n - d_n), \qquad 0 < b < 1$

$$0 \leq d_n \leq x_n, \qquad n = 1, 2, \ldots$$

The dynamic programming formulation is

$$f_1(x_1) = \min_{0 \leq d_1 \leq x_1} [c_1 d_1^2 + c_2(x_1 - d_1)^2]$$

and

$$f_n(x_n) = \min_{0 \leq d_n \leq x_n} [c_1 d_n^2 + c_2(x_n - d_n)^2 + f_{n-1}(b(x_n - d_n))], \qquad n = 2, 3, \ldots$$

Starting with a one-stage process, we find that a necessary and sufficient condition for d_1 to be a minimum is

$$c_1 d_1 - c_2(x_1 - d_1) = 0$$

so

$$d_1(x_1) = \left(\frac{c_2}{c_1 + c_2}\right) x_1$$

and

$$f_1(x_1) = \left(\frac{c_1 c_2}{c_1 + c_2}\right) x_1^2$$

Substituting the result for $f_1(x_1)$ into the two-stage equation, we have

$$f_2(x_2) = \min_{0 \leq d_2 \leq x_2} [c_1 d_2^2 + c_2(x_2 - d_2)^2 + \frac{c_1 c_2}{c_1 + c_2} b^2(x_2 - d_2)^2]$$

Again it is simple, although algebraically messy, to determine $d_2(x_2)$ and

$f_2(x_2)$. Partially differentiating the above expression in brackets with respect to d_2 and setting the derivative to zero yields

$$d_2(x_2) = \left[\frac{c_2 + \dfrac{c_1 c_2 b^2}{c_1 + c_2}}{c_1 + c_2 + \dfrac{c_1 c_2 b^2}{c_1 + c_2}} \right] x_2$$

and

$$f_2(x_2) = \left[\frac{c_1 c_2 + \dfrac{c_1^2 c_2 b^2}{c_1 + c_2}}{c_1 + c_2 + \dfrac{c_1 c_2 b^2}{c_1 + c_2}} \right] x_2^2$$

We could continue to compute the sequence $d_3(x_3)$, $f_3(x_3)$, and so on. The only difficulties would be algebraic. Even for specific values of c_1, c_2, and b, the computation of $d_{10}(x_{10})$, or even worse, $d_{50}(x_{50})$, is extremely cumbersome. Furthermore, assuming that we do have, say, a fifty-stage process, it is not until $d_{50}(x_{50})$ is computed that we can retrace the optimal solution. Perhaps, by just solving for $\lim_{n \to \infty} d_n(x_n)$, we can obtain a good approximation to $d_n(x_n)$ for large values of n.

Before turning to the infinite-stage problem, we can extract some useful general results from the finite problem. Note that for $n = 1, 2, d_n(x_n)$ is a linear function of x_n, and $f_n(x_n)$ is a quadratic function of x_n. We want to establish this in general. We proceed by induction and assume

$$f_{n-1}(x_{n-1}) = k_{n-1} x_{n-1}^2 = k_{n-1} b^2 (x_n - d_n)^2$$

then

$$f_n(x_n) = \min_{0 \le d_n \le x_n} [c_1 d_n^2 + c_2 (x_n - d_n)^2 + k_{n-1} b^2 (x_n - d_n)^2]$$

The solution for $d_n(x_n)$ is given by the equation

$$2c_1 d_n - 2(c_2 + k_{n-1} b^2)(x_n - d_n) = 0$$

or

$$d_n = \left(\frac{c_2 + k_{n-1} b^2}{c_1 + c_2 + k_{n-1} b^2} \right) x_n$$

and

$$f_n(x_n) = \left(\frac{c_1 c_2 + c_1 k_{n-1} b^2}{c_1 + c_2 + k_{n-1} b^2} \right) x_n^2$$

Hence our assumptions about the linearity of $d_n(x_n)$ and the quadratic nature of $f_n(x_n)$ are true for all n. In particular, we will make use of this result as n approaches infinity.

For the infinite-stage system, we have the equation

$$f(x) = \min_{0 \le d \le x} [c_1 d^2 + c_2 (x - d)^2 + f(b(x - d))]$$

In general, there are questions concerning the existence and uniqueness of solutions to such a functional equation. Bellman [10] covers this problem in great detail and establishes the existence and uniqueness of a solution for the illustrative problem.†

The problem of finding a solution still remains, since the unknown function f appears on both sides of the equation. But for the example, we have shown that $f(x)$ is a quadratic function, so there are no formidable difficulties. Using the result

$$f(x) = kx^2 \quad \text{where } k \text{ is unknown}$$

we have

$$kx^2 = \min_{0 \le d \le x} [c_1 d^2 + c_2(x - d)^2 + kb^2(x - d)^2]$$

The right-hand side of the equation just given is the same as the right-hand side of the recursive equation obtained in the proof of the quadratic nature of $f_n(x_n)$, so

$$d(x) = \left(\frac{c_2 + kb^2}{c_1 + c_2 + kb^2} \right) x$$

This result for $d(x)$ allows us to determine k, that is,

$$kx^2 = \left(\frac{c_1(c_2 + kb^2)}{c_1 + c_2 + kb^2} \right) x^2$$

or
$$b^2 k^2 + (c_1 + c_2 - c_1 b^2)\, k - c_1 c_2 = 0$$

Therefore

$$k = \frac{c_1 b^2 - c_1 - c_2 \pm [(c_1 + c_2 - c_1 b^2)^2 + 4b^2\, c_1 c_2]^{1/2}}{2b^2}$$

Unfortunately, the term under the square root is not a perfect square, but it can be shown that we want the positive value of the square root and that it leads to a nonnegative, real value of k.

Taking the particular case $c_1 = 3$, $c_2 = 1$, $b^2 = \frac{1}{2}$ yields $k = 1$, $f(x) = x^2$, and $d(x) = x/3$. Comparing $x/3$ with $d_1(x_1) = x_1/4$, and $d_2(x_2) = 0.314x_2$, we see that convergence is quite rapid even for this rather large value of b. Convergence accelerates as b gets smaller. Thus at any stage after two or three, the infinite-stage solution $d(x)$ can be used to approximate the sequence $d_n(x_n)$.

Although we obtained the steady state solution very easily in the illustration, in general, solving the infinite-stage optimization equation can be laborious since an unknown function appears on both sides of the equation. Bellman [10] gives methods for solving this type of equation. We shall study them in the Section 3.

---

† Theorem I (page 12) [10].

3. Successive Approximations

We shall develop iterative procedures for solving the infinite-stage optimization equation

$$f(X) = \max_D \ [r(X, D) + f(t(X, D))]$$

In some way, the difficulty caused by the unknown optimal function f appearing on both sides of the equation must be overcome.

There are two ways to proceed. Since the object is to eliminate the unknown function in the brackets, an obvious procedure is to make a guess for $f(X)$ and then proceed iteratively. That is, let $f_0(X)$ be the initial guess, and define

$$f_1(X) = \max_D \ [r(X, D) + f_0(t(X, D))]$$

and, in general,

$$f_n(X) = \max_D \ [r(X, D) + f_{n-1}(t(X, D))], \qquad n = 1, 2, \ldots$$

Applying this method of successive approximations to the illustration of Section 2 and setting $f_0(x) = 0.0$, yields

$$f_1(x) = \min_{0 \le d \le x} \ [c_1 d^2 + c_2(x - d)^2]$$

and

$$f_n(x) = \min_{0 \le d \le x} \ [c_1 d^2 + c_2(x - d)^2 + f_{n-1}(b(x - d))], \qquad n = 2, 3, \ldots$$

These recursive equations are identical to the original recursive equations that were given in Section 2. In essence then, we are back where we started from. If using the infinite-stage solution to determine the structure of the finite-stage solution is our objective, we find that this method of successive approximation is unsatisfactory, since the successive approximation involves the solution of the original finite-stage problem. There is, however, a more powerful procedure.

Just as successive approximations can be initiated with a guess of the optimal return, so it is also possible to begin with a guess of the optimal policy. This duality of choice exists because, given a policy or decision function $D(X)$, we can find the corresponding return function from the equation

$$f(X) = r(X, D(X)) + f(t(X, D(X)))$$

Similarly, given a return function $f(X)$, we can solve the equation just given for the corresponding optimal policy function $D(X)$.

Denote the first guess of an optimal policy function by $D_0(X)$. Then the function $f_0(X)$ may be found by solving

$$f_0(X) = r(X, D_0(X)) + f_0(t(X, D_0(X)))$$

Since the unknown function $f_0(X)$ appears on both sides of the equation, its solution may be computationally difficult. Usually, numerical methods are used to obtain approximate solutions.

Given $f_0(X)$, we find the optimal policy to the problem of

$$\max_{D} \; [r(X, D) + f_0(t(X, D))]$$

This policy is denoted by $D_1(X)$. Then the function $f_1(X)$ may be found by solving

$$f_1(X) = r(X, D_1(X)) + f_1(t(X, D_1(X)))$$

Bellman [10] calls this procedure *approximation* in *policy space,* because the approximation is guided by the optimal sequence of decision functions. He indicates that rigorous proof for the convergence of the sequences $D_n(X)$ and $f_n(X)$ determined from approximation in policy space to the optimal policy and return $D(X)$ and $f(X)$ is sometimes difficult to obtain. In many special cases, convergence can be established and is often very rapid. For example, there is an efficient algorithm for solving infinite-stage Markovian decision processes based on policy space approximations.

We actually used approximation in policy space before, although we did not call it such. The one-at-a-time method,† based on guessing part of an optimal policy, was used for state variable reduction. Here our objective is quite different, but the basic idea of guessing an optimal or part of an optimal policy is the same.

Flow charts for the first successive approximation procedure (which might be called approximation in return space) and successive approximations in policy space are given in Figures 3 and 4 respectively. There is a subtle difference between the two which is deeper than the superficial difference in the initial guess. Actually each procedure could be started with a guess of either the optimal policy or return. The essential difference is that approximation in return space involves only a series of sequential optimizations. This is almost identical to finite-stage dynamic programming. Approximation in policy space involves sequential optimization together with successive adjustments of the optimal return using the functional equation

$$f(X) = r(X, D(X)) + f(t(X, D(X)))$$

---

† Chapter IV, Section 11.

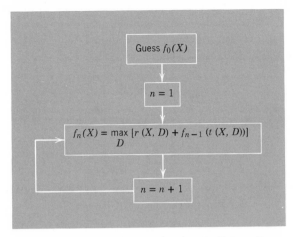

Fig. 3. Algorithm for Approximation in Return Space.

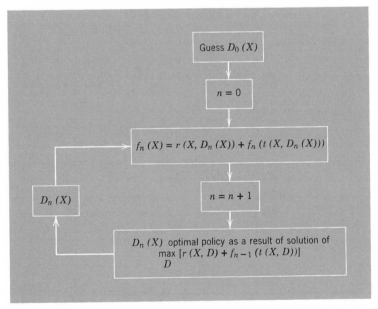

Fig. 4. Algorithm for Approximation in Policy Space.

To fix ideas about approximation in policy space, we return to the example of Section 2. The infinite-stage equation is

$$f(x) = \min_{0 \le d \le x} [c_1 d^2 + c_2 (x - d)^2 + f(b(x - d))]$$

As an initial guess for an optimal policy, we set

$$d_0(x) = \left(\frac{c_2}{c_1 + c_2}\right) x$$

We make this choice of $d_0(x)$ because it corresponds to an initial choice of $f_0(x) = 0.0$. Thus we can make a numerical comparison between the results from the two approximation procedures.

Substituting $d_0(x)$ into the equation for $f(x)$ yields

$$f_0(x) = \left(\frac{c_1 c_2}{c_1 + c_2}\right) x^2 + f_0\left(\left(\frac{bc_1}{c_1 + c_2}\right) x\right)$$

Solving this equation using the known quadratic nature of $f(x)$, we obtain

$$f_0(x) = k_0 x^2, \quad k_0 = \frac{c_1 c_2 (c_1 + c_2)}{(c_1 + c_2)^2 - b^2 c_1^2}$$

We now determine $d_1(x)$ as the policy that minimizes

$$c_1 d^2 + c_2 (x - d)^2 + k_0 b^2 (x - d)^2$$

$$\text{subject to } 0 \leq d \leq x$$

This yields

$$d_1(x) = \left(\frac{c_2 + k_0 b^2}{c_1 + c_2 + k_0 b^2}\right) x$$

and

$$f_1(x) = \left(\frac{c_1(c_2 + k_0 b^2) + c_1^2 c_2}{(c_1 + c_2 + k_0 b^2)^2}\right) x^2 + f_1\left(\left(\frac{bc_1}{c_1 + c_2 + k_0 b^2}\right) x\right)$$

Solving this equation, we obtain

$$f_1(x) = k_1 x^2, \quad k_1 = \frac{c_1(c_2 + k_0 b^2)^2 + c_1^2 c_2}{(c_1 + c_2 + k_0 b^2)^2 - b^2 c_1^2}$$

To compare numerically the results obtained from both approximation schemes, we choose the parameter values $c_1 = 3$, $c_2 = 1$, $b^2 = \frac{1}{2}$ for which it may be recalled that $f(x) = x^2$ and $d(x) = x/3$. Table 2 gives a summary of the results. The policy approximation procedure converges faster since it employs both optimization and adjustment of the optimal return using the infinite-stage equation.

Table 2

	Return Space		Policy Space	
Guess	$f = 0.0$		$d = 0.250x$	
n	f_n	d_n	f_n	d_n
0	0.0	—	$1.043x^2$	$0.250x$
1	$0.750x^2$	$0.250x$	$1.000x^2$	$0.337x$
2	$0.945x^2$	$0.314x$	$1.000x^2$	$0.333x$
3	$0.987x^2$	$0.329x$		
4	$0.995x^2$	$0.332x$		

4. Infinite-Stage Markovian Decision Processes

A Markov chain is described by a transition matrix $P = \{p_{ij}\}$, where p_{ij} is the probability of transition from state i to state j. In a Markov decision process there is also a return matrix $R = \{r_{ij}\}$, where r_{ij} is the return associated with a transition from state i to j. Decision making arises when we permit a choice among various transition and return matrices. To be specific, assume that if the system is at state i, then $d_n = k$, $k = 1, \ldots, K$ implies that the transition probabilities and returns are $p_{ij}(d_n = k)$ and $r_{ij}(d_n = k)$ respectively.[†] Furthermore, assume that if the decision alternatives are time-invariant, that is, if $d_m = d_n$

$$p_{ij}(d_n) = p_{ij}(d_m) \quad \text{and} \quad r_{ij}(d_n) = r_{ij}(d_m)$$

Under these assumptions we derived the recursive equations [‡]

$$\bar{f}_1(i) = \max_{d_1 = 1, \ldots, K} q_i(d_1), \quad i = 1, \ldots, M$$

and

$$\bar{f}_n(i) = \max_{d_n = 1, \ldots, K} [q_i(d_n) + \sum_{j=1}^{M} p_{ij}(d_n) \bar{f}_{n-1}(j)], \quad i = 1, \ldots, M$$
$$n = 2, \ldots, N$$

with

$$q_i(d_n) = \sum_{j=1}^{M} p_{ij}(d_n) r_{ij}(d_n), \quad i = 1, \ldots, M$$

The optimal expected return from a system in state i with n transitions remaining is given by $\bar{f}_n(i)$.

We are interested in the optimal decisions and returns for large values of n. We have shown, by example, that as n gets large, d_n depends only on the state and not on the stage of the system, and that the optimal return per stage approaches a constant. Our object is generalizing these results for steady state behavior and developing a procedure based on approximation in policy space for finding the optimal decisions and optimal return per stage. The development follows Howard [38], and is only an introduction to his results on the relations between dynamic programming and Markov processes.

Before delving into infinite-stage Markov decision processes, we give some basic results for steady state Markov chains. We have shown that the probability of being in state j at stage $n - 1$, denoted by $\pi_{n-1}(j)$, is given by the simultaneous linear difference equations,

---

† Although we have not subscripted k with an i, the number of alternatives from each state can be different.

‡ Chapter V, Section 4.

$$\pi_{n-1}(j) = \sum_{i=1}^{M} p_{ij}\pi_n(i), \qquad j = 1, \ldots, M$$

Suppose there are N stages, so that the vector π_N denotes the starting state; then under special conditions on the transition matrix P

$$\lim_{n, N \to \infty} \pi_{N-n}(i) = \pi(i)$$

exists independently of the starting state π_N. The probabilities $\pi(i)$ are called the *steady state probabilities* and are interpreted as the probability of being in state i after a large number of transitions, regardless of the starting state. Following Howard, we call Markov chains with this property *completely ergodic*. Completely ergodic Markov chains are quite common in practice. A necessary and sufficient condition for complete ergodicity is that some power of the P matrix (that is, P^n, where n is any integer) contains all positive elements. Thus if all of the elements of P are positive, the Markov chain is completely ergodic. Taking the limit of the state probability equations, we have

$$\pi(j) = \sum_{i=1}^{M} p_{ij}\,\pi(i), \qquad j = 1, \ldots, M$$

There are M linear, homogeneous equations in M unknowns. It can be shown that only $M - 1$ of them are independent. Thus $M - 1$ of the equations together with

$$\sum_{j=1}^{M} \pi(j) = 1$$

determine the steady state probabilities.

For example, given

$$P = \begin{pmatrix} \frac{1}{2} & \frac{1}{2} \\ \frac{3}{4} & \frac{1}{4} \end{pmatrix}$$

we obtain the equations

$$\pi(1) = \tfrac{1}{2}\pi(1) + \tfrac{3}{4}\pi(2)$$

$$\pi(2) = \tfrac{1}{2}\pi(1) + \tfrac{1}{4}\pi(2)$$

$$\pi(1) + \pi(2) = 1$$

Taking one of the first two equations and the third and solving simultaneously, the solution is found to be $\pi(1) = \tfrac{3}{5}$ and $\pi(2) = \tfrac{2}{5}$.

To proceed one step at a time, we introduce returns into the infinite-stage Markov process. Let the return from a transition from state i to j be r_{ij}. For a completely ergodic Markov process, the expected return per stage, after a large number of transitions, is given by

$$g = \sum_{i=1}^{M} \sum_{j=1}^{M} r_{ij} \, p_{ij} \, \pi(i)$$

Our justification of this equation is informal. The probability of being in state i in the steady state is $\pi(i)$. Hence, the steady state probability of a transition from state i to state j is

$$p_{ij} \, \pi(i)$$

The expected return from a transition from state i to state j, in steady state, is

$$r_{ij} \, p_{ij} \, \pi(i)$$

Summing over i and j, we obtain

$$g = \sum_{i=1}^{M} \sum_{j=1}^{M} r_{ij} \, p_{ij} \, \pi(i)$$

Substituting

$$q_i = \sum_{j=1}^{M} r_{ij} p_{ij}$$

we can simplify the equation for g to

$$g = \sum_{i=1}^{M} q_i \, \pi(i)$$

In other words, the expected return from a single transition is computed simply by multiplying the immediate expected return from a state (q_i) by the steady state probability of being in that state ($\pi(i)$) and then summing over all states.

For the example with the transition matrix as given previously and

$$R = \begin{pmatrix} 0 & 6 \\ -3 & 8 \end{pmatrix}$$

we have

$$q_1 = \tfrac{1}{2}(0) + \tfrac{1}{2}(6) = 3$$

$$q_2 = \tfrac{3}{4}(-3) + \tfrac{1}{4}(8) = -\tfrac{1}{4}$$

and

$$g = 3(\tfrac{3}{5}) - \tfrac{1}{4}(\tfrac{2}{5}) = \tfrac{17}{10}$$

We emphasize that g is independent of the starting state. However, this does not mean that the total expected return is independent of the starting state. The total expected return for a system in state i with n transitions remaining (denoted by $v_n(i)$) is given by the equations

$$v_1(i) = q_i, \qquad i = 1, \ldots, M$$

and
$$v_n(i) = q_i + \sum_{j=1}^{M} p_{ij} v_{n-1}(j), \qquad i = 1, \ldots, M$$

Since the expected return from a single transition is g for large n, $v_n(i)$ is a linear function of n with slope g; that is, for large n,

$$v_n(i) = ng + v_i$$

where the intercept v_i depends on the starting state. We note that

$$v_n(i) - v_n(j) = v_i - v_j$$

so that $v_i - v_j$ is a measure of the relative advantage (or disadvantage) of starting in state i rather than j.

Substituting the linear approximation for $v_n(i)$, valid for large n, into the defining equations for $v_n(i)$ yields

$$ng + v_i = q_i + \sum_{j=1}^{M} p_{ij} [(n-1)g + v_j]$$

or
$$v_i = q_i + \sum_{j=1}^{M} p_{ij} v_j - g, \qquad i = 1, \ldots, M$$

We have M simultaneous linear equations in $M + 1$ unknowns ($v_1, \ldots, v_M, g$); furthermore g can be determined independently, using the equation

$$g = \sum_{i=1}^{M} q_i \pi(i)$$

Although this reduces the problem to M equations in M unknowns, the equations still cannot be solved for the absolute values of v_i. The reason is that only $M - 1$ of the equations are independent. On the other hand, if we fix one of the v_i's arbitrarily, say $v_M = 0$, the remaining v_i's and g can be determined. The values of v_i determined will be relative to v_M, and thus differ from the actual values of v_i by a constant. The value of g determined will be correct, since we have shown that g is independent of the v_i's.

For the P and R matrices just given, we have

$$v_1 = 3 + \tfrac{1}{2} v_1 + \tfrac{1}{2} v_2 - g$$
$$v_2 = -\tfrac{1}{4} + \tfrac{3}{4} v_1 + \tfrac{1}{4} v_2 - g$$

Upon setting $v_2 = 0$, we obtain

$$g + \tfrac{1}{2} v_1 = 3$$
$$g - \tfrac{3}{4} v_1 = -\tfrac{1}{4}$$

which has the solution $g = \tfrac{17}{10}$ and $v_1 = \tfrac{13}{5}$. Had we set $v_1 = 0$, the solution obtained would have been $g = \tfrac{17}{10}$ and $v_2 = -\tfrac{13}{5}$. Any initial choice of v_1 or v_2 yields $g = \frac{17}{10}$ and $v_1 - v_2 = \frac{13}{5}$. These relative values are vital for the approximation in policy space.

The goal in an infinite-stage decision process is to maximize the expected return per stage, which we denote by $g(d)$. As before, $d = k$, $k = 1, \ldots, K$, implies that the transition probabilities and returns from state i are $p_{ij}(d = k)$ and $r_{ij}(d = k)$ respectively. The subscript n has been omitted from d because we are interested in finding the steady state policy that maximizes g, independent of the stage. It is sufficient to consider such a policy, when dealing with a completely ergodic Markov chain, because, for large n, the state probabilities are independent of n and the initial state.†

Of course, one way to maximize $g(d)$ is to compute g for all decision policies. But with M states and K feasible decisions from each state, there are K^M policies, which is a large number for even relatively small values of M and K. A much more efficient way to find the policy that maximizes $g(d)$ is to use approximation in policy space to solve an infinite-stage recursion equation.

Let $\bar{f}$ be the optimal expected return per stage as the number of stages becomes very large, that is,

$$\bar{f} = \lim_{n \to \infty} \frac{f_n(i)}{n}, \qquad i = 1, \ldots, M$$

We note that $\bar{f}$ is independent of the starting state and, in fact,

$$\bar{f} = \max_{d = 1, \ldots, K} g(d)$$

where

$$g(d) = q_i(d) + \sum_{j=1}^{M} p_{ij}(d)\, v_j(d) - v_i(d)$$

We begin the approximation in policy space by guessing a policy d_0 and calculating the corresponding expected return g_0 and the relative values v_{i0} as explained above. Howard calls this the *value determination operation*. Then to determine a better policy, if one exists, we maximize g using the current values of v_i, that is, (v_{i0}) by solving

$$\max_{d = 1, \ldots, K} \left[q_i(d) + \sum_{j=1}^{M} p_{ij}(d)\, v_{j0} - v_{i0} \right], \qquad i = 1, \ldots, M$$

Howard calls this the *policy improvement routine*. In the maximization it would make no difference if a constant were added to each v_i. This is fortunate since we know only the relative values of v_i.

---

† When all of the g's are equal, the object is to maximize the v_i's. See Howard [38] for an example.

The value of d that maximizes g is used as a next guess for an optimal policy (d_1). Given d_1, we use the value determination operation to determine the corresponding values of g_1, and v_{i1}. In general, $g_1 \geq g_0$; if $g_1 = g_0$, then $g_1 = f$, and d_1 is an optimal policy. Otherwise we return to the policy improvement routine using v_{i1} and determine a new decision policy. Howard calls the value determination operation, together with the policy improvement routine, the *policy iteration method*. It is a particular application of approximation in policy space. The policy improvement routine is the optimization part of approximation in policy space. The value determination operation solves for the corresponding optimal return. Howard has proved that the policy iteration method yields monotone convergence to the optimal g, that is, $g_m > g_{m-1}$, or when there is no improvement ($g_m = g_{m-1}$) the optimal average expected return and an optimal decision policy have been found.

He has extended the policy iteration method in several ways, including the removal of the complete ergodicity assumption and the consideration of cost discounting. He has also developed similar algorithms for continuous time Markov processes.†

We conclude with an illustration of the policy iteration method. There are two alternative decision and return matrices, with $d = 1$

$$P_1 = \begin{pmatrix} \frac{1}{2} & \frac{1}{2} \\ \frac{3}{4} & \frac{1}{4} \end{pmatrix} \quad \text{and} \quad R_1 = \begin{pmatrix} 0 & 6 \\ -3 & 8 \end{pmatrix}$$

and with $d = 2$

$$P_2 = \begin{pmatrix} 1 & 0 \\ \frac{1}{2} & \frac{1}{2} \end{pmatrix} \quad \text{and} \quad R_2 = \begin{pmatrix} 2 & 4 \\ 1 & -1 \end{pmatrix}$$

In Chapter V, Section 4, we solved this problem for four stages and found that with more than one stage remaining, if the system is in state two, the optimal decision is $d = 1$, and if the system is in state one, the optimal decision is $d = 2$, and also $g = 2$. Let us verify that this is the steady state solution.

To illustrate the policy iteration method, we begin with another solution, say $d_0 = 1$ from both states. The relevent probabilities and returns are then P_1 and R_1. Earlier we found that in this case, $g_0 = \frac{17}{10}$, and with $v_{20} = 0$, $v_{10} = \frac{13}{5}$. This completes our first value determination operation, and we turn to the policy improvement routine. For state one,

$$g(1) = 3 + \tfrac{1}{2}(\tfrac{13}{5}) - \tfrac{13}{5} = \tfrac{17}{10}$$

and

$$g(2) = 2 + 1(\tfrac{13}{5}) - \tfrac{13}{5} = 2$$

† It is interesting that an infinite-stage Markov decision process also can be solved by linear programming.

hence
$$d_1 = 2$$

For state two,

$$g(1) = -\tfrac{1}{4} + \tfrac{3}{4}(\tfrac{13}{5}) = \tfrac{17}{10}$$

and
$$g(2) = 0 + \tfrac{1}{2}(\tfrac{13}{5}) = \tfrac{13}{10}$$

hence
$$d_1 = 1$$

Turning again to the value determination operation, and using d_1, the relevant probabilities and returns are

$$P = \begin{pmatrix} 1 & 0 \\ \tfrac{3}{4} & \tfrac{1}{4} \end{pmatrix} \qquad R = \begin{pmatrix} 2 & 4 \\ -3 & 8 \end{pmatrix}$$

Setting $v_{21} = 0$, we have

$$v_{11} = 2 + v_{11} - g_1$$

and
$$0 = -\tfrac{1}{4} + \tfrac{3}{4}v_{11} - g_1$$

Thus $g_1 = 2$ and $v_{11} = 3$. Using $v_{11} = 3$ and $v_{21} = 0$ in the policy improvement routine yields for state one,

$$g(1) = 3 + \tfrac{1}{2}(3) - 3 = \tfrac{3}{2}$$

and
$$g(2) = 2 + 1(3) - 3 = 2$$

hence
$$d_2 = 2$$

For state two,

$$g(1) = -\tfrac{1}{4} + \tfrac{3}{4}(3) = 2$$

and
$$g(2) = 0 + \tfrac{1}{2}(3) = \tfrac{3}{2}$$

hence
$$d_2 = 1$$

The last two iterations produced the same decisions, consequently the optimal decision from state one is $d = 2$ and from state two, $d = 1$, with $g = 2$. We verified our hypothesis that the solution determined from the four-stage process is, in fact, the steady state solution.

5. The Calculus of Variations

Problems in the calculus of variations involve the determination of a function that optimizes an integral of the function. One of the simplest cases is to determine a function $x(t)$ optimizing the integral

$$\int_{t_1}^{t_2} F(t, x, x') \, dt, \qquad x' = \frac{dx}{dt}$$

and satisfying the boundary conditions

$$x(t_1) = x_1 \quad \text{and} \quad x(t_2) = x_2$$

It is assumed that F has continuous second partial derivatives with respect to t, x, and x'.

In a decision-making context, we assume that at the point (x, t), we make the decision x' and obtain a return of $F(t, x, x')\, dt$ and an output of $(x + dx)$ at the point $(t + dt)$. This problem is a special case of the variational problem posed in Section 1, except that a second boundary condition $x_2 = x(t_2)$ has been added. The vector state variable X is a scalar variable x, the vector decision variable U is a scalar variable u, and

$$x' = g(t, x, u) = u$$

Since x' can be substituted directly for u in $F(t, x, u)$ to obtain $F(t, x, x')$, the constraint $x' = g(t, x, u)$ can be omitted.

The main result for this problem is the famous Euler condition

$$\frac{d}{dt}(F_{x'}) - F_x = 0$$

or in expanded form †

$$F_{x'x'}\, x'' + F_{xx'}\, x' + F_{tx'} - F_x = 0$$

The Euler condition is necessary for a maximum or a minimum. It is analogous to the condition that the first derivative must vanish in the determination of ordinary maxima and minima by the differential calculus.

Before proceeding further, we give the classic example of proving that the shortest distance between two points on a plane is a straight line. The distance between two points on a plane (t_1, x_1) and (t_2, x_2) connected by a continuously differentiable curve $x(t)$ can be expressed as

$$\int_{t_1}^{t_2} [1 + (x')^2]^{1/2}\, dt$$

We want to choose the curve $x(t)$ between the points (t_1, x_1) and (t_2, x_2) that minimizes the integral just given.

Evaluating the partial derivatives $F_{x'}$ and F_x, we obtain

$$F_{x'} = x'[1 + (x')^2]^{-1/2}$$

and

$$F_x = 0$$

---

† The notation F_x indicates a partial derivative of F with respect to x. For example

$$F_x = \frac{\partial F}{\partial x} \quad \text{and} \quad F_{xx'} = \frac{\partial^2 F}{\partial x \partial x'}$$

Thus the Euler condition yields

$$x'' \left[\frac{\partial}{\partial x'} [x'(1 + (x')^2)^{-1/2}] \right] = 0$$

This is satisfied by $x'' = 0$. Hence

$$x' = c_1 \quad \text{and} \quad x = c_1 t + c_2$$

The constants c_1 and c_2 are determined from the boundary conditions x_1 and x_2.

Our understanding of the physical situation is now needed to draw the conclusion that the straight line is, in fact, the minimizing curve. To be rigorous, all that we have shown is that a straight line satisfies the necessary conditions for a minimizing curve. Direct calculation can be used to distinguish among various alternatives that satisfy the Euler condition. This is usually easier than applying the Legendre, Weierstrass, or other conditions that differentiate between relative maxima, minima, and other stationary points.

Unfortunately, for situations beyond the very elementary, it is unusual to obtain closed-form solutions from the Euler condition. The Euler condition is a second-order partial differential equation and, for all but the simplest forms of F, is nonlinear. Thus the applicability of the calculus of variations as an optimization tool is greatly diminished unless we settle for numerical solutions. But even the determination of numerical solutions is easier said than done. The numerical solution of the Euler equation presents a thorny problem. The problem arises because of the boundary conditions

$$x_1 = x(t_1) \quad \text{and} \quad x_2 = x(t_2)$$

that must be satisfied. The numerical solution of two-point boundary differential equations is enormously more difficult than the corresponding problem with only initial or final conditions. The reason is quite simple.

To evaluate the two constants in the solution of a second-order differential equation, two boundary conditions are needed. When both of these conditions are, say, initial conditions, that is,

$$x_1 = x(t_1) \quad \text{and} \quad x_1' = x'(t_1)$$

there is a satisfactory numerical procedure. The basic method of solution is to begin at t_1, and calculate x_1'' from the differential equation using the known values of t_1, x_1, and x_1'. Finite difference methods are then employed to calculate approximate values of x at $t_1 + \Delta$ from x_1'—and x' at $t_1 + \Delta$ from x_1''. That is,

$$x_1' \cong \frac{x(t_1 + \Delta) - x_1}{\Delta}$$

and
$$x_1'' \cong \frac{x'(t_1 + \Delta) - x_1'}{\Delta}$$

Given the values of $x(t_1 + \Delta)$ and $x'(t_1 + \Delta)$, we can calculate x'' at $t_1 + \Delta$ from the differential equation. Continuing in this manner, we calculate successive values of x, x', and x'' at $t_1 + 2\Delta, \ldots, t_2$. In essence, we solved a difference equation whose solution $x(t_1)$, $x(t_1 + \Delta), \ldots, x(t_2)$ approximates the original differential equation at the points $t_1, t_1 + \Delta$, $\ldots, t_2$.

Now suppose the two boundary conditions are

$$x_1 = x(t_1) \quad \text{and} \quad x_2 = x(t_2)$$

as in the Euler equation. If we initiate the calculations at t_1, we have to guess a value for $x'(t_1)$ in order to calculate $x''(t_1)$. The same procedure applies if the calculations are begun at t_2. Given the calculated value of $x''(t_1)$, which may not be correct since it depends on the value assumed for $x'(t_1)$, the calculations proceed as before. But when t_2 is reached the value of x calculated at this point may not be, and in general will not be, x_2 unless we have a crystal ball for guessing $x'(t_1)$. We then must proceed iteratively by adjusting $x'(t_1)$, and repeating the whole procedure over and and over again until a value of $x'(t_1)$ is found which is compatible with x_2.

Unfortunately even when there is no end condition given a *natural boundary condition* takes over. If there is no prescribed value of $x(t_2)$, the Euler condition still holds, if at t_2, the condition

$$F_{x'} = 0$$

is satisfied. This condition is known as a natural boundary condition and, of course, applies at t_1 also, if x_1 is not prescribed. So a two-point boundary differential equation must be solved in all cases. In the example of determining the curve of minimum-arc length, suppose x_2 were not specified. Then from the condition $F_{x'} = 0$, we have

$$F_{x'} = x'[1 + (x')^2]^{-1/2} = 0 \quad \text{or} \quad x = c$$

In other words if an end-point is not fixed, the minimizing straight line is one of zero slope—a rather obvious result.

There are several extensions of the elementary Euler condition. Suppose the function $x(t)$ is restricted by the integral constraint,

$$\int_{t_1}^{t_2} G(t, x, x') \, dt = 0$$

By using a Lagrange multiplier, we can replace the original integral to be optimized by

$$\int_{t_1}^{t_2} F(t, x, x') \, dt + \lambda \int_{t_1}^{t_2} G(t, x, x') \, dt = \int_{t_1}^{t_2} [F(t, x, x') + \lambda \, G(t, x, x')] \, dt$$

This yields the Euler-Lagrange necessary condition that

$$\frac{d}{dt}[F_{x'} + \lambda G_{x'}] - F_x - \lambda G_x = 0$$

On the other hand, there is no corresponding simple modification of the Euler equation for ordinary inequality constraints of the form

$$h(x(t)) \leq k$$

Of course, so long as the optimizing curve lies within the feasible region, the Euler condition applies. However, at the boundary, the Euler condition does not apply, and other methods must be used.

The Euler condition is readily extended to several independent and dependent variables. For example, with two independent and dependent variables, the integral to be optimized is

$$\iint F(s, t, x, x_s, x_t, y, y_s, y_t) \, ds \, dt,$$

where the functions $x = x(s, t)$ and $y = y(s, t)$ are to be determined. The two Euler equations obtained as necessary conditions are

$$\frac{\partial}{\partial s}(F_{x_s}) + \frac{\partial}{\partial t}(F_{x_t}) - F_x = 0$$

$$\frac{\partial}{\partial s}(F_{y_s}) + \frac{\partial}{\partial t}(F_{y_t}) - F_y = 0$$

The Euler condition can also be generalized to include higher derivatives of the dependent variables in the function F. More detail can be found in any of several books on the calculus of variations, for example, Bliss [16]. We shall fill in only a few holes. Using a dynamic programming approach, we derive a partial differential equation for the variational problem of Section 1, and then specialize the result to obtain the Euler condition for the problem of this section. This establishes the formal relationship between dynamic programming and the calculus of variations. This approach also is used to obtain the maximum principle of Pontryagin. Finally, we consider obtaining numerical solutions to variational problems. By using dynamic programming in discrete form, we do not need to solve two-point boundary equations.

6. A Derivation of the Euler Condition by Dynamic Programming

We return to the variational problem of Section 1, except for the simplification of dealing with scalar variables. We want to find the function

$u(t)$ maximizing the integral

$$\int_{t_1}^{t_2} F(t, x, u)\, dt$$

$$\text{subject to } x' = g(t, x, u)$$

$$x_1 = x(t_1)$$

By formulating the variational problem as a dynamic program, it can be reduced to an ordinary optimization problem.

Let

$$f(t, x(t)) = \max_{\substack{u(t) \\ [t, t_2]}} \int_{t}^{t_2} F(t, x, u)\, dt$$

Because of the additivity of integrals the expression for $f(t, x(t))$ can be written as

$$f(t, x(t)) = \max_{\substack{u(t) \\ [t, t_2]}} \left[\int_{t+\Delta}^{t_2} F(t, x, u)\, dt + \int_{t}^{t+\Delta} F(t, x, u)\, dt \right]$$

Following the derivation of the recursive equation for discrete multistage optimization, the maximization over the interval $[t, t_2]$ is broken into the two intervals $[t, t + \Delta]$, $[t + \Delta, t_2]$. Thus

$$f(t, x(t)) = \max_{\substack{u(t) \\ [t, t+\Delta]}} \left[\max_{\substack{u(t) \\ [t+\Delta, t_2]}} \int_{t}^{t+\Delta} F(t, x, u)\, dt + \int_{t+\Delta}^{t_2} F(t, x, u)\, dt \right]$$

The first integral does not depend on the inner maximization, consequently

$$f(t, x(t)) = \max_{\substack{u(t) \\ [t, t+\Delta]}} \left[\int_{t}^{t+\Delta} F(t, x, u)\, dt + \max_{\substack{u(t) \\ [t+\Delta, t_2]}} \int_{t+\Delta}^{t_2} F(t, x, u)\, dt \right]$$

But by definition

$$\max_{\substack{u(t) \\ [t+\Delta, t_2]}} \int_{t+\Delta}^{t_2} F(t, x, u)\, dt = f(t + \Delta, x(t + \Delta))$$

Substituting this identity into the equation for $f(t, x(t))$, we obtain the basic recursion equation for the variational problem, namely

$$f(t, x(t)) = \max_{\substack{u(t) \\ [t, t+\Delta]}} \left[\int_{t}^{t+\Delta} F(t, x, u)\, dt + f(t + \Delta, x(t + \Delta)) \right]$$

This equation is analogous to the basic recursion equation for discrete multistage problems. The last term, $f(t + \Delta, x(t + \Delta))$ is the optimal return from $t + \Delta$ to t_2 as a function of the output state $x(t + \Delta)$, and corresponds to $f_{n-1}(x_{n-1})$. The integral represents the immediate return, corresponding to $r_n(x_n, d_n)$. The max is similar to $\max_{\substack{u(t) \\ [t, t+\Delta]}}$ $\underset{d_n}{}$.

We shall make considerable use of this equation. By letting $\Delta \to 0$ Euler equations and the maximum principle of Pontryagin can be derived. Taking Δ to be small but finite leads to an efficient computational algorithm for finding numerical solutions.

For small values of Δ

$$\int_t^{t+\Delta} F(t, x, u) \, dt$$

can be replaced by $F(t, x, u)\Delta$. Thus

$$f(t, x(t)) = \max_{\substack{u(t) \\ [t, t+\Delta]}} [F(t, x, u)\Delta + f(t + \Delta, x(t + \Delta))]$$

By expanding $f(t + \Delta, x(t + \Delta))$ in a Taylor series about $(t, x(t))$, we can simplify matters by eliminating $f(t, x(t))$ from both sides of the equation just given. Recall that the Taylor series expansion of a function $f(t)$ about $t = a$ is given by

$$f(t) = f(a) + (t - a) f'(a) + \frac{(t - a)^2}{2!} f''(a) + \ldots +$$

In our problem

$$f'(a) = f'(t, x(t)) = f_t + f_x \, g(t, x, u)$$

Thus assuming f can be partially differentiated with respect to t and x,

$$f(t + \Delta, x(t + \Delta)) = f(t, x(t)) + \Delta(f_t + f_x \, g(t, x, u))$$

$$+ \text{ terms with higher powers of } \Delta.$$

Using this value for $f(t + \Delta, x(t + \Delta))$ in the previous equation for $f(t, x(t))$, we obtain

$$f(t, x(t)) = \max_{\substack{u(t) \\ [t, t+\Delta]}} [F(t, x, u)\Delta + f(t, x(t)) + \Delta(f_t + f_x \, g)]$$

In making this last substitution, it was permissible to ignore terms multiplied by Δ^2 and higher powers of Δ, since we shall divide the equation just given by Δ and take the limit as $\Delta \to 0$.

Since f does not have u as an argument, it can be subtracted from both sides of the equation above. Thus

$$0 = \max_{\substack{u(t) \\ [t, t+\Delta]}} [F(t, x, u)\Delta + \Delta(f_t + f_x \, g)]$$

Finally, dividing both sides by Δ and taking the limit as $\Delta \to 0$, we obtain

$$0 = \max_{u(t)} [F(t, x, u) + f_t + f_x \, g]$$

In this equation the maximization is at a point. Consequently, we reduced the original variational problem to an ordinary maximization problem. A necessary condition for a maximum is that the first partial derivative with respect to u vanish; consequently

$$F_u + f_x g_u = 0$$

And at the maximum, the function to be maximized is identically zero so

$$F + f_t + f_x g = 0$$

The elimination of the unknown function f from the last two equations yields a nonlinear partial differential equation in terms of F, g, t, x, and u, whose solutions satisfy the necessary conditions for a maximum. Solving the first equation for f_x, we obtain

$$f_x = \frac{-F_u}{g_u} = P(t, x, u)$$

Substituting this result into the second equation and solving for f_t yields

$$f_t = \frac{F_u g}{g_u} - F = S(t, x, u)$$

The last two expressions can be combined by noting that

$$\frac{\partial}{\partial t} [P(t, x, u)] = \frac{\partial}{\partial x} [S(t, x, u)]$$

By definition

$$\frac{\partial}{\partial t} [P(t, x, u)] = P_t + P_x \frac{\partial x}{\partial t} + P_u \frac{\partial u}{\partial t}$$

and

$$\frac{\partial}{\partial x} [S(t, x, u)] = S_x + S_t \frac{\partial t}{\partial x} + S_u \frac{\partial u}{\partial x}$$

But at any particular point t, except $t = t_1$, the state variable x varies independently of t, thus

$$\frac{\partial}{\partial t} [P(t, x, u)] = P_t + P_u u_t$$

and

$$\frac{\partial}{\partial x} [S(t, x, u)] = S_x + S_u u_x$$

Equating the right-hand sides of the last two equations, we obtain the nonlinear partial differential equation

$$P_t + P_u u_t = S_x + S_u u_x$$

as a necessary condition for a maximum.

We can show that the particular case of $u = g = x'$ yields the Euler condition of Section 5. Noting that $g_u = 1$, we obtain

$$P(t, x, x') = -F_{x'}$$

and $$S(t, x, x') = x' F_{x'} - F$$

Then by partial differentiation

$$P_t = -F_{tx'}$$

$$P_{x'} x_t' = -F_{x'x'} x''$$

$$S_x = F_{xx'} x' - F_x$$

S_u can be ignored since $x'_x = 0$. Substituting these results into the partial differential equation yields the Euler condition in expanded form,

$$F_{x'x'} x'' + F_{xx'} x' + F_{tx'} - F_x = 0$$

This derivation has followed Bellman [10]. For other similar results see Bellman [10, 12], Bellman and Dreyfus [13], and Roberts [60]. An advantage of this approach is that by reducing the problem to an ordinary optimization, additional results follow almost immediately. For example, we deduced the condition

$$F_u + f_x g_u = 0$$

by requiring that the first derivative with respect to u vanish. For the special case of $u = x' = g$, the equation just given reduces to

$$F_{x'} + f_x = 0$$

For a local maximum, it is sufficient that the second derivative be negative where the first derivative vanishes. Thus we derive the Legendre condition that

$$F_{x'x'} < 0$$

for a local maximum.

7. The Maximum Principle of Pontryagin

A set of necessary conditions for a maximum given in terms of non-linear differential equations has recently been developed by the Russian mathematician, Pontryagin [58]. Following Kopp [42], we develop Pontryagin's maximum principle from a dynamic programming point of view. We want to find the function $u(t)$ that maximizes the integral †

$$\int_{t_1}^{t_2} F(t, x, u) \, dt$$

$$\text{subject to } x' = g(t, x, u)$$

$$x_1 = x(t_1)$$

---

† Vector variables and a somewhat more general objective function can be considered without any complications.

This problem can be transformed into a terminal optimization problem by defining a new state variable y,

$$y_1 = y(t_1) = 0$$

$$y(t) = \int_{t_1}^{t} F(t, x, u) \, dt, \qquad t_1 \leq t \leq t_2$$

Note that

$$y' = F(t, x, u)$$

Consequently, the original problem may be restated as

$$\max_{\substack{u(t) \\ [t_1, t_2]}} y(t_2)$$

$$\text{subject to } x' = g(t, x, u)$$

$$y' = F(t, x, u)$$

and

$$x_1 = x(t_1), \qquad y_1 = y(t_1) = 0$$

In the terminology of the calculus of variations, problems of maximizing some function of the initial and/or final states are Mayer problems; variational problems of the type we have considered so far are Lagrange problems; and those that are of both Mayer and Lagrange form are called Bolza problems. To derive the maximum principle, we must begin with a Mayer problem. Hence we made the transformation just given. Incidentally, this transformation to a Mayer problem can be made for any variational problem originally in Lagrange form.

Following the derivation in Section 6, let

$$f(t, x(t), y(t)) = \max_{\substack{u(t) \\ [t, t_2]}} y(t_2)$$

$$= \max_{\substack{u(t) \\ [t, t+\Delta]}} \max_{\substack{u(t) \\ [t+\Delta, t_2]}} y(t_2)$$

Since

$$f(t + \Delta, x(t + \Delta), y(t + \Delta)) = \max_{\substack{u(t) \\ [t+\Delta, t_2]}} y(t_2)$$

we obtain the functional equation

$$f(t, x(t), y(t)) = \max_{\substack{u(t) \\ [t, t+\Delta]}} [f(t + \Delta, x(t + \Delta), y(t + \Delta))]$$

Expanding $f(t + \Delta, x(t + \Delta), y(t + \Delta))$ in a Taylor series about $f(t, x(t), y(t))$ and neglecting second-order and higher terms yields

$$f(t + \Delta, x(t + \Delta), y(t + \Delta)) = f(t, x(t), y(t)) + \Delta (f_t + f_x g + f_y F)$$

Combining the last two equations by substituting the Taylor series expansion for $f(t + \Delta, x(t + \Delta), y(t + \Delta))$ gives

$$f(t, x(t), y(t)) = \max_{\substack{u(t) \\ [t, t+\Delta]}} [f(t, x(t), y(t)) + \Delta (f_t + f_x g + f_y F)]$$

Subtracting f from both sides and then dividing by Δ yields in the limit as $\Delta \to 0$

$$0 = \max_{u(t)} [f_t + f_x g + f_y F]$$

Since f_t is not a function of u, the objective is to maximize $f_x g + f_y F$.

We now define auxiliary variables, which may be recognized as time-dependent Lagrange multipliers

$$p(t) = -f_x \quad \text{and} \quad q(t) = -f_y$$

From $f_x(t_2) = 0$ and $f_y(t_2) = 1$, the end conditions $p(t_2) = 0$ and $q(t_2) = -1$ are obtained.

Let

$$H(t, x, u) = pg + qF$$

Since $pg + qF = -[f_x g + f_y F]$, the objective can be restated as

$$\min_{u(t)} H(t, x, u)$$

Let $\bar{g}$ and $\bar{F}$ be the values of g and F evaluated at the optimum value of u. Then

$$\bar{0} = f_t - p\bar{g} - q\bar{F}$$

or

$$-f_t = -p\bar{g} - q\bar{F}$$

Partially differentiating the above equation with respect to x, we obtain

$$p' = -f_{tx} = -p\bar{g}_x - q\bar{F}_x$$

This equation can be used to calculate the values of p along the optimal curve. Similarly

$$q' = -f_{ty} = -p\bar{g}_y - q\bar{F}_y$$

But g and F are not functions of y; thus

$$q' = 0 \quad \text{and} \quad q(t) = -1, \qquad t_1 \leq t \leq t_2$$

Summarizing the above results, we want to find $u(t)$ that minimizes

$$H(t, x, u) = pg - F$$

$$\text{subject to} \quad p' = -pg_x + F_x, \quad p(t_2) = 0$$

and

$$x' = g(t, x, u), \quad x(t_1) = 0$$

Actually we derived a minimum principle for H. Pontryagin starts with a minimization problem, and shows that H must be maximized—hence the name "maximum principle."

To illustrate the maximum principle in a very simple case, we return to finding a curve of minimum length between the fixed point (x_1, t_1) and the line $t = t_2$. For this problem

$$u = x' = g$$

and
$$F = (1 + (x')^2)^{1/2}$$

Thus
$$H(t, x, x') = px' - (1 + (x')^2)^{1/2} \quad \text{and} \quad p' = 0$$

Then from $p(t_2) = 0$, it follows that

$$p(t) = 0, \qquad t_1 \le t \le t_2$$

and
$$H(t, x, x') = -(1 + (x')^2)^{1/2}$$

Partially differentiating H with respect to x' yields the necessary condition

$$H_{x'} = -x'(1 + (x')^2)^{-1/2} = 0$$

Consequently, we obtain the expected result

$$x' = 0 \quad \text{or} \quad x = c_1$$

In the more general case, the state and decision variables are vectors $X = (x_1, \ldots, x_n)$ and $U = (u_1, \ldots, u_m)$ respectively, and the objective is to maximize

$$\sum_{i=1}^{n} c_i x_i(t_2)$$

subject to the differential equations

$$x_i' = g_i(t, X, U), \qquad i = 1, \ldots, n$$

and the initial conditions

$$X_1 = X(t_1)$$

A derivation similar to the one just given yields the maximum principle

$$\min_{U(t)} H(t, X, U)$$

where
$$H(t, X, U) = \sum_{i=1}^{M} p_i g_i$$

subject to $p_i' = -\sum_{j=1}^{M} p_j \dfrac{\partial g_j}{\partial x_i}, \quad p_i(t_2) = -c_i$

and
$$x_i' = g_i(t, X, U), \quad X_1 = X(t_1), \qquad i = 1, \ldots, n$$

An important asset of Pontryagin's principle is that constraints of the form $a(t) \leq U(t) \leq b(t)$ can be handled in the minimization of H. However the solution of two-point boundary value differential equations is still required, since the end conditions on the state variables x_i are at t_1, whereas the auxiliary variables p_i are constrained at t_2. As we shall see in Section 8, the dynamic programming approach eliminates solving differential equations with boundary conditions at both ends. Instead we face the problems of state variable dimensionality.

There is a corresponding maximum principle for discrete multistage optimization problems [29]. However, the discrete maximum principle is not nearly as fruitful as its counterpart for variational problems since, under some circumstances, the condition corresponding to minimize H is not necessary for a maximum.

8. Numerical Solution of Variational Problems by Dynamic Programming

Although it is theoretically interesting to derive known results such as Euler equations and the maximum principle using a dynamic programming approach, the capability of generating new results is the really important issue.

Most variational problems of practical importance lead to Euler equations that cannot be solved for closed-form solutions, and in some cases, because of constraints, there is no Euler equation at all. By using Pontryagin's maximum principle, we can overcome the difficulty caused by constraints on the decision variables. However, the numerical solution of Pontryagin's equations and/or the Euler equations is greatly complicated by two-point boundary value, nonlinear differential equations. Fortunately a discrete finite multistage dynamic programming approach avoids the trial-and-error procedure of solving these differential equations. Thus the greatest value of dynamic programming in the calculus of variations is in the obtaining of numerical solutions. For the problem of finding $u(t)$ that maximizes

$$\int_{t_1}^{t_2} F(t, x, u)\, dt$$

$$\text{subject to } x' = g(t, x, u)$$

$$x_1 = x(t_1)$$

in Section 5, we developed the functional equation

$$f(t, x(t)) = \max_{\substack{u(t) \\ [t, t+\Delta]}} \left[\int_t^{t+\Delta} F(t, x, u)\, dt + f(t + \Delta, x(t + \Delta)) \right]$$

To calculate numerical solutions we replace the variational model by a discrete multistage model. In particular, the continuous interval $t_1 \leq t \leq t_2$ is replaced by the discrete one $n = 0, \ldots, N$ where $N = t_1$, $N - 1 = t_1 + \Delta, \ldots, 1 = t_2 - \Delta$, $0 = t_2$. The end condition $x_1 = x(t_1)$ becomes $x_N = k$. At the point n, the differential equation

$$x'(t) = g(t, x, u)$$

is written as

$$x_n' = g_n(x_n, u_n)$$

By making the approximation

$$x_n' \cong \frac{x_{n-1} - x_n}{\Delta}$$

we obtain

$$\frac{x_{n-1} - x_n}{\Delta} = g_n(x_n, u_n)$$

or

$$x_{n-1} = h_n(x_n, u_n, \Delta)$$

Similarly, we make the approximation

$$\int_t^{t+\Delta} F(t, x, u)\, dt \cong F(t, x, u)\Delta$$

and use the notation

$$F(t, x, u)\Delta = F_n(x_n, u_n)\Delta$$

The optimal return $f(t, x(t))$ is denoted by $f_n(x_n)$.

Substituting the definitions and approximations just given into the functional equation, we obtain recursive equations of familiar form:

$$f_n(x_n) = \max_{u_n} [F_n(x_n, u_n)\Delta + f_{n-1}(x_{n-1})]$$

with

$$x_{n-1} = h_n(x_n, u_n, \Delta), \qquad n = 1, \ldots, N, \ x_N = k$$

and

$$f_0(x_0) = 0$$

Actually there is no need to multiply F_n by Δ when carrying out the optimizations, since Δ multiplies every stage return by the same constant.

The maximum return $f_N(x_N = k)$ is, of course, an approximation to the maximum value of the original integral, that is,

$$f_N(x_N = k) \cong \max_{\substack{u(t) \\ [t_1, t_2]}} \int_{t_1}^{t_2} F(t, x, u)\, dt$$

The maximizing function $u(t)$ is approximated from $u_N = u_N(x_N)$, $u_{N-1}(x_{N-1})$, and so on. Given the approximating points to the optimum curve, we can construct a smooth curve from which it may be possible to draw an hypothesis concerning an analytic solution. We can make as good an approximation as we want by choosing Δ and the corresponding spacings between sufficiently small feasible x values. Naturally, these spacings are limited by computational feasibility.

The dynamic programming algorithm ensures that the end condition $x_N = k$ and the natural-boundary condition at x_0 are satisfied, without us going through the trial-and-error iterations of numerical solution of two-point boundary differential equations. If there is also a fixed condition at t_2, that is,

$$x_0 = c$$

the recursion equations are identical to the ones just given except that at stage one,

$$x_0 = c = h_1(x_1, u_1, \Delta)$$

is inverted to yield

$$u_1 = \hat{h}_1(x_1, c, \Delta)$$

and

$$f_1(x_1) = F(x_1, \hat{h}_1)\Delta$$

Constraints on the decision variables of the form

$$a_n \leq u_n \leq b_n$$

which sometimes rule out the existence of an Euler equation, cause no difficulty in the numerical solution of the recursive equations. When there are constraints on the decision variables, we simply solve the recursive equations

$$f_n(x_n) = \max_{a_n \leq u_n \leq b_n} [F_n(x_n, u_n)\Delta + f_{n-1}(x_{n-1})] \qquad n = 1, \ldots, N$$

Finally, constraints on the state variables of the form

$$A_n \leq x_n \leq B_n$$

which cause immense difficulty in the classical treatment and also rule out the use of the maximum principle, actually simplify the dynamic programming analysis. To deal with these constraints, we follow the obvious rule of considering only optimal returns and decision functions for the feasible values of the state variables.

There is, however, one serious deficiency in the dynamic programming approach. We have belabored it time and time again. When the state variable dimensionality is too high, it may not be possible to solve the recursive equations even using state variable reduction methods. Perhaps, in these unfortunate cases, a synthesis of the maximum principle and dynamic programming may yield computational feasibility.

EXERCISES

1. Consider

$$\max_{d_n} \sum_{n=1}^{N} c_1 d_n + c_2 (x_n - d_n), \quad c_1, c_2 > 0$$

$$\text{subject to } 0 \leq d_n \leq x_n$$

$$x_{n-1} = a_1 d_n + a_2 (x_n - d_n), \quad n = 1, \ldots, N$$

$$0 \leq a_1 < 1, \, 0 \leq a_2 < 1$$

and obtain the steady state solution, that is, $\lim_{N \to \infty} f_N(x_N)$ and $\lim_{N \to \infty} d_N(x_N)$ as a function of $c_1, c_2, a_1,$ and a_2.

2. Obtain steady state solutions for parts a, b, c, d of Problem 10, Chapter III.

3. In the gold-mining problem (Problem 12, Chapter V), assume that as long as the machine is not damaged, it can be used over and over again for an arbitrarily long period of time. Determine how the machine should be used to maximize the amount of gold mined.†

4. In Problem 4 of Chapter V, determine a policy to maximize the expected gain per stage independent of the starting state, assuming that the number of transitions is very large.

5. In Problem 5 of Chapter V assume that we want to maximize the average profit per week over a very long period of time. Determine an advertising policy, for all weeks, which will achieve this objective.

6. Prove the monotone convergence of Howard's policy iteration method.

7. Following the dynamic programming approach of Section 6, derive the Euler-Lagrange necessary condition for

$$\max_{x(t)} \int_{t_1}^{t_2} F(t, x, x') \, dt$$

$$\text{subject to } \int_{t_1}^{t_2} G(t, x, x') \, dt = K$$

$$x(t_1) = x_1, x(t_2) = t_2$$

8. Prove that in Problem 7 the Lagrange multiplier (λ) of the Euler-Lagrange equation is given by

$$\lambda = \frac{\partial f}{\partial K}$$

9. Consider the problem of controlling a chemical reactor. The desired concentration of material leaving the reactor is x^*, the initial concentration is $x_0 = c$, and the concentration at time t is given by the differential equation

$$x'(t) = \left(\frac{1 - x}{1 + x} \right) u(t)$$

---

† The solution may be found in Bellman [10].

The object is to find the control function $u(t)$ minimizing

$$\int_0^T [(x(t) - x^*)^2 + (u(t))^2] \, dt$$

subject to $a \leq u(t) \leq b$

(a) State Pontryagin's principle for this problem.

(b) Suppose $x^* = 0.8$, $x_0 = 0.2$, $a = 0$, and $b = 1$. Choose a grid and solve numerically for $u(t)$ by applying the maximum principle and then by using dynamic programming.

10. Derive Pontryagin's principle for the problem

$$\max_{u(t)} \int_{t_1}^{t_2} F(t, X, U) \, dt$$

$$U = (u_1, \ldots, u_m) \qquad X = (x_1, \ldots, x_n)$$

subject to $x_i' = g_i(t, X, U), \qquad i = 1, \ldots, n$

$$X(t_1) = X_1$$

VIII

Conclusions

1. General Remarks

In developing the theory and computational aspects of dynamic programming, we have made liberal use of illustrative problems. But these illustrations were devoid of verbal context. This was done deliberately, so that we could concentrate on deriving the recursion equations and the solution from the mathematical statement. Our object was to show when it is possible to decompose a multivariable optimization model by using recursive optimization, what the advantages are in doing this, and, in particular, *how to do it*.

Claims have been made that there is a great mystery in the formulation of dynamic programming problems. It can be confusing to transform a verbal problem statement directly to the recursive equations. But if this is difficult, the solution is simply to write down an ordinary mathematical statement of the problem and from it derive the recursive equations. This is the principle we followed, and this is why we begin with a mathematical statement. We hope that sufficient guidance has been provided so that the mystique has been removed.

The great popularity of linear programming is supposedly its simplicity and easy recognition, and the availability of "canned" computer programs. We believe that dynamic programming has these advantages too—but they are not so obvious. The basic idea of decomposition is easy to understand. Once we become familiar with the kind of multivariable functions that can be decomposed and with the role of state variables in dynamic programming, recognition becomes no problem. There are several general flow charts in Chapter III. These can be transformed into computer programs into which we can substitute the particular return and transformation functions as data. Routines of this type are already in use; it is just a question of making them generally available.

One reason that dynamic programming has not been used as extensively as it should is that the original presentation involved advanced mathematics. Bellman's *Dynamic Programming* [10] is primarily concerned with the existence of solutions to functional equations, and the mathematical structure of infinite-stage solutions, rather than numerical solutions to finite-stage problems. Since this was the only book for some time, dynamic programming was beyond the grasp of people with limited mathematical abilities. This is a pity, because the simple problem of determining numerical solutions to finite-stage problems is not beyond the ability of many high-school students. Having a numerical solution to a particular problem is indeed a modest result compared with having a general solution to a class of problems; but, although a numerical solution may not be very satisfying to a theoretical mathematician, it can be of utmost importance to an engineer or an economist. Furthermore, with high-speed digital computers, numerical solutions are easier to obtain. Occasionally, from a series of numerical solutions a general theory can be constructed.

2. Applications

There are some important general classes of problems so amenable to a dynamic programming approach that it would be an injustice not to mention them. A considerable amount of numerical and theoretical results have been obtained on multistage inventory models, exemplified by the recent collection of articles edited by Scarf et al. [62], and the earlier book by Arrow, Karlin, and Scarf [5]. In an inventory problem, the object is to determine optimal replenishment rules to minimize the combined costs of carrying inventory, ordering or production, and shortage. In the simplest inventory models, it is assumed that the optimal stock levels in each period are independent. This assumption does not hold in many realistic situations. One reason is that demands for inventory in each period are often interdependent. It is intuitive that multistage inventory models can be solved by dynamic programming. The fundamental idea is that the optimal stock level in a month should minimize the cost in that month n and yield an optimal inventory at the beginning of month $n-1$.

Nonlinear allocation problems of the form

$$\max_{D_1,\ldots,D_n} \sum_{n=1}^{N} g_n(D_n)$$

$$\text{subject to } \sum_{n=1}^{N} h_{ni}(D_n) \leq k_i, \qquad i = 1,\ldots,M$$

are suitable to a dynamic programming approach. We studied several problems of this type in Chapters III and IV. There are an almost endless number of interpretations of the allocation model. In the economic interpretation, D_n is a vector which represents the amount of resource—in money, materials, and labor—allocated to the nth source (industry or factory). The terms in the objective function $r_n(D_n)$ represent the return from the nth source, and h_{ni} are constraints, such as limited availability of resource. For a particular application to advertising expenditure see Maffei [46]. An application concerned with the use of ground-water resources is given by Burt [17]. Burt and Harris [18] give an application to the allocation of a fair number of representatives to each of the 50 states. Kettelle [41] discusses the optimum allocation of parallel components in an electronic system to maximize reliability.

The serial structure of processing units in the chemical and oil industries creates a perfect environment for dynamic programming applications. Even individual pieces of equipment, such as distillation towers, are multistage units. Dynamic programming has been applied by Mitten and Nemhauser [52, 53], and Nemhauser [54] to the design of multistage separation equipment and to complex plants that may include nonserial structures. A monograph by Aris [2] deals extensively with the application of dynamic programming to chemical reactor design. Roberts [60] has written about applications of dynamic programming to optimal design and control in the process industries.

Combinatorial optimization problems have been studied extensively using dynamic programming. Dimensionality has proved to be a formidable adversary. Nevertheless, some powerful procedures have been developed, and in some cases analytical solutions have been obtained. Bellman [11] and Held and Karp [36] discuss the subject in general. A dynamic programming assembly line balancing algorithm has been obtained by Held et al. [37]. Gonzalez [31] developed a dynamic programming algorithm for the traveling-salesman problem. Bellman [10] gives numerous results on problems of determining optimal testing sequences.

Finding an optimal control function is generally a problem in the calculus of variations. Such problems occur, for example, in controlling a missile or a complex chemical plant. Recently, considerable effort has been devoted to these problems, using dynamic programming. The main reference is Bellman's second book on dynamic programming, *Adaptive Control Processes* [12]. Tou [63] contains a detailed analysis of the dynamic programming approach to control problems with quadratic objective functions.

Table 1 summarizes the interpretations of stages, input states, output states, decisions, and objectives for a variety of problems that can be formulated as multistage decision systems.

Table 1 SOME MULTISTAGE DECISION PROCESSES

	Chemical Process	Allocation Problem	Production and Inventory Scheduling	Missile Control System	Combinational Optimization Problem
Objective	Maximize profit	Maximize total return from all activities	Minimize cost of inventory	Minimize deviations from desired trajectory	Optimal sequence
Stage	Reactor	Activity	Time period	Time period	Position n in the sequence
Input State	Composition of entering materials	Amount of resource that could be allocated	Inventory at the beginning of the period	Position at the beginning of the period	Arrangement of first $n-1$ items
Decisions	Reaction temperature, catalyst	Amount of resource allocated	Amount of goods ordered or produced during the period	Direction	Item placed in position n
Output State	Composition of leaving materials	Amount of resource remaining	Inventory at the end of the period	Position at the end of the period	Resulting arrangement

IX

References

The following list of references is meant to be representative of some of the books and articles on dynamic programming and related subjects used in the preparation of this book. The bibliographies listed contain numerous entries on dynamic programming [6–9, 14, 19, 20, 59] but none is both current and comprehensive. Articles on the theory and application of dynamic programming have appeared in a wide variety of journals. *Operations Research, Management Science, Naval Research Logistics Quarterly, Econometrica,* the *Journal of Industrial Engineering,* and the *Journal for the Society of Industrial and Applied Mathematics* are the American journals that probably contain the greatest number of articles on dynamic programming. *The International Abstracts in Operations Research* contains abstracts of articles on dynamic programming taken from an almost exhaustive list of relevant journals.

1. R. L. Ackoff, S. K. Gupta, and J. S. Minas, *Scientific Method: Optimizing Applied Research Decisions,* John Wiley and Sons, New York, 1962.
2. R. Aris, *The Optimal Design of Chemical Reactors,* Academic Press, New York, 1961.
3. R. Aris, *Discrete Dynamic Programming,* Blaisdell, New York, 1964.
4. R. Aris, G. L. Nemhauser, and D. J. Wilde, "Optimization of Multistage Cycle and Branching Systems by Serial Procedures," *A.I.Ch.E. Journal,* **10,** 913–919 (1964).
5. K. J. Arrow, S. Karlin, and H. Scarf, *Studies in the Mathematical Theory of Inventory and Production,* Stanford University Press, Stanford, California, 1958.
6. J. Batchelor, *Operations Research: An Annotated Bibliography,* Vol. I, Saint Louis University Press, St. Louis, 1959.
7. J. Batchelor, *Operations Research: An Annotated Bibliography,* Vol. II, Saint Louis University Press, St. Louis, 1962.

8. J. Batchelor, *Operations Research: An Annotated Bibliography,* Vol. III, Saint Louis University Press, St. Louis, 1963.

9. J. Batchelor, *Operations Research: An Annotated Bibliography,* Vol. IV, Saint Louis University Press, St. Louis, 1964.

10. R. Bellman, *Dynamic Programming,* Princeton University Press, Princeton, New Jersey, 1957.

11. R. Bellman, "Mathematical Aspects of Scheduling Theory," *J. Soc. Ind. App. Math.,* **4,** 168–205 (1956).

12. R. Bellman, *Adaptive Control Processes: A Guided Tour,* Princeton University Press, Princeton, New Jersey, 1961.

13. R. Bellman and S. E. Dreyfus, *Applied Dynamic Programming,* Princeton University Press, Princeton, New Jersey, 1962.

14. R. Bellman and R. Karush, "Dynamic Programming: A Bibliography of Theory and Application," Rand Corp. Memorandum RM–3951–PR, 1964.

15. A. T. Bharucha-Reid, *Elements of the Theory of Markov Processes and Their Applications,* McGraw-Hill, New York, 1960.

16. G. A. Bliss, *Calculus of Variations,* University of Chicago Press, Chicago, 1925.

17. O. Burt, "Optimal Resource Use Over Time with an Application to Ground Water," *Management Science,* **11,** 80–93 (1964).

18. O. Burt and C. Harris, Jr., "Apportionment of the U.S. House of Representatives: A Minimum Range, Integer Solution, Allocation Problem," *Operations Research,* **11,** 648–652 (1963).

19. Case Institute, *A Comprehensive Bibliography on Operations Research through 1956,* John Wiley and Sons, New York, 1958.

20. Case Institute, *A Comprehensive Bibliography on Operations Research 1957–1958,* John Wiley and Sons, New York, 1963.

21. A. Charnes and W. W. Cooper, *Management Models and Industrial Applications of Linear Programming,* Vols. I and II, John Wiley and Sons, New York, 1961.

22. H. Chernoff and L. E. Moses, *Elementary Decision Theory,* John Wiley and Sons, New York, 1959.

23. C. W. Churchman, R. L. Ackoff, and E. L. Arnoff, *Introduction to Operations Research,* John Wiley and Sons, New York, 1957.

24. G. B. Dantzig, *Linear Programming and Extensions,* Princeton University Press, Princeton, New Jersey, 1963.

25. S. Dreyfus, "Computational Aspects of Dynamic Programming," *Operations Research,* **5,** 409–415 (1957).

26. A. Dvoretzky, J. Kiefer, and J. Wolfowitz, "The Inventory Problem: I. Case of Known Distributions of Demand," *Econometrica,* **20,** 187–222 (1952).

27. A. Dvoretzky, J. Kiefer, and J. Wolfowitz, "The Inventory Problem: II. Case of Unknown Distributions of Demand," *Econometrica,* **20,** 450–466 (1952).

28. H. Everett, "Generalized Lagrange Multiplier Method for Solving Problems of Optimum Allocation of Resource," *Operations Research,* **11,** 399–417 (1963).

29. L. T. Fan and C. S. Wang, *The Discrete Maximum Principle: A Study of Multistage Systems Optimization,* John Wiley and Sons, New York, 1964.
30. C. D. Flagle, W. H. Huggins, and R. H. Roy, *Operations Research and Systems Engineering,* The Johns Hopkins Press, Baltimore, 1960.
31. R. H. Gonzalez, "Solution of the Traveling Salesman Problem by Dynamic Programming on the Hypercube," *Tech. Rep.,* No. 18, O.R. Center, M.I.T. (1962).
32. R. L. Graves and P. Wolfe (eds.), *Recent Advances in Mathematical Programming,* McGraw-Hill, New York, 1963.
33. G. Hadley, *Linear Programming,* Addison–Wesley, Reading, Massachusetts, 1962.
34. G. Hadley, *Nonlinear and Dynamic Programming,* Addison–Wesley, Reading, Massachusetts, 1964.
35. H. Hancock, *Theory of Maxima and Minima,* Dover, New York, 1960.
36. M. Held and R. M. Karp, "A Dynamic Programming Approach to Sequencing Problems," *J. Soc. Indust. and Appl. Math.,* **10,** 196–210 (1962).
37. M. Held, R. M. Karp, and R. Shareshian, "Assembly-Line Balancing–Dynamic Programming with Precedence Constraints," *Operations Research,* **11,** 442–459 (1963).
38. R. A. Howard, *Dynamic Programming and Markov Processes,* John Wiley and Sons, New York, 1960.
39. S. Johnson, "Optimal Two- and Three-Stage Production Schedules with Setup Times Included," *Nav. Res. Log. Quart.,* **1,** 61–68 (1954).
40. J. G. Kemeny and J. L. Snell, *Finite Markov Chains,* D. Van Nostrand, Princeton, New Jersey, 1959.
41. J. D. Kettelle, Jr., "Least-Cost Allocation of Reliability Investment," *Operations Research,* **10,** 249–265 (1962).
42. R. E. Kopp, "Pontryagin Maximum Principle," in *Optimization Techniques* (G. Leitmann, ed.), Academic Press, New York, 1962.
43. H. W. Kuhn and A. W. Tucker (eds.), "Contributions to the Theory of Games II," *Annals of Mathematical Studies,* **24,** Princeton University Press, Princeton, New Jersey, (1953).
44. H. W. Kuhn and A. W. Tucker, "Nonlinear Programming," *Proceedings of the Second Berkeley Symposium on Mathematical Statistics and Probability,* 481–490, University of California Press, 1951.
45. R. D. Luce and H. Raiffa, *Games and Decisions: Introduction and Critical Survey,* John Wiley and Sons, New York, 1957.
46. R. B. Maffei, "Planning Advertising Expenditures by Dynamic Programming Methods," *Management Technology,* **1,** 94–100 (1960).
47. A. S. Manne, "Linear Programming and Sequential Decisions," *Management Science,* **6,** 259–267 (1960).
48. D. D. McCracken, *Digital Computer Programming,* John Wiley and Sons, New York, 1957.
49. J. C. McKinsey, *Introduction to the Theory of Games,* McGraw-Hill, New York, 1952.

50. L. G. Mitten, "An Analytic Solution to the Least Cost Testing Sequence Problem," *J. of Ind. Eng.*, **11**, 17 (1960).

51. L. G. Mitten, "Composition Principles for Synthesis of Optimal Multistage Processes," *Operations Research*, **12**, 610–619 (1964).

52. L. G. Mitten and G. L. Nemhauser, "Multistage Optimization," *Chemical Engineering Progress*, **59**, 52–60 (1963).

53. L. G. Mitten and G. L. Nemhauser, "Optimization of Multistage Separation Processes by Dynamic Programming," *Can. J. of Chemical Eng.*, **41**, 187–194 (1963).

54. G. L. Nemhauser, "Applications of Dynamic Programming in the Process Industries," *Am. Inst. Ind. Eng. Proceedings*, 279–292 (1963).

55. G. L. Nemhauser, "Decomposition of Linear Programs by Dynamic Programming," *Naval Research Logistics Quarterly*, **11**, 191–196, (1964).

56. M. Pollack and W. Wiebenson, "Solution of the Shortest Route Problem —A Review," *Operations Research*, **8**, 224–230 (1960).

57. G. Polya, *How to Solve It*, Doubleday, New York, 1957.

58. L. S. Pontryagin, V. G. Boltyanskii, R. V. Gamkrelidze, and E. F. Mishchenko, *The Mathematical Theory of Optimal Processes*, (translated by K. N. Trirogoff), Interscience, New York, 1962.

59. V. Riley and S. I. Gass, *Linear Programming and Associated Techniques*, The Johns Hopkins University Press, Baltimore, 1958.

60. S. M. Roberts, *Dynamic Programming in Chemical Engineering and Process Control*, Academic Press, New York, 1964.

61. T. L. Saaty, *Mathematical Methods of Operations Research*, McGraw-Hill, New York, 1959.

62. H. E. Scarf, D. M. Gilford, and M. W. Shelly (eds.), *Multistage Inventory Models and Techniques*, Stanford University Press, Stanford, California, 1963.

63. J. T. Tou, *Optimum Design of Digital Control Systems*, Academic Press, New York, 1963.

64. J. Von Neumann and O. Morgenstern, *Theory of Games and Economic Behavior*, Princeton University Press, Princeton, New Jersey, 1944.

65. A. Wald, *Statistical Decision Functions*, John Wiley and Sons, New York, 1950.

66. D. J. Wilde, *Optimum Seeking Methods*, Prentice-Hall, Englewood Cliffs, New Jersey, 1964.

Index

253